THE BIRDS OF
BUCKINGHAMSHIRE

THE BIRDS OF BUCKINGHAMSHIRE

Second Edition

Edited by

David Ferguson

BUCKINGHAMSHIRE BIRD CLUB

First published 1993
Second edition published 2012 by Buckinghamshire Bird Club

ISBN 978 0 907823 94 0

Printed by SS Media Ltd., UK.

CONTENTS

INTRODUCTION TO THE SECOND EDITION

Since the publication of the first edition of *The Birds of Buckinghamshire* in 1993, many changes have taken place among the birds of the county. The list has increased by 24 species while eight have bred for the first time. Among the breeders are two species that have benefited from the warming climate - Little Egret and Cetti's Warbler, two that have benefited from man's ability to create mounds of rubbish - Herring Gull and Lesser Black-backed Gull - and one - Cormorant - that has utilised gravel pits. In the south of the county the most obvious newcomer is the Red Kite, now a familiar sight even over urban areas.

Inevitably other species have declined or disappeared altogether. Modern agricultural methods, in particular the sowing of winter cereals and the use of pesticides, has brought about a catastrophic decline in farmland birds. The decline of Corn Bunting that is mentioned in the first edition has continued to the point where it is now a very local bird. Yellowhammer, Skylark, Grey Partridge, Yellow Wagtail and Lapwing, all birds of farmland, have also decreased in numbers to varying degrees. Many woodland birds have also suffered population declines. Here the causes are varied and not easy to understand. The reason for the near extinction of the Willow Tit in the county is certainly different from the problems that Lesser Spotted Woodpeckers face, for instance.

All these changes mean that, for a significant number of our birds, the maps in the first edition are out of date. When the British Trust for Ornithology announced that it was about to start fieldwork for a new National Atlas it was an easy decision for the committee of the Buckinghamshire Bird Club to agree that this effort should also be aimed towards a new county atlas.

The last Buckinghamshire atlas used paper forms and hand-drawn maps. The new atlas was based around the BTO's atlas website which allowed records to be entered directly through a home computer. Records were updated daily so that it was possible to target under-recorded areas and so increase the efficiency of recording. Paper forms were still used and these were entered by BTO staff after the season ended. The county results were sent to the club and from this data, maps were produced.

Another great change in birding has been the replacement of the film camera with the digital camera. Bird photography, with its uncooperative subjects, could waste a lot of film. Digital photography only wastes a tiny amount of electricity and, although traditionalists may dispute this, the quality is better. The species photographs in this edition are a celebration of this new technology. Many of the county's birders have become photographers, either by using small cameras attached to their telescopes (digiscoping) or by using long lenses. Birds that would have been impossible to photograph using a film camera can now have their images captured for posterity. The gull photographs taken at roost are a good example. The birds are far out in the middle of a lake, it is dusk in winter, and yet technology accompanied by patience and skill can overcome these obstacles.

There have been changes in the last twenty years to many of our main birding sites. Willen Lake in autumn was once an expanse of mud, a perfect feeding area for migrant waders. Now the mud is reduced to a few small patches, the surroundings have been urbanised and waders are scarce. College Lake, now in the care of BBOWT, has undergone many changes since its brief mention in the first edition but has settled down into a major wetland site. The rowing complex at Dorney is now complete and has furnished some interesting wader records.

There have been changes too in birding coverage. Quainton Hills have probably been unchanged for decades but they were only discovered as a passerine migration spot in 2006. The Ivinghoe Hills, although known for many years as a migration point, have only received the coverage they deserve since the late 1990s.

Every county has its unexplored corners. The atlas project, with its insistence that every square is covered, forced birders into these corners with the result that the unexpected was occasionally encountered. We now know more about the distribution of the county's birds than ever before.

It is conventional to dedicate a work of this kind to the efforts of many, but it is true. Without the birders of Buckinghamshire this book could not have been written.

To achieve continuity with the first edition the original introduction has been left intact

INTRODUCTION TO THE FIRST EDITION

This book aims to summarise the status of the birds which have occurred in the present county of Buckinghamshire. The boundaries of the county have in fact changed very little for several hundred years. It is a medium-sized more or less rectangular county situated in the midlands of England approximately 80 km from north to south and 30-40 km from east to west. Most of the county lies between the Rivers Thames in the south and the Great Ouse in the north with the major dividing line of the Chiltern Escarpment running southwest to northeast between them. To the north of this, about two thirds of the area, the landscape is predominantly mixed farmland with a few scattered woodlands and with a rather low human population density, except in Aylesbury and MIlton Keynes. The south, occupying the remaining third, is more wooded, especially on the Chilterns themselves and today is much more densely populated.

The population of the county is now about 725,000 with the majority in the urban areas in and around High Wycombe, Beaconsfield and towards Slough (itself since 1974 in Berkshire), Marlow, Amersham and in recent years increasingly in the administrative capital of Aylesbury and the new town of Milton Keynes. In between are some areas which, for southern England, have a very low population indeed.

Ornithologically the county has not been very well served in the past partly because there are relatively few well known birdwatching sites, at least in national terms. Also it was not until the advent of the Buckinghamshire Bird Club (hereafter referred to as the BBC) in the early 1980s that there was a co-ordinating body able to cover the whole county effectively. The southern part had been very well served by the Middle Thames Natural History Society for many years previous to this but, until 1975 when a very active group of birdwatchers was formed, the north of the county in particular was too far away from this Society's main recording area. Indeed until the 1970s there were very few people and hence birdwatchers at all in the northern part of the county. The growth of Milton Keynes brought both many more people and the development of some excellent new birdwatching sites to the area.

There have been a few compilations of the birds of the county, most recently by Fraser and Youngman (1976), and together with the more recent records compiled by the BBC in the 1980s these form the basis of this book. Two complications have been the geographically minor, but ornithologically quite important, boundary changes, in particular Slough and its immediate environs which were in the county until 1974, and that a small part of the Tring Reservoir complex is actually in Buckinghamshire rather than Hertfordshire. We have tried to ensure that all the records quoted have been recorded within the confines of the county as it stands today although a few old records from boundary areas may have slipped through.

We have also tried to be as consistent as possible over assessing records of less common species. All recent records have been vetted by the BBC's Records Committee but a great many earlier records have had to be accepted as they stand.

During the early 1980s the Club took over the running of the fieldwork for an atlas of the breeding birds of the county. This continued for several years and the resulting maps are published in this book to give an indication of the status of the county's breeding species. Full details of the methods used and some comments on the interpretation of the resulting maps are included below.

The book starts with some introductory chapters on the history of Buckinghamshire's birdwatchers, the main habitats to be found and a short essay on migration within the county. All these and the main bulk of the book, the species accounts, have been written by a variety of birdwatchers and scientists who have an interest in the birds of the county and who are credited with their texts. Authors of the species accounts were asked to follow certain guidelines when writing and to use material from Buckinghamshire where possible in preference to that from other areas. In particular the simple repeating of general information which appears in other books is avoided although some has been necessary to put the Buckinghamshire information into context.

It will be obvious that the species accounts vary considerably in length. The longer ones mainly result from the particular species having been the subject of a special study in the county, often by the author of the text concerned, rather than that the species is particularly common, or rare. Where possible the editors have tried to retain the sometimes distinctive styles of these and the other authors. The result is that the book is a compilation of knowledge about the birds of the county and knowledge of the birds in general which was gained in the county. The bibliography contains the majority of significant references about the birds of the county, and serves in part as a complement to the much earlier very full bibliography in Hartert and Jourdain (1920) which listed all the old references to individual records up to that date.

There have been several particular surveys of birds in addition to the county breeding survey referred to above, and which have been mentioned specifically where relevant. Most of the national bird surveys which have taken place, largely under the auspices of the British Trust for Ornithology, have included the county. These include the ringing scheme and its associated recoveries, the Common Birds Census, the Nest Record Scheme and several shorter term ones including single species surveys. The National Wildfowl Counts organised by the Wildfowl and Wetlands Trust have been carried out regularly on the major water bodies for many years. The BBC has also run some surveys of its own and in particular a Garden Bird Survey which started in the winter of 1986/87 and continues. Particular surveys of wintering plovers and more detailed studies by individuals working in the county are also noted where relevant.

ACKNOWLEDGEMENTS

A book of this kind cannot be produced without the help of a large number of people. The writers of the species accounts are listed below, the species photographs are individually credited and the main atlas surveyors are listed in an appendix, but there are a number of individuals whose work has largely been in the background.

John Gearing organised atlas surveys (followed by pub lunches) in under-recorded parts of the county. Without his work the maps would not have been as comprehensive as they are. He also continued the work of the late Graeme Taylor on the Garden Bird Survey from which some interesting and useful graphs have been produced.

The proof-reading and photograph selection was undertaken by Rob Andrews, John Barnes, Adam Basset, Mick A'Court, John Gearing, Ed Griffiths, Neill Foster, Rosie Hamilton, Kevin Holt, Lynn Lambert, Jackie Newcombe, Dave Parmenter, Steve Rodwell, Jim Rose and Roger Warren.

The species accounts were written by different authors. In many cases, the author's initials are given at the end of the account. Where no initials are given then the account is of one of the rarer birds and was written by a combination of John Marchant (for the first edition) and David Ferguson, with help from Andy Harding.
    The authors of individual species accounts are:

Rob Andrews (RDA)
Philip Burton (PJKB)
Susan Cowdy (SC)
David Ferguson (DMF)
Rob Fuller (RJF)
Darrell Hamley (DBH)
Andy Harding (AVH)
Jim Knight (JK)
Henry Mayer-Gross (HM-G)
Robert Morgan (RAM)
Jim Rose (JER)
Peter Stevens (PJS)
Norman Stone (NHFS)
Richard Tomlin (RJT)
Mike Wallen (MSW)
Phil Whittington (PAW)
Chris Young (CEY)

Finally, Dawn Balmer, Simon Gillings and the rest of the atlas team at the BTO provided a prompt and helpful service. And, of course, without the BTO's decision to produce a new atlas this book would never have been written in the first place.
    To all these, and particularly to anyone we have inadvertently left out, we are very grateful.

ORNITHOLOGISTS, COLLECTORS AND FIELDWORKERS IN BUCKINGHAMSHIRE THROUGH THE YEARS

Susan Cowdy, Peter Lack and David Ferguson

Early Records

The first explicit mention of birds in Buckinghamshire seems to be in the Domesday Book of 1085. It is stated there that William the Conqueror held two eyries of Hawks in the county: firstly, Manno the Breton owned some land in Chalfont St Giles which 'included woodland to feed 600 swine and in the same wood was a falcon's eyrie'; and, secondly, at Chalfont St Peter, Bishop Bayeux owned some woodland which held a 'hawk's eyrie'. We can only guess at the species involved.

We know of no other mention until the beginning of the sixteenth century when a letter to Cardinal Wolsey stated that the timber for St George's Chapel in Windsor Castle came from Dreynford Wodde at Agmondesham (the present day Brentford Wood at Amersham), where there 'hath been this twenty or thirty years an Ayreye of Goossehawks contynually there bredying. By mysorder they were put from there' (quoted by R.H.Tighe in Annals of Windsor -- see Fraser (1953)).

Hawks seem to have been the major interest because the first mention of a collector in the county was at about the same time. In 1530 Thomas Hawtry, the owner of the Chequers Estate, together with Edward and Harry Hampden and other 'evil-disposed persons, riotously with force and arms entered Frith Wood and caused the tree wherein the Goshawk bred to be scaled and so took out of the nest all the said eyries of young hawks and bore them away to hitherto keep at their wills and pleasures'. Sir John Hampden, as Sheriff, reported the matter to his royal master the King (Henry VIII), and added that he had caused the nest to be kept under continuous watch, at not little cost to himself, with the object that the young hawks should be taken and delivered 'to the commodity and pleasure of your Royal Highness'. This was by no means the end of the story though; for when Hampden sent messengers to collect information on the spot, 'Thomas Hawtry with a dozen others issued out of an ambush on the Ellesborough road and beat and grievously wounded the messengers'. After this, all the accused were summoned to appear before the Court of the Star Chamber, although the upshot of the affair is not told (Jenkins 1967).

A whole series of observations which were made during the late 18th century were recorded in a manuscript which was found in Dinton Hall near Aylesbury. The notes were started in 1772 by Sir John Van Hatten and were continued by a grandson, the Rev. W. Goodall, into the beginning of the nineteenth century. Hartert (see below) later saw this treatise and verified the statements made in it and used them in his two later papers on the birds of the county. Unfortunately this manuscript cannot now be found and must be presumed lost.

It is, however, from about the middle of the nineteenth century that we have a rather better idea of what occurred in the area. There was still considerable persecution going on, as an addendum to the book Aedes Hartwelliana (Smythe 1864) explains. Admiral Smythe lived in Hartwell House and there is a chapter describing the persecution in *A Defence of Birds*. The author discusses the 'vexed questions about birds and bird-murderers'. He denounced sparrow clubs and gives a list of innocuous species which became a quarry for sparrow club heroes, and there is a vivid description of the holiday pastimes of the 'Aylesbury street-arabs'.

Reasons are also given for the rapid thinning of bird communities while their enemies are on the increase. The problems faced by the birds of the time included such as:

'Predatory cottage urchins, hobbety boys and idle adults.
Shrikes and the tribe of butcher birds.
Sparrow clubs and Sunday bird-murderers.
Supplying taxidermy's demands, and the associated wilful waste.
Assarting of wood, groves, spinneys, coppices and the like.
Aylesbury street-arabs' holiday pastime.
Birds' nest plunderers, and birds' egg collectors.
Buzzards, kestrels and hawks in general.
Carrion, Hooded or Gor Crows.
Dogs, cats, rats, fitchets and weasels.
Fire-arms, bows and arrows, stones and sticks.
Hard frosts, sudden storms and severe winters.
Mongel sportsmen and small class poachers.
Owls and strix-hooters of all sorts.
Poisoned food, bird-lime, gins and springes.'

It is a wonder that there were any left!

Mid nineteenth and early twentieth centuries

The first attempt to write about all the birds of the county was by the Rev Bryant Burgess who published a list of bird species recorded in the county in volume 1 (1858) of the Records of Buckinghamshire. He was rector at Latimer and Rural Dean of Amersham. As was typical of country parsons of the time, he had many interests, other than birds. Foremost was archeology. He was a founder member of the Buckinghamshire Archeological and was one of its Honorary Secretaries for some years. Several of the early volumes of 'Records' contain articles by him.

The Birds of Berkshire and Buckinghamshire published in 1865 and written by Alexander W.M. Clark Kennedy, 'an Eton boy', is a remarkable book. The author was only 16 years old when it was written and it is unique too in that the illustrations are the first hand-coloured photographs used in a book on birds. Clark Kennedy's ardent wish was to see the ornithology of each British county represented in a book, but he himself did not do anything very much more ornithological in his life. In compiling the book he was in contact with many Buckinghamshire ornithologists of his day, in particular the Rev. Harpur Crewe of Drayton Beauchamp, and he apparently relied heavily on the records of the Rev Burgess, but most of the records and observations concern the southern part of the county and across the River Thames in Berkshire.

In the following 50 years there was no concerted effort to compile records from the county although there are various individual reports of less common birds in such as The Field (see below). However, in 1905 Ernst Hartert, who was Curator of the Tring Museum from 1903 to 1930, wrote a paper, in collaboration with the Hon. Walter Rothschild, on the birds of Buckinghamshire as a chapter in the *Victoria County History* (Hartert & Rothschild 1905). They wrote then: 'compared with many other counties the number of collectors and field-ornithologists is small, and it seems to us that the country people generally are less observant than they are in some other parts of England'. Ernst Hartert was reckoned by Richard Meinertzhagen to be the best ornithologist of his day, and one who had a great sense of humour and was a charming companion. Rothschild (later Lord

Rothschild) himself was the owner of Tring Museum and he too admired and appreciated Hartert's matchless curating and unflagging industry. Despite his travels all over the world in search of exotic flora and fauna, Rothschild's first interest was in the local Tring area and he and Hartert wrote several papers on the natural history of the nearby areas including the bird one noted above.

Rothschild too was evidently a remarkable man. He was extremely diffident and shy and either had nothing to say at all or gave vent to trumpeting: altogether a charismatic enthusiast who was very generous to all who came his way.

In 1920 Hartert wrote a second major paper on the birds of the county, this time including the Tring Reservoirs, most of which are in neighbouring Hertfordshire, and this time with Pastor F.C.R. Jourdain. Apart from some detailed notes about the birds known from the area, this paper is remarkable for the list of 185 references from 1827 to 1920 which Jourdain compiled. These include many odd records from The Field and all other journals and magazines which he could find. The paper included notes from their own observations, those of Clark Kennedy and from several birdwatchers of the day including Rev H.D. Astley, A. Heneage Cocks, Alan F. Crossman, Heatley Noble, Charles Wilson and Edwin Hollis. The last named was Curator of the Buckinghamshire County Museum in Aylesbury from 1908 to 1941, who was a keen collector and taxidermist and who made a very fine collection of birds and eggs from the county during his term of office. Sadly during the Second World War the bird skins became rather badly moth-eaten and were destroyed by a subsequent curator.

A rather different book was written in the late nineteenth century by the Rev Hubert Astley called *My Birds in Freedom and Captivity*, described by the author as 'only a homely account' of the birds in the gardens of his beautiful home, Chequers Court near Ellesborough (Astley 1900). He too was an extraordinary man for his time. He was one of the first people to put up nestboxes, and these attracted many species, including Common Redstarts which are decidedly uncommon there today. He was also one of the first bird protectionists and calls on the county magistrates to enforce the bird protection laws and to bestir the county police. In addition to local observations he travelled on the continent and in Egypt, and gives graphic descriptions of extreme cruelty to birds. He was particularly fond of wagtails. For example he bought 200 Blue-headed Wagtails from a man in Naples for 5 francs, then opened the large flat cage to the amazement of the bird seller. He had found that the townspeople bought the birds as 'flycatchers', clipping their wings and letting them run loose in their yards and rooms. A more local story was from his schooldays at Eton in the 1870s. At that time there was a ghastly old woman, 'Old Mother Lipscombe', who sat by the school gates selling fruit and local wild birds' eggs, and he lists many of the species she had for sale.

A final string to his bow concerns what may be the first ringing of any birds in Britain. He had a considerable bird collection and in June 1899 he obtained some nestling White Storks from Leadenhall Market, and then..

'..I bought some silver rings, on which I had the year and the name of their English home engraved, and slipped one on to the ankle of each bird. This was not easy, for the ring must not be too large for the stork's leg, and yet large enough to go over the foot. Of course one might have them made with a snap which would close for ever, when shut to; but it would be a more costly business.'

The birds spent the summer flying around Chequers, roosting on the chimney pots, then, in September, flew away, never to be seen again.

From 1920 after the publication of the paper by Hartert and Jourdain (1920) annual reports of birds seen in the county were published as part of the annual report of the then newly started Oxford Ornithological Society. These reports covered Oxfordshire, Berkshire and Buckinghamshire although reading through them it appears that Buckinghamshire was still relatively unrecorded compared to the others.

The reports continued in this way, many compiled and edited by Bernard Tucker, until that for 1953. As with present day county reports and books, the bulk of them consists of a list with notes of the birds seen during the year. However, the newly fledged society also organised several special surveys of particular species covering all three counties, especially during the 1930s. The Great Crested Grebe, Redstart, Tufted Duck and Pochard among others received such a survey. Full details of the results of these surveys are published in the annual reports and form an important record of the distribution of the species at that time. The status of several of the species has changed substantially since.

Although not directly concerned with the birds of Buckinghamshire, a meeting of some significance to the world of ornithology took place in the county in 1945. This is part of a letter written by R. M. Lockley:

'There had been great enthusiasm among us during the war to set up a chain of bird observatories as soon as peace came; and, in December 1945, the nucleus of the first Bird Observatories Committee got together at E. J. M. Buxton's cottage at Long Crendon, Buckinghamshire: W. B. Alexander, John Buxton, Dr Bruce Campbell, George Waterston and myself; and co-opted R. M. Garnett (then busy erecting a Heligoland trap at Spurn, Yorkshire) and Frank Elder of the Isle of May. In due course, the British Trust for Ornithology took over this committee. In 1947, Fair Isle and Lundy Bird Observatories were born, followed by Spurn (1948), Gibraltar Point and Cley (1949); and, while temporarily resident in Jersey, Channel Islands, I was instrumental in persuading the Ornithological Section of the Societe Jersiaise to open in 1950 the present observatory at St Ouen's Pond.'

In 1947 Miss K. Price, who had previously been editor of the Oxford Ornithological Society report, compiled an annotated list (usually 2-3 lines per species) of the 'Birds of Buckinghamshire' as part of the centenary volume of the Buckinghamshire Archaeological Society (Price 1947).

The status of each species in the county was summarised although it was not nearly so detailed as the earlier papers by Hartert and his colleagues. In the introduction to the paper she adds:

'Reading through old county reports one is struck by the number of birds that were shot for identification or out of stupidity; this is now fortunately a rare thing, but it means that there is an element of doubt concerning a number of recent records.

It was not until about 1925 that we began to get reports of birds seen at sewage farms. It will be noticed that a good many species, especially waders, have so far only been met with on Slough sewage farm. Others are seen there almost annually but hardly ever recorded elsewhere in Buckinghamshire. The Chiltern Hills, in the western part of the county, is the only area where Stone Curlew, Cirl Bunting and Wood-lark are found. The Wryneck only breeds in the south-eastern part of the county.'

Unfortunately for Buckinghamshire ornithology Slough Sewage Farm is now not in the county as it was excised during the boundary changes in 1974 and put in Berkshire, as were some of the reservoirs nearby.

After 1953 the Oxford Ornithological Society ceased to report the birds of Buckinghamshire and the annual reporting of records was taken over by the Middle

Thames Natural History Society. However, until 1974 it only covered the area south of the Chiltern Escarpment with the north of the county not covered at all. From 1974 the report covers the whole county and it carried on in this format until the Buckinghamshire Bird Club took over the report for 1980. This has continued ever since.

The period of the Middle Thames Society stewardship of the county records also saw updates of the county list largely at the instigation of A.C. Fraser. *The Birds of the Middle Thames*, covering southern Buckinghamshire was first published in 1954 (Fraser 1954), was revised in 1967 and again in 1976 when, in collaboration with Ron Youngman, who was then County Recorder, it became a fully annotated list of birds of the whole county (Fraser and Youngman 1976). The opportunity was taken also to include the results of the BTO Atlas of Breeding Birds (Sharrock 1976) as it affected the birds of the county.

There were a few other groups active in the county during the latter part of this period. The Amersham and District Ornithological Society (now the Amersham Birdwautching Club) continues to record birds in an area within about 10 km of Amersham, and served then, as it does today, as a focus for many of the birdwatchers in its vicinity.

At the end of 1974 the Milton Keynes Natural History Society spawned a monthly bird bulletin. Mirroring its parent body its area of interest spread farther out than just Milton Keynes and actually covered much of the north of the county. Over the following year or two this bulletin became larger and in 1977 became the North Bucks Bird Report, and the group whose activities centred on the publication formed themselves into a more formal group, the North Bucks Birders, in 1980. During the late 1970s they passed their records for the county report to the Middle Thames Natural History Society but other contact between the two groups was minimal largely because of the distance involved, 80-90 km.

There have been one or two other publications relating to the birds of the county in this period. In 1934 Godfrey Harrison published *A Bird Diary* which includes references to birds in the Amersham/Beaconsfield area, and is illustrated by wood engravings by Robert Gibbings. From his home at Little Missenden he visited Shardeloes Lake where he saw (probably the first) Canada Geese in 1934, commenting that he hoped they would disappear! He and his wife were keen bird mentors (but not collectors) and he writes vivid accounts of the behaviour of different species. He delighted in the common species: 'the Reed Bunting with his black head, singing his ridiculous song', and recalling how he and his wife were in full enjoyment of 'that existence for which ornithology is only an education and a discipline - the unconscious consciousness of the companionship of birds; seeing hearing and interpreting is a pleasure and a delight untold'.

The second is a more well-known book, *The Goshawk* by T.H.White, who was a schoolmaster at Stowe School and a knowledgeable ornithologist and falconer. This eloquent and absorbing book was written a few years before 1939 but publication was withheld for 15 years because as the author wrote: 'There was a guilty secret that had to be concealed at all costs'. This concerned a pair of Hobbies breeding in the area where he lived. White explains: 'The secret was the hobbies, one of the rarest falcons who migrate to breed in England, so rare that one must not tell anybody about them and particularly not in print. All the names in my book are real names. Any unscrupulous ornithologist had only to identify the place or me and then diminish the number of English nesting Hobbies by one pair'. The book was eventually published because an airport was built next to the site (now Silverstone Racing Circuit on the Buckinghamshire/Northamptonshire border), which caused the 'lovely hobbies to clear off on their own accord'. The book is a delight to read.

In more recent years the county has benefited from the fact that the British Trust for Ornithology headquarters was situated in Tring, only just outside the county boundary in

Hertfordshire, from 1963 until 1991, and also the Bird Room of the British Museum (Natural History) moved to Tring during 1971. This has resulted in several eminent ornithologists making their homes in the area and there have been several detailed studies of particular species and areas as a result.

1981 to the Present

Birdwatchers did not really have a focus for their interests over the whole county until 1981 as there was no specific bird club covering the county. During 1981 a group of people in the middle of the county decided that a county bird club was needed to co-ordinate all activities and this resulted in the founding of the Buckinghamshire Bird Club. This had its first public meeting in Wendover in October 1981, since when it has met six or seven times each winter and has organised many field meetings both in the county and farther afield throughout the year.

From its start the Club took over the production of an annual report on the birds of the county from the Middle Thames Natural History Society and produced the report for 1980 as a starting point. This annual report has always had the full co-operation of the North Bucks Birders and, until the society folded in 1989, the Middle Thames Natural History Society bird section.

Early in the Club's history it was decided that the county's breeding birds should be surveyed with the objective of producing maps to a tetrad resolution. The methodology would follow that of the BTO's breeding atlas of the 1960s and the results published in a county avifauna, *The Birds of Buckinghamshire.* This was the first comprehensive book on the county's birds and was published in 1993. It gathered data from many sources: the county atlas survey, wildfowl counts, the county garden birds survey, and the county annual reports.

A characteristic of the present birding scene is its integrated nature. As well as the two clubs mentioned earlier, the North Bucks Birders and the Amersham Birdwatching Club, there are also two RSPB Members Groups in the county, the North Bucks group based in Milton Keynes, and the Aylesbury group. The advent of the internet and email made communications that much easier. The Club's website began operating in 1999 and an online recording system in 2009.

The result is that the county is probably now covered by birdwatchers better that it ever has been. This is demonstrated by the fact that all the county's 553 tetrads were visited for the second atlas of 2007 - 2011. The major sites in the county are regularly watched by a number of dedicated observers with the result that much more is known about migration through the county, particularly on the hills.

The pressure on wildlife habitats caused by an ever increasing human population has meant that the Club has become more involved with other conservation groups in attempting to minimise the damage. The Club's remit has always been recording and education but in 2009 conservation was added. This allowed the Club to sponsor various conservation projects in the county including a hide at College Lake, tern rafts at Little Marlow and help with the purchase of the BBOWT reserve at Gallows Bridge Farm.

BIRD HABITATS AND SELECTED SITES IN BUCKINGHAMSHIRE

Rob Andrews

This chapter is based to a large extent on Rob Fuller's excellent account of the bird habitats in Buckinghamshire in the first edition of The Birds of Buckinghamshire. In the interests of consistency and as a comparison this account follows the same format, giving a brief summary of the habitat, an outline of the significant changes over the last twenty years and the effect this has had on the birdlife of the county. Some of the more noteworthy sites are described in more detail. Finally, an attempt is made to look into the future, although the dramatic changes in the environment and the lack of knowledge of the requirements of many of our birds makes this an uncertain task.

Buckinghamshire is still a largely rural county although the expanding conurbation of Milton Keynes now dominates the north-east. The county is divided almost equally in two by the diagonal south-west to north-east line of the Chiltern escarpment. The geology of the northern half mainly is a mixture of clays interspersed with limestone ridges running parallel to the escarpment. The exception is the greensand ridge on the Bedfordshire border on with the Brickhill Woods lie. The land is largely agricultural although there is a broken line of ancient woodlands again running at a diagonal. In places the increasingly rare habitat of unimproved herb-rich grassland still survives.

To the south of the escarpment beechwoods dominate. In the far south-east the chalk disappears under sandstone and in a few places heathland remains. Thus, although Buckinghamshire is an inland lowland county, there is an impressive range of habitats.

The Wormsley Valley: A typical piece of Buckinghamshire Chiltern landscape with wooded hillsides, wide valleys and mixed farmland. This part of the county was the release site for the reintroduction of the Red Kite. This scheme was a huge success with the species now a familiar sight in the Chilterns and further north. This continuing increase has also been mirrored by Common Buzzard and, more recently, Raven.

Farmland

Farmland forms the largest percentage of the countryside in the county and so has the largest impact on our avifauna through the types of crops grown and the management of the land. Humans have shaped this landscape for hundreds of years, initially enabling many species to adapt successfully to the changes made by man. This trend started to reverse in the 1970s as modernisation of farming practices began to take effect. Since then many of our farmland species have continued to decline. The main reasons appear to be the increased use of pesticides, a decline in the diversity of habitats and the general tidying up of the land.

Crops and grassland

Crops and grassland still cover approximately 60% of the land area in the county and although the types of crops grown have altered very little over the last couple of decades, there have been a few subtle changes.

Mixed farming dominates the county but there is a lot of variation in different parts of Bucks with the area north of the Chilterns characteristically holding more sheep and cattle than the more crop-biased south.

Probably the most striking difference in the last twenty years is the increase in land use for horses, particularly in the south of the county. The majority of these will be on land that was already 'improved' grassland so the change of use has had little negative impact. It is too early to assess the changes to bird populations at the moment but it will be interesting to see if species like Swallow and Yellow Wagtail benefit from the increase in this habitat. Swallows have suffered from many barns being converted to residential dwellings in the last two decades so hopefully an increase in potential nesting sites from newly built stables will go some way to compensating this.

The damper meadows have continued to decline but the BBOWT reserve at Gallows Bridge Farm is a fine example of this rare habitat and a small part of a more ambitious project to link similar areas on a larger scale, described later in this chapter.

Oilseed rape has also continued to increase as a crop in Bucks and may continue to do so with its growing popularity as a healthy vegetable oil and the increasing demand for bio-fuels.

The damp meadows of Gallows Bridge Farm, an important site for breeding Curlew and wintering wildfowl and plovers. These wet meadows have become very scarce in the county.

Use of crops and grass by birds

These days a walk through farmland in spring and summer can be a quiet experience compared with 30-40 years ago. The characteristic song of the Skylark can still be heard over crop fields in most parts of Buckinghamshire but they have declined in the last twenty years and are now quite patchy in distribution. Thankfully their numbers now appear to have stabilised, largely due to field margins being left fallow.

Very few other species use crops for actually nesting in and they have never been as widespread as the Skylark. Corn Buntings and Yellow Wagtails can still be found in a few areas and Reed Buntings sometimes find Oilseed rape to their liking, although they have failed to colonise it as the early signs suggested. Lapwings are very scarce farmland breeders now due to the change in sowing times and spraying. Grassland species like Curlew are still hanging on in a few areas, largely thanks to sympathetic landowners and conservation organisations but their productivity appears to be very low at present, with predation a problem. Redshank and Common Snipe no longer breed in these fields, although the former has successfully colonised some of our lakes. Meadow Pipits are still present in a few suitable meadows, with the stronghold being the chalk grassland of the Chilterns.

The crop fields attract far more species when they have been ploughed and throughout the winter if left as stubble, although the latter is an increasingly rare sight. Rooks, Jackdaws, Starlings, Black-headed Gulls and Lesser Black-backed Gulls are characteristic of recently ploughed land but the pickings are short term and these birds move from one area to another as a new field is ploughed up.

Studies into the diets of wintering passerines have shown that the seeds of annual weeds associated with crops are a vitally important food source. The development of pre-emergent herbicides has all but wiped out these crop field weeds. The demise of the weeds has also removed the invertebrates that used to feed on them and in turn removed a major food source for partridge chicks.

Down Farm near Pitstone: The wide field margins and permanent grass meadows of this area have been beneficial to a number of species, particularly Skylark and Corn Bunting. From this spot on one evening in June, as well the two species already mentioned, the calls of Quail, Meadow Pipit, Linnet, Yellowhammer and Common Whitethroat could be heard nearby.

Turf farms can also be attractive to species such as wagtails and thrushes, with the sward kept short by mowing or sheep grazing. Also when the turf is stripped off the ground below can be covered in freshly exposed worms and leatherjackets, producing a feast for many birds including migrants like Northern Wheatear and Whinchat.

Changes in farming practice and bird populations
The changes in farming practices in the last twenty years have been smaller than in the same time period before this. Most of the damage to our farmland bird populations had already been done and many species have continued to contract in numbers and range as the modern agricultural practices continue to take their toll. Tree Sparrows have declined by 94% in Britain in the last 50 years and a similar pattern has occurred in Bucks. They are now completely absent from the area south of the Chilterns and only found in isolated patches in the north. Corn Bunting is another species virtually absent from the south of the county now, with other species like Yellowhammer, Lapwing and Grey Partridge found in far lower numbers than before. The more long-term food source of winter stubble, particularly important for species like finches and buntings, has declined further with the increase in autumn sown crops.

Occasionally a piece of farmland will provide suitable feeding for winter birds and give an indication how the trend of declines could be reversed. An open grain store at Granborough attracted double figure counts of Tree Sparrows in the first decade of the new millennium and as recently as 2010 a flock of 100 was discovered feeding in a game cover strip near Little Linford Wood.

There are now various agri-environment schemes being implemented, such as leaving a wide field margin uncultivated, that will hopefully begin to reverse some of the declines before it is too late.

There will no doubt be many changes to farming over the next few decades, as pressure for food from a growing population increases and the need to cut down on fossil fuels becomes a necessity.

Woodland
Buckinghamshire is well known for being a particularly wooded county, still covering more than 8% of the area of the county. This is especially true of the Chilterns where approximately 20% of the land is wooded. In contrast the Vale of Aylesbury lacks any large areas of woodland with just a few patches of coverts until reaching the ancient Bernwood Forest to the north-west and the conifer dominated plantations of the Brickhill Woods to the north-east. As with farmland, many birds associated with woodland have also declined over the last few decades and in common with that habitat there are believed to be a number of reasons.

Ancient woodland
The county still contains a reasonably high proportion of ancient woodland, currently around 8,000ha and any losses in the last twenty years have been mainly around the margins during building development, which can certainly affect its quality even if only small sections are taken.

Many of these ancient woods were replanted with conifers as can be seen at sites like Shabbington Wood and College Wood. Although these woodlands can be of great botanical interest, their value to birdlife depends on the structure and the type of vegetation present, which is looked at in more detail below.

The Chilterns Woodlands

Think of the Chilterns and you think of one type of tree, the Beech, the tree most associated with the county and the one that gives most woodland of the Chilterns its distinct character. Many of these woods, particularly the vast beech hangers on the steeper slopes, lack any significant patches of shrub layer. Consequently their attractiveness to breeding birds is limited to species using the canopy or hole nesters. However, wherever the soil is deeper, the variety of growth is more varied with species such as Cherry, Oak, Ash and Hornbeam adding to the interest.

Many woods in the Chilterns have grown up on former open common land, the best examples being parts of Ashridge, Burnham Beeches, Penn Wood and Naphill Common. Many of these commons would have been open heathland, the remnants of which will be described below.

Decaying tree in Ashridge Forest: This large area of woodland, managed by the National Trust, contains a wide variety of habitats rich in birdlife. Dead trees are left to decay naturally where it is safe and some areas are felled to open up the canopy to encourage a healthy shrub layer.

Left: An open ride in Rushbeds Wood with a recently coppiced area to the right showing the dense shrub layer that has grown up. The demise of coppicing has had a negative impact on many woodland species, especially Nightingale, but also Willow Tit.

Right: In the same wood a former area of coppice not cut for many years showing the lack of a dense shrub layer. Deer browsing has also reduced the quality of the shrub layer in many woods.

The dominant tree on these former commons is usually birch, which because of the open nature of its foliage, lets in plenty of light and so supports a rich shrub layer, as in parts of Ashridge near Ringshall.

There has been no large scale felling in these woods during the last twenty years, although the demand for wood has increased in recent years so this may change. Some small scale felling has taken place in Penn Wood since it was bought by the Woodland

Trust as part of the management plan to restore parts of the site to wood pasture.

Birds likely to colonise these more open areas with sprouting saplings include summer visitors like Willow Warblers, Chiffchaffs and Garden Warblers. Recently felled areas were once colonised by Tree Pipits but their population has crashed nationally for reasons not completely understood and it is now an uncommon visitor to the county. Penn Wood also holds an important finch roost during the winter months with nationally significant counts of Brambling. Most of these birds roost in the rides of Rhododendron located in the centre of the wood, showing not only the value of having a diversity of plant species including evergreens but also the importance of the size of the wood in determining the warmth of night temperatures in the centre.

A number of other species have declined in these woods including Lesser-spotted Woodpeckers, while Hawfinch, Common Redstart and Wood Warbler sadly appear to have disappeared as breeding species in the county. Areas of woodland with Hornbeam and Cherry may still be worth searching for Hawfinch though, as the population in Britain can be supplemented in some years by birds from the continent in the winter, so a few may stay to breed.

The size of the woodland will also affect the quality of the habitat with some woodland being constantly fragmented or reduced around the edges as pressure from housing and business gradually infringe on land. This may appear minimal at the time but over the years as more trees disappear the result is a sparse area of woodland with little variety and less cover for birds. A prime example of this is Kingswood, north of High Wycombe, which once had a large amount of dense cover but the building of houses has nibbled into the edges and it is now possible in the winter to see buildings through the wood while standing on the other side. This type of reduction must also have an effect on the temperature of a wood in cold winters with the wind able to penetrate the whole site and so potentially affecting birds feeding and roosting there.

The clay vale woods

These woods are usually more varied in tree species than the beech woods of the Chilterns and most are remnants of larger ancient forests. The majority are found around Yardley Chase, Whittlewood Forest, Whaddon Chase and the land between Bernwood Forest and the Claydons. The varied number of tree species is predominantly made up of oak, mixed with ash, field maple and hazel and many of these have a long history of coppicing with many showing old hazel stools. Once an integral part of the rural economy, coppicing largely ceased as a woodland management practice 70-80 years ago. Some coppicing is now carried out as part of a management plan for wildlife, such as in Rushbeds Wood, a BBOWT reserve near Brill. Areas of hazel and ash are coppiced on a cycle of around 10 years allowing light to reach the forest floor and encourage other species to grow. After a few years there is a dense shrub layer attractive to species of warbler and in the past Nightingales were found in some of these woods. The demise of coppicing no doubt had an impact on this latter species but it is doubtful that it is the only aspect responsible for its decline. There is also growing evidence that browsing from deer is having a negative impact on the structure of the shrub layer and the birds that use it but more study is needed to gauge the level of this change.

Coniferous Woodland

Conifer woods are often thought to be a sterile habitat for birds but this is often not the case. The largest conifer plantations include a vast swathe on former heathland across the greensand ridge of the Brickhills, with other large areas such as Wendover Woods and

Homefield Wood in the Chilterns.

The best known colonist of our conifer woods is the Firecrest, originally putting Wendover Woods on the national map, this species is also found in other mostly coniferous woods in the Chilterns and appears to be thriving again in recent years.

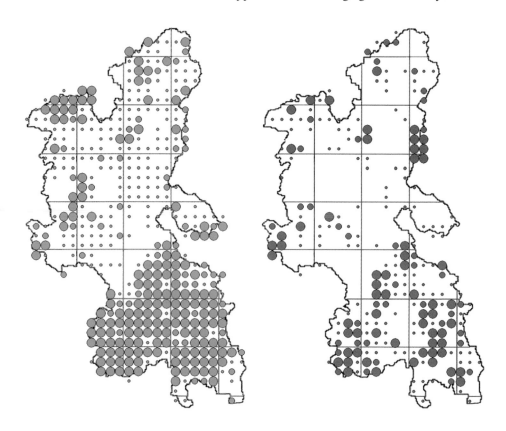

Distribution of broad-leaved woodland.
Large dots represent > 20 ha per tetrad, medium dots 10 - 20 ha and small dots < 10 ha.

Distribution of coniferous woodland.
Large dots represent > 20 ha per tetrad, medium dots 10 - 20 ha and small dots < 10 ha.

Sections of these large conifer plantations are harvested in cycles of many years and so varying stages of growth provide a diverse structure in a similar way to the old coppiced woods. A newly felled area of Black Park attracted the first breeding Woodlarks in the county for many years in 1994, after more than a twenty year absence, so scrutiny of similar sites in the future could be fruitful. A large part of Wendover Woods was clear felled in the 1990s and in the next decade a fascinating colonisation of species occurred as dense vegetation grew up around the newly planted conifers. Typical birds of this dense vegetation such as Grasshopper, Willow and Garden Warblers were regular here up until 2009 when the growth became too high and Grasshopper Warblers abandoned the site. This is a pattern that has been reflected at other sites like Back Wood in the Brickhills where this species moves to younger areas when the growth has become too tall. The mature stands are far from birdless with Coal Tits and Goldcrest abundant, Treecreepers found in increasing numbers and Siskins regular. Another species that is being seen more regularly and must breed occasionally is Crossbill, the ultimate specialist of these types of wood.

Hedges and Scrub
These two habitats have changed very little in the last two decades. A few hedges continue to be lost and new ones planted but clearly the quality of new hedges will take many years to reach the potential of an established one.

There are some fine examples of ancient hedgerows in the county, particularly in the Chilterns, with one in Princes Risborough known to have existed since AD903 and thought to be the oldest hedge in England.
These ancient hedges, as well as many others dating from the Enclosure Acts of the eighteenth and early nineteenth centuries, are now recognised as exceptionally important species rich habitats.

Not surprisingly the hedgerows with the largest range of plant species, especially trees, contain the most bird species. The quality of individual hedges varies greatly though with sections containing too many trees preventing the lower shrubs from growing strongly and so limiting the number of species that can utilise them. Heavy trimming results in a short, weak structure supporting few species but at the other end of the spectrum lack of pruning will produce tall, spindly growth shading out the lower vegetation and so weakening the density. A rotational system where hedges are cut every couple of years would provide maximum benefit for breeding birds and allow sections to fruit for wintering thrushes. Hedgerows have become especially important for breeding farmland birds as the pesticides have reduced feeding opportunities in the crops so birds rely on the usually unsprayed hedgerow edges to find enough food.

Areas of scrub on Steps Hill: The photo on the left shows how the dense low growth disappears as the plants mature. Many of the species associated with the dense low growth, including Garden Warbler and Lesser Whitethroat abandon these areas when the shrub layer becomes too sparse. Fortunately this site is actively managed with many areas cleared on rotation to create dense growth of varying stages, as shown in the photo on the right.

Species most commonly found in our hedgerows include Chaffinch, Blackbird, Song Thrush, Robin, Wren, Dunnock, Woodpigeon and Blue and Great Tits. They are also important for summer migrants like Common Whitethroat, Lesser Whitethroat and

Blackcap. Smaller numbers of species such as Bullfinch, Great Spotted and Green Woodpeckers occur and isolated populations of Tree Sparrow can also still be found in some areas.

Scrub is an unpredictable habitat occurring in patches all over the county where land is no longer used and there has been no grazing or mechanical control to prevent it establishing.

The largest and most stable areas tend to occur along the Chiltern escarpment where large patches are managed to provide vegetation of varying heights and densities. Scrub is usually extremely rich in birdlife but the populations of individual species vary greatly as the vegetation grows up. Skylarks and Meadow Pipits dominate in the open grassland and will tolerate small patches of isolated bushes, although Skylark will soon move out as these increase. As the scrub cover increases Meadow Pipits will sometimes be replaced by Tree Pipits but as mentioned earlier there are other factors limiting their occurrence in Bucks. Other species characteristic of this open scrub include Linnet, Whitethroat and Yellowhammer, with the possibility of Grasshopper Warbler if there are areas of bramble. As the canopy closes these are replaced by species associated with hedgerows as mentioned above with the addition of Willow Warbler, Chiffchaff and Garden Warbler.

Scrub also occurs in large densities along disused railway cuttings and around gravel pits. These have been some of the last sites for heavily declining species in the county like Turtle Dove, Nightingale and Cuckoo.

Being similar in habitat type to coppiced woodland, the effects of deer browsing appear to be having an impact on the quality of the vegetation. Muntjacs, in particular, will browse the low level vegetation favoured by the likes of Garden Warbler and Willow Tit.

This is a fairly easy habitat to create so it would be an ideal opportunity for conservation organisations to turn more land into scrub in the future and manage it on a rotational system.

Heathland

Although accounting for just a tiny percentage of land area in the county, heathland is potentially one of the most important habitats in Bucks, certainly in terms of the less common species it may attract. It is also a nationally important habitat with nearly half the area of European heathland found in Britain, despite us having only 16% of the area found here some 150-200 years ago.

Heathland is a semi-natural habitat that was probably first created on a large scale by early settlers during the stone and bronze ages, who cleared trees for firewood and farming. Finding the topsoil too thin for growing crops, they began using the land for grazing livestock and harvested heather for thatching or fuel. This gradually impoverished the soil fertility further, preventing coarse grasses and other invasive plants from taking over, benefiting species like Heather and Gorse that could survive on the low nutrient soils. Grazing also helped prevent invading tree species from taking over and shading out the heather, resulting in the characteristic open habitat that typifies heathland.

The special birds of heathland, for example Dartford Warbler, Woodlark and Nightjar are typical of large areas of suitable habitat, although the latter two can also occur in woodlands that have been clear felled. None of these species are regular breeders in the county and it seems likely that we receive the 'overspill' from the strongholds in Berkshire and Surrey where there are large areas of suitable habitat and healthy populations of most heathland species.

There are three main sites large enough to be of significant interest - Black Park and Stoke Common in the south of the county and Rammamere Heath in the north.

Aside from the usual threat of development, which shouldn't be an issue for the main sites mentioned above, the largest threat is through lack of management. Fires have also taken their toll over the last couple of decades or so but the special value of this habitat is at last being recognised. Long-term management plans are in place to create new areas and maintain the existing habitat to maximise its potential for wildlife. The organisations responsible for pushing these initiatives forward should be applauded for their efforts. It is hoped that other areas where heathland used to exist, such as Littleworth Common, will also be turned back to prime habitat and link some of the isolated pockets.

Heathland: Active management of heathland is essential to the survival of this nationally important habitat. The left photo, taken at Black Park, shows the varying stages of heather growth with older woody plants in the foreground, younger growth behind and then a freshly cut area behind this. This diversity of plant age, including the unmanaged area at the back with mature trees ensures that a large variety of invertebrate species can survive. The right photo, taken at Stoke Common, shows a gorse dominated heath. Studies have shown that the presence of gorse on heaths can have a significant positive effect for Dartford Warblers and other species, providing a dense snow free feeding area during harsh winter weather.

Wetlands

The various wetland sites, in general, attract the widest variety of species in the county and so attract the attention of birdwatchers more than any other habitat. With the exception of the rivers and streams all of these are man-made and have been created for a variety of reasons including chalk and gravel extraction, flood relief and drinking water.

In contrast to the previous habitats, the fortunes for our wetland birds have been mostly positive with the likes of Oystercatcher, Little Egret and Cetti's Warbler establishing themselves as regular breeders in the last 20 years.

Lakes and Reservoirs

By far the most popular of these wetlands for birders are the significant number of lakes scattered throughout the county varying in size, depth and type of vegetation. The vast majority of these can be found along the valleys of the Great Ouse, the Colne and the Thames mostly as a result of aggregate extraction but there are also reservoirs at Foxcote and Weston Turville. The remaining water bodies are mostly ornamental lakes and ponds that can also prove attractive to certain species.

It is the practice of mineral extraction though that has had the largest effect on the status of our waterbirds. After their intended reason for creation has been exhausted, the options for future use can be varied with some used for landfill but the majority kept as lakes for recreation or in some cases sites for nature to flourish.

In the early days the vegetation is sparse and can attract breeding species associated with beaches like Ringed and Little-ringed Plovers and Common Tern, while as the vegetation increases slightly Lapwing, Redshank and more recently Oystercatcher will join them. These open sites also prove very attractive to passage waders while there is sufficient open ground available.

As the vegetation continues to increase and cover any open ground many of the species above will disappear unless the site is actively managed to control the natural succession. For this reason most of these species are found on nature reserves where the open ground can be preserved and in some cases water levels can be manipulated to replicate winter flooding.

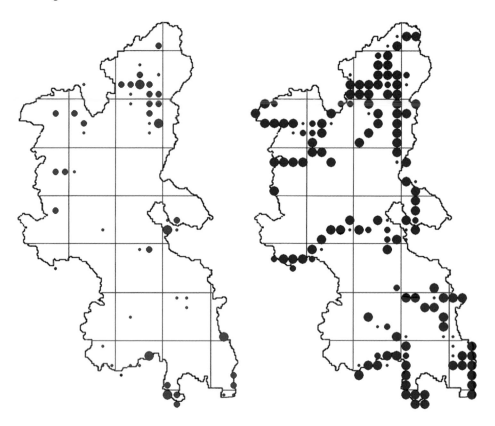

Distribution of standing water bodies (mainly gravel pits, reservoirs and brick pits).
Large dots represent > 30 ha per tetrad, medium dots 15 - 30 ha and small dots < 15 ha.

Distribution of rivers.
Large dots represent > 2 km per tetrad, medium dots 1 - 2 km and small dots < 1 km.

Another feature that greatly enhances the potential of a lake is an island, or better still a series of islands of differing heights, shapes and vegetative structure. Breeding productivity is usually higher due to the increased protection from ground predators, although the introduced mink can still prove a serious threat.

The presence of large enough trees on these sites can result in a heronry becoming established and this in turn can attract Little Egrets to breed, as has happened in recent years in the north of the county.

The following section describes the major water bodies in the county, from north to south, with the more significant sites described in more detail. Details of location and access for the main sites can be found in the site guide elsewhere in this book.

The Milton Keynes area contains the largest concentration of lakes in the county and some of the best birding. The jewel in the crown of these is Linford, also known as the Hanson Environmental Study Centre, a gem of a site with habitats ranging from damp woodland, reedbeds, meadows and a large low lying gravely bund. Situated on the northern edge of the city it is constantly under threat, with two new housing estates now encroaching from each side and the possibility of it being turned into a country park in the future. This was the first site to attract breeding Little Egrets to the county and has also attracted a long list of county scarcities, not to mention a few firsts for the county. The bund is an important habitat for breeding waders when in suitable condition, as well as passage birds, and the densely vegetated patches are excellent for breeding warblers. Crucially the access is by permit and we can only hope that this remains the case in the future.

Rivalling Linford for its reputation in attracting scarce birds is Willen Lake. Located almost in the centre of Milton Keynes and with open access to all, this is a complete contrast as a birding experience to the previous site. Designed as a balancing lake to take floodwater from the River Ouzel, it actually consists of two lakes divided by the H5 grid road. The south lake is used heavily for watersports and other recreational activities limiting the interest for birdwatching but it is always worth a look for passage terns and roosting gulls. The north lake is thankfully quieter and more bird friendly with the shallower water attracting flocks of wildfowl, along with a large island and areas of reedbed and scrub to add to the diversity. There is a hide on the southern shore overlooking a close wader scrape and a mud and gravel spit on the island – important sites for passage waders. Willen has a well-deserved reputation for turning up the unexpected with an incredible list of rarities and an undeniable attraction for scarce county birds. Although higher water levels and disturbance have had an impact, Willen still seems to conjure up surprises and the benefit of having an undisturbed island ensures that individuals will stick around this heavily utilised site.

Many other lakes can be found around the city, although none rival the two detailed above for their attractiveness to birdlife or diversity of habitats but are certainly worthy of exploration.

Just outside Buckingham, in the North-west of Bucks, is found one of our two reservoirs, Foxcote, owned by Anglian Water and managed by BBOWT as one of their reserves and a couple of kilometres south-east of here can be found the under-watched Hyde Lane Gravel Pits.

Continuing south to a small village named Hillesden, a series of small pools have been created by an enthusiastic landowner and have already proved attractive to a number of waders. Oystercatchers have bred successfully here, along with Little-ringed Plover and

Redshank but recently success has been limited due to predation and disturbance. Remarkably the first Wilson's Phalarope for the county appeared here in 2006, testament to the fact that anything can turn up if attractive habitat is provided.

A little further south can be found the former brick pits of Calvert lakes. They comprise of two lakes, the east one being a BBOWT reserve and the larger west lake used for sailing and fishing. The BBOWT reserve contains a wider variety of habitat including reedbed, scrub, meadows and scrapes. Cetti's Warbler is becoming regular here and the surrounding scrub has become one of the last remaining sites for the fast disappearing Turtle Dove. Winter usually produces a Bittern or two and the sailing lake is a prime site for wintering gulls, with regular sightings of the rarer species, particularly Iceland, Glaucous and Caspian on a virtual annual basis.

The private lakes at Wotton House in the west are an attractive site for wintering wildfowl and have also tempted in a passage Osprey on a few occasions.

Just to the north of the Chilterns can be found Weston Turville Reservoir, constructed in 1795 to supply water to the Wendover arm of the Grand Union Canal. Owned by British Waterways and managed by BBOWT this small reservoir has the main attraction of an extensive reedbed. Reed Warblers breed in large numbers, with a few pairs of Sedge Warblers. Grasshopper Warbler is sometimes present and Cetti's is being seen, or more often heard, with increasing regularity. This is the only regular breeding site for Water Rail in Bucks and a reliable place to find wintering Bitterns.

Further east we find another BBOWT reserve, College Lake, an old chalk quarry that has been transformed into a mosaic of habitats including a deep lake, a shallower lake with islands, meadows, scrub and woodland. This is an excellent site for breeding waders, with Redshank , Oystercatcher and Lapwings all regular. There is also an important Common Tern colony here and if the water levels are low, passage waders will be attracted to the exposed mud. The extremely deep main lake usually remains largely unfrozen in freezing conditions and consequently is a refuge for wintering wildfowl pushed off the nearby Tring Reservoirs complex when iced over.

The extensive reedbed at Weston Turville Reservoir: a vitally important habitat for breeding and wintering species.

The Chilterns is almost devoid of significant areas of water with just a few small lakes along the Rivers Chess and Misbourne. Shardeloes Lake on the Misbourne is probably the pick of these being a small ornamental lake with lots of dense bushes and overgrown islands. This is a good site for breeding wildfowl and roosting thrushes in the winter. It was also a regular site for breeding Ruddy Duck, before the controversial cull brought that to an unfortunate end.

At the eastern edge of the county a string of gravel pits line the River Colne, the result of gravel extraction, from Tilehouse Lakes at the northern end to Thorney Country Park to the south. which despite being placed adjacent to the junction of the M4 and M25 motorways has attracted Red-breasted Merganser and Purple Sandpiper in the past so has potential to turn something up despite being not particularly well watched.

The remainder of our lakes are found along the Thames Valley. The newest of these is Dorney Lake, constructed and owned by Eton College, it was designed specifically as a rowing course and was completed as recently as 2006. The lake is fairly sterile with limited vegetation but the surrounding gravel areas have proved attractive to breeding Little Ringed Plovers and the short grass is suitable for wagtails and pipits. The area of most interest to visiting birders is the small nature reserve south of the rowing lake where a shallow flooded pool is a haven for wading birds and dabbling duck. Shallow marsh is an all too scarce habitat in Bucks and this site shows how important it is to passage waders with a large variety of species being seen in the last few years, including a number of locally rare ones. The first Glossy Ibis for over one hundred years was also found the habitat to its liking in 2011. Following the Thames north a short distance we reach Taplow Gravel Pit, a private pit mainly used for watersports and fishing, it is attractive to wintering wildfowl and has attracted Black-throated and Great-northern Divers in the past.

Continuing upriver a series of gravel pits are located to the east of Marlow. The best of these is the eastern most lake known as Little Marlow or Spade Oak Nature Reserve, one of the best sites in the county and certainly the top South Bucks site. The main feature of the lake is the large sand spit that extends out from the northern shore, formed by the waste left over after cleaning the extracted gravel. This low, open 'beach' is usually full of birds and credit must go to a small group of enthusiastic local birders who maintain this habitat with regular cutting of the vegetation. In winter the spit is used by grazers such as geese and Wigeon and is also favoured by thousands of gulls during late afternoon before they go to roost. During passage periods a number of wader species are attracted to the muddy edges and Jack Snipe is occasionally found in the winter. Another important feature of the site is the well-vegetated island providing safe nesting for a colony of Grey Herons and Cormorants.

Although this is currently still a working site, this is set to come to an end in the next few years and turned solely into a nature reserve. It is hoped that landscaping will be carried out to create further habitats where the current workings are located.

Rivers, streams and Canals

As mentioned earlier we are fortunate in the county that two of the largest rivers in England, the Great Ouse and the Thames, run through part of our landscape. These large rivers, although not supporting anything like the variety of species found on our lakes, are important for a number of species and can be crucial in harsh winter weather when they remain ice-free. Although the variety of breeders may be low on the larger rivers they do have their specialities and remarkably a pair of Goosander bred in the county for the first time in 2007, on the Great Ouse near Olney, with a repeat performances in 2010 and 2012.

Smaller rivers include the Ouzel, Ray and Thame to the north of the Chilterns, with the Chess, Misbourne, Colne and Wye to the south. The usual species associated with rivers like Kingfisher and Grey Wagtail continue to thrive.

The River Ouse at Tyringham: The Ouse along with its adjacent meadows is an important river in the county. This location has become well known for attracting Hobbies in late summer.

A completely man-made river in the south of the county, known as the Jubilee River, was created in the late 1990s to take overflow from the River Thames and so alleviate flooding to the towns of Maidenhead, Eton and Windsor. Approximately 11.5km long and an average of 45metres wide the river was designed with wildlife in mind, with islands created and reedbeds planted up. The banks are remarkably natural looking along most of the river and in the last ten years it has matured and attracted a large number of species.

Many streams and brooks can be found in the flatter area of the Vale of Aylesbury resulting in damper areas, although these are extremely limited and large areas of damp meadow have been mostly drained. These losses have been compensated to an extent by the formation of all the lakes mentioned above but Common Snipe has disappeared as a breeding species due to its need for extensive wet grass areas, a habitat not found in abundance on these newer sites.

The Grand Union Canal is a significant feature running through much of the eastern side of the county, attractive to Kingfishers, Little Grebes and Common Terns in search of an easy meal.

The future of our wetland sites looks more encouraging in the 21st century and who knows what could follow the lead of Little Egrets as colonists. With more than a hint of optimism, Cattle and Great White Egrets, Night and Purple Herons and Little Bittern to name just a few!

Artificial and Urban Habitats
A section on our more built up towns may not seem a particularly inspiring choice of location in which to go birding and although they will never be able to support the diversity found in the countryside, there can be more to these concrete jungles than meets the eye.

The most obvious sites to begin with are the gardens as they make up a large proportion of green space in our towns and are the one habitat that *we* can manage to whatever extent we like. These can potentially provide nesting and feeding sites for a number of species if planted sympathetically and there is a growing trend for laying gardens out with wildlife in mind. The usual principles of creating areas for safe nesting, feeding and roosting are the basic requirements and there are many native and ornamental shrubs that can provide all three without taking up vast amounts of space.

Winter feeding has grown in popularity in the last 20 years or so and has certainly helped many species at a time when farmland has been such a barren habitat. The buildings themselves can be important for breeding birds too, for example House Martins and Swifts almost completely dependent on these structures, with Starlings and House Sparrows less so.

Towns often have large areas of parkland, formal gardens or churchyards. Often these are too manicured to attract a vast array of species but can still be an oasis of greenery in an otherwise inhospitable landscape. A few churchyards still seem to be attractive to Spotted Flycatchers, probably in part due to suitable nesting sites in climbers on walls and lack of pesticides used. Maybe future councils could adopt a policy of allowing more wild areas to develop in parkland, enhancing the diversity, as found in some of the parkland of Milton Keynes. This relatively new city was carefully planned to include large areas of parkland, inter-connected with pathways and planted with large numbers of shrubs and trees.

Aylesbury County Hall: The site of successful breeding by Peregrines in 2012 after a specially constructed nesting platform was placed on the building. This exciting event was captured on video cameras connected to the council's website (inset).

In the last decade our towns have provided a particularly memorable winter bird spectacle, with the increasing frequency of Waxwing flocks appearing in the county. Although these flocks are highly eruptive and irregular in Britain with no two winters the same, the increased planting of ornamental trees and shrubs in our urban areas must be a factor in holding birds in the county for longer. By the time Waxwings work their way south through Britain to this area most of the hedgerow berries have been eaten by thrushes, so these artificial orchards are a magnet for these not particularly shy birds.

Watching and photographing Waxwings at close range in a shopping centre car park as people walk past with trolleys has to be one of the more surreal experiences of a birders' year, usually met with an equal amount of amusement and interest from passers-by!

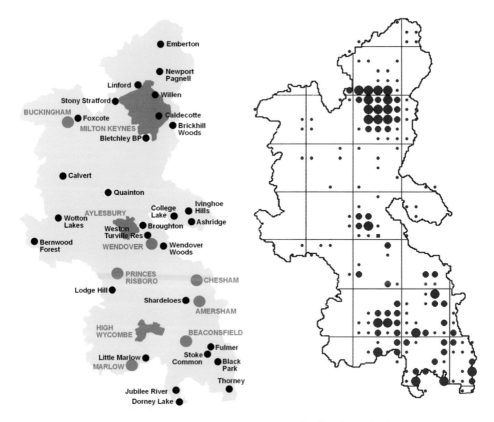

Distribution of urban areas. Large dots represent >267 ha, medium dots 133 - 267 ha, and small dots <133 ha.

Towns are also used by some species for communal roosts, in particular Pied Wagtails and Starlings, which take advantage of the slightly warmer night temperatures.

Recently a new exciting development has occurred with the arrival of Peregrines in the centre of Aylesbury. A nesting platform was positioned on a ledge and after some false starts a pair successfully raised two juveniles. Cameras have also been set up and it is hoped that this will become an annual event to raise awareness and interest with the general public in birds and especially raptors.

Of all the artificial habitats, perhaps the least appealing but strangely magnetising to certain birders, are the rubbish tips. Their popularity is largely down to one group of birds, the gulls, and they have changed the status of many species. In the last decade Herring and Lesser Black-backed have started to breed on factory roofs in nearby towns, with the year round supply of food providing easy pickings. Wintering flocks have also increased in numbers, including many scarce species and flocks of Red Kites have also started taking advantage of this resource.

The Future

It is always preferable if possible to finish an article such as this on a positive note and despite all the pressures on the birdlife of Buckinghamshire there are many examples, a few already mentioned above, of species increasing in the county.

So what ups and downs can we expect in the future? The pressure on land in this increasingly busy part of the country is heavier than ever and so the remaining areas must be protected where possible and well managed. There is also the opportunity to create new habitat to compensate for any losses and to be creative in these sites to maximise the diversity of birds and other wildlife attracted to it.

Boardwalk through flooded marsh and woodland at Linford Reserve: A good example of how modern reserves can enhance people's experiences with nature, giving an intimate view into a rare habitat, created by industrial mineral extraction and careful habitat creation. Many reserves similar to this one provide an impressive range of facilities for visitors, with strategically positioned hides, visitor centres and paths - the challenge being to ensure that the wildlife is not disturbed by the inevitable increase in visitors.

Some examples of wetland sites that have been transformed into nature reserves after mineral extraction have already been mentioned above. BBOWT's flagship reserve in the county is College Lake, a site that has been subject to many changes in the last decade with improved visitor facilities, including a large visitor centre, well-marked paths and a re-landscaped marsh. It is now an important education centre, receiving visits from many schools in the area, the aim to build an interest of the natural world in the next generation.

BBOWT have also launched an ambitious project called 'Living Landscapes' centred on the Upper River Ray floodplain. This scheme, in partnership with the RSPB and local landowners, will link a vast area of land along the Ray all the way to the Otmoor reserve in Oxfordshire. Already an important area for breeding waders, it is hoped that an increase in wet grassland and pools will help conserve these populations and even bring back species like Common Snipe.

Schemes such as this will be vital in the future, as our land becomes more fragmented and populations more isolated. Although birds are not as prone to isolation as other animals they suffer more from predation if surrounding areas are bereft of any quality habitats, with these 'green islands' acting like a honey pot to predators.

Nature reserves will still be a vital refuge as they can be specifically managed to suit certain species and usually have a higher level of protection against development. There are threats even to SSSIs though.

At the time of writing the government has given its approval to a new high speed rail link between London and Birmingham. The proposed route for this new line cuts straight through the Chilterns and out into the Vale of Aylesbury, carving through ancient woodland and several nature reserves. There is still a way to go before this project is built and this is not the place to discuss the impact on our birdlife but I include it here as an example of the very real threats facing our county and its wildlife.

The Aston Clinton super dairy under construction on the site of former damp grassland meadows where Lapwings bred the previous year and flocks of Golden Plover could be found during the winter. Many other sites like this will be under threat in the coming decades.

Our urban areas are increasing too with Milton Keynes continuingly expanding and Aylesbury growing at a rapid rate with 3000 houses currently being built to the north of the town and plans having been submitted for a similar number to the south-east.

The recent approval and building of a new 'super dairy' at Aston Clinton on an important damp meadow area was a major blow for the local environment and a prime example how threatened the countryside is in our county.

There is no doubt that the next few decades will continue to produce many changes to our birdlife through the shaping of habitats. With thought, creativity and much perseverance it is to be hoped the positive changes will prevail.

References

Ausden, M & Fuller, R.J. 2009. Birds and habitat change in Britain – Part 2. British Birds: 102. 52-71.
Brooke, S. 1998. Broughton near Aylesbury – A Site Guide. Buckinghamshire Bird Report 1998: 16-20.
Clews, B. 2001. New Wetlands in the Thames Valley. Buckinghamshire Bird Report 2001: 15-16.
Clews, B & Trodd, P. 2002. Where to watch birds in the Thames Valley and the Chilterns. Helm. London.
Cowdy, S. 1992. The Changing Pattern of Some Buckinghamshire Birds. Buckinghamshire Bird Report 1991: 10-12.
Crathorne, B&L. 2000. Changes in a Breeding Bird Community – Medmenham during 1974-2000. Buckinghamshire Bird Report 2000:21-29.
Fuller, R.J. 1995. Changes in Breeding Populations of Curlews and Lapwings in Central Buckinghamshire 1981-1990. Buckinghamshire Bird Report 1994: 11-16.
Fuller, R.J & Ausden, M. 2008. Birds and Habitat Change in Britain – Part 1. British Birds:101. 644-675.

Fuller, R.J., Noble, D.G., Smith, K.W. & Vanhinsbergh, D. 2005. Recent Declines in Populations of Woodland Birds in Britain: British Birds: 98. 116-143.

Glue, D.E. 1996. Aylesbury Sewage Treatment Works 1993-1996. Buckinghamshire Bird Report 1995: 15-18.

Glue, D.E. 1993. Impact of Prolonged drought during 1989-92 on Birdlife of Aylesbury Sewage Treatment Works. Buckinghamshire Bird Report 1992: 13-16.

Griffiths, E. 2001. The Changing Habitats of College Lake. Buckinghamshire Bird Report 2001: 17-20.

Hill, R. 2004. Changes in breeding populations of Little-ringed and Ringed Plovers in Buckinghamshire. Buckinghamshire Bird Report 2004: 16-21.

Hill, R. 2003. A Site Guide to Little Linford Wood. Buckinghamshire Bird Report 2003: 21-23.

Hill, R. 1997. Ecological and Recreational Effects on Wintering Wildfowl on a Gravel Pit Complex. Buckinghamshire Bird Report 1996: 17-21.

Hill, R. 2005. The Common Tern in Buckinghamshire. Buckinghamshire Bird Report 2005: 23-28.

Hill, R and Nichols, S. 2009. Olney and the North-East – a Site Guide. Buckinghamshire Bird Report 2009: 29-35.

Holt, K. 2007. The Bramblings of Penn Wood. Buckinghamshire Bird Report 2007: 18-22.

Lack, P and Ferguson, D. 1993. The Birds of Buckinghamshire.

Nichols, S and Hill, R. 2008. The Ouse Valley – East. Buckinghamshire Bird Report 2008: 24-34.

Nichols, S and Hill, R. 2007. The Ouse Valley – West. Buckinghamshire Bird Report 2007: 23-31.

Phillips, J. 1994. Unusual Gulls at a Buckinghamshire Roost. Buckinghamshire Bird Report 1993: 7-10.

Rose, J.E. and Wallen, M.S. 1992 Little Marlow Gravel Pit. Buckinghamshire Bird Report 1991: 15-16.

Sutherland, W.J and Hill, D.A. 2000. Managing Habitats for Conservation. University Press, Cambridge.

Watts, T. 2009. Bitterns at Calvert – Winter 2009. Buckinghamshire Bird Report 2009: 18-24.

Watts, T. 2005. Improvements to BBOWT Calvert Jubilee. Buckinghamshire Bird Report 2005: 17-19.

BUCKINGHAMSHIRE SITES

In the species accounts and in the annual reports of the Buckinghamshire Bird Club a small number of sites are mentioned many times. This article shows what they look like, where they are and what birds you might expect to see.

Ashridge

Location: SP9713. 5km WNW of Tring. Most of the site is in Hertfordshire.
Access: unrestricted.
Parking: many parking areas around the site.
Facilities: visitor centre, café and toilets along Monument Drive.
Habitat: mixed woodland with large clearings.
Birds: wide range of woodland birds including Woodcock and Lesser Spotted Woodpecker. Formerly held breeding Wood Warbler, Common Redstart, Tree Pipit, Hawfinch and Lady Amherst's Pheasant.

Black Park

Location: TQ010840. 2km W of Iver Heath.
Access: unrestricted.
Facilities: café and toilets on south side of lake.
Parking: pay and display at TQ005833. Free parking in lay-bys on minor road at TQ010846.
Habitat: Broad-leaved woodland in north section, otherwise black pine plantation, southern heathland, alder carr and a lake.
Birds: Mandarin, irregular Crossbill, wintering Siskin and Lesser Redpoll. Nightjar, Woodlark and Dartford Warbler have bred.

Caldecotte Lake

Location: SP890350. 2km W of Bow Brickhill.
Access: unrestricted.
Parking: pay and display at SP887356 (north basin), street parking in estate on east side of south basin.
Facilities: pub on west side of north basin.
Habitat: two artificial basins separated by a road and joined by a short channel. Small nature reserve with screen at south end of south basin.
Birds: breeding Common Terns, Reed Warblers, Cetti's Warblers. Winter wildfowl and passage terns.

Calvert

Location: SP681250. Immediately NW of Calvert.
Access: two lakes. East lake is a BBOWT managed reserve with access by permit only (contact BBOWT at 01865 775476 or info@bbowt.org.uk). West lake is a sailing lake. Access is by public footpath on north side.
Parking: east lake: small parking area on road between the two lakes. West lake: north end of Charndon at SP672249.

Facilities: none.
Habitat: deep lakes with steep sides. Small area of mud on east lake.
Birds: large winter gull roost with regular Glaucous and Iceland Gulls, winter wildfowl, occasional passage waders, rarer grebes.

College Lake

Location: SP932141. 1 km WSW of Marsworth.
Access: many paths.
Parking: on site.
Facilities: information centre with toilets. Several hides.

Habitat: former chalk quarry converted to a nature reserve managed by BBOWT consisting of a deep, steep-sided lake, a marsh with islands, traditional corn fields, chalk grassland and scrub.
Birds: breeding Redshank, Little Ringed Plover, Oystercatcher, Common Tern, Kingfisher. Small numbers of passage waders, winter wildfowl.

Dorney Lake

Location: entrance at SP924790, 0.5 km west of Dorney village.
Access: unrestricted except 'nature reserve' area between return lake and R Thames. Closed during special events.
Parking: free car park at SP924789.
Facilities: none.
Habitat: venue for 2012 Olympic rowing events. Two 2 km long rectangular lakes running in parallel, the rowing lake and the narrower and less used return lake. Between the return lake and the River Thames are several scrapes which are designated as a nature reserve. The rest of the area is closely mown grass with an arboretum along the northern edge. There are two small reed-fringed ponds here. The adjacent Dorney Common has a small stream along its eastern edge by Eton Wick which holds breeding Cetti's Warbler and once hosted a Spotted Crake.
Birds: breeding Little Ringed Plover, Ringed Plover, Redshank, Little Grebe. Passage Northern Wheatear. Small numbers of passage waders including local rarities. These always occur either on the gravel shores of the return lake or in the nature reserve which can be viewed (with difficulty) from the causeway between the two lakes.

Foxcote

Location: SP713363. 3 km NNE of Buckingham.

Access: this is a BBOWT permit only reserve (contact BBOWT at 01865 775476 or info@bbowt.org.uk). There is a footpath to a hide via a gate which may be locked. The dam is strictly off limits. The reservoir is viewable from the road but a telescope is required.

Parking: small lay-by on road between Leckhampstead and Maids Moreton at SP713361.

Facilities: hide.

Habitat: drinking water reservoir with dam. Areas of mud in autumn.

Birds: autumn waders, winter wildfowl.

Gallows Bridge Farm

Location: SP668203. 2km W of Grendon Underwood.

Access: short track from car park via an unlocked gate to two hides. There is no access to the rest of the site.

Parking: on site.

Facilities: two hides.

Habitat: part of BBOWT's Upper Ray Valley complex of reserves. Two hides overlooking small scrape and the extensive wet meadows beyond.

Birds: breeding Curlew, Little Ringed Plover. Small numbers of passage waders. Wintering Peregrine, Merlin, Golden Plover, Short-eared Owl. Occasional Hen Harrier.

Ivinghoe Hills

Location: SP962161. 1km W of Ivinghoe. The site includes Steps Hill and Incombe Hole.
Access: unrestricted.
Facilities: none.
Parking: parking off the minor road to Ringshall at SP962161 and SP963160.
Habitat: chalk grassland and scrub.
Birds: passage songbirds including Northern Wheatear, Common Redstart and Ring Ouzel. Breeding Corn Bunting.

Jubilee River

Location: begins at SP904819 where it leaves the Thames at Maidenhead and ends at SP976781 where it rejoins the Thames between Eton and Datchet.
Access: footpath and cycle track on southern bank.
Parking: free parking at SP915804 and SP928795.
Facilities: none.
Habitat: artificial river created as flood relief. Many gravel islands. Dorney Wetlands at the eastern end is mostly in Berkshire.
Birds: breeding Little Ringed Plover, Common Tern, Water Rail. Wintering ducks in small numbers.

Linford

Location: SP843429. 1 km E of Haversham.
Access: permit only (01908 504810 for permit). Distant views from Swan's Way.
Parking: on site. N of Wolverton Road at SP849425.
Habitat: working gravel pits with reed beds, mud and gravel; pasture and hedges.
Facilities: three hides (permit holders only).
Birds: one of the best sites in the county for rarities. Passage waders, winter wildfowl, passage songbirds, breeding Little Egret.

Little Marlow

Location: SU880876. 1km W of Bourne End.
Access: public footpath and permissive footpath around lake going away from the water at the workings.
Parking: by Little Marlow church at SU874879, car park by Spade Oak pub at SU884875, and at end of private road at SU876876.
Facilities: none.
Habitat: designated as a local nature reserve known as Spade Oak NR. Gravel pit no longer worked but used to dump sand. This will cease in 2012. Small reed beds, wooded islands and large sand spit.
Birds: breeding Common Tern, Grey Heron, Cormorant, Reed Warbler. Small numbers of passage waders, wintering wildfowl, large gull pre-roost.
Note: the lake to the W is not accessible. The lake by the A404 has small numbers of wintering wildfowl.

Lodge Hill

Location: SP794001. 2 km W of Loosley Row.
Access: Ridgeway Path crosses summit of hill. Many footpaths in surrounding farmland.
Parking: on minor roads around the hill.
Habitat: isolated hill on Chiltern escarpment. Chalk scrub and arable farmland much of which is spring sown.
Facilities: none.
Birds: breeding Corn Bunting, passage Northern Wheatears and wintering Golden Plovers.

Manor Farm

Location: SP806417. 0.5 km W of Old Wolverton.
Access: footpaths.
Parking: car parks. Off Old Wolverton Industrial Estate opposite Motor Serv at SP809415; Haversham car park at SP818422.
Facilities: none.
Habitat: working gravel pits with varying amounts of mud; pasture, hedges and River Ouse. It is intended to become a nature reserve around 2015.
Birds: passage waders, Little Egret.

Quainton Hills

Location: SP750825. Immediately N of Quainton.

Access: public footpaths.

Parking: nearest is in Quainton by the church. Roadside parking on all the surrounding roads.

Facilities: none.

Habitat: heavily grazed pasture with hedges and a small copse at the summit.

Birds: passage songbirds including Northern Wheatear, Common Redstart, Ring Ouzel.

Shardeloes Lake

Location: SU942980. 3km W of Amersham.

Access: public footpath along S side of lake.

Parking: on minor road off A413 roundabout at SU948979.

Facilities: none.

Habitat: reed-fringed lake with willow carr at W end.

Birds: small numbers of winter waterfowl, regular migrant Spotted Flycatchers. Breeding Water Rail.

Stoke Common

Location: SU988854. 2km N of Stoke Poges.

Access: unrestricted.

Parking: lay-bys on Stoke Common Road on north of site, in Vine Road off B416 (on south edge of west section)..

Facilities: none.

Habitat: southern heathland, conifer plantation. In two sections divided by B416. The larger E section becomes very wet in winter. The site is managed to preserve the heathland.

Birds: Mandarin, irregular Crossbill, wintering Common and Jack Snipe. Nightjar, Woodlark and Dartford Warbler have bred.

Stony Stratford Nature Reserve

Location: SP785411. 1 km E of Old Stratford on S side of A5.
Access: footpaths within reserve.
Parking: two car parks. Off the Stony Stratford - Wolverton Road at SP407798; off the Stony Stratford bypass at SP400790.
Facilities: none.
Habitat: damp, grazed fields which can flood in winter, pools and a small scrape.
Birds: winter wildfowl, small passage of regular waders. Oystercatchers have bred.

Wendover Woods

Location: SP890090. 2km NW of Wendover.
Access: unrestricted.
Parking: pay and display on the ridge at SP890090. The entrance is at SP899084 on the St Leonards road. There are free lay-bys on The Hale road at SP893075 and SP880075.
Facilities: café and toilets at the pay and display car park.
Habitat: conifer and beech woodland with a large area of young plantation off The Hale road.
Birds: breeding Firecrest and regular Crossbill, wintering Siskin and Lesser Redpoll.

Weston Turville Reservoir

Location: SP862096. 1.5 km N of Wendover.
Access: permissive path around site (not always close to water).
Parking: lay-by at SP858097 by road from World's End to Weston Turville.
Facilities: two hides.
Habitat: fishing and sailing lake with large reed bed at S end. Damp woodland.
Birds: wintering Bittern, small numbers of wintering wildfowl. Breeding Water Rail, Reed Warbler, Sedge Warbler.

Willen Lakes

Location: SP880403. 3km ENE of Central Milton Keynes.
Access: unrestricted.
Parking: pay and display at SP878398 (S lake); free at SP877411 (N lake).
Facilities: café on west side of south basin. Hide on south side of north lake.
Habitat: two artificial lakes joined by a narrow channel. The south lake is reserved for watersports, the north lake is a nature reserve with an island and a hide on the south shore.
Birds: one of the best sites in the county for rarities although lack of mud in autumn and urbanisation, including building a road between the two lakes, has reduced its attraction. Passage waders, winter wildfowl. Breeding Common Tern, Cetti's Warbler.

References:

Nichols, S & R Hill. 2008. The Ouse Valley - West. Buckinghamshire Bird Report 2007.

Nichols, S & R Hill. 2009. The Ouse Valley - East. Buckinghamshire Bird Report 2008.

Nichols, S & R Hill. 2010. Olney and the North-east. Buckinghamshire Bird Report 2009.

Nichols, S & R Hill. 2011. Milton Keynes - a site guide. Buckinghamshire Bird Report 2010.

BIRD MIGRATION IN BUCKINGHAMSHIRE

Mike Wallen

When modern birds began to evolve around 125 million years ago, the super-continent of Panagea had been drifting apart for 75 million years. Birds began to migrate over long distances when their summer and wintering areas grew further apart. The first ringing scheme to study this extraordinary phenomenon took place in Germany in 1899. By 1909 the BTO began ringing birds, but a significant step was taken when, at an historic meeting in the Buckinghamshire village of Long Crendon in 1947, the idea for a chain of bird observatories was mooted.

Ringing birds with aluminium rings was the primary method for studying bird migration until quite recently. Schemes using coloured plastic rings that enable individual birds to be identified without trapping them, have produced interesting local results, which are described below, but the most dramatic advances have been in radio and satellite tracking.

One example of this, which has a tangential local interest, concerns 'Beatrice', an Osprey breeding in Scotland and wintering in southern Spain. She was satellite tagged in 2008 when she was eight years old and has been followed ever since. Her consistency has been remarkable. All her northbound landfalls on the English south coast have been between 30th March and 3rd April. On her journeys south she has passed over or very close to Buckinghamshire. At 15.00 hrs on 13 Aug 2010 she was just south of Banbury, Oxfordshire. Four hours later she was mid-channel, south of the Isle of Wight. On 18 Aug 2008 she was near Dagnall and at mid-day she was flying at 47 km/hour over Latimer. The following morning she was five miles SE of Maidenhead which meant a route over south Buckinghamshire. Needless to say, no local birders saw her.

Ringing

There are several ringing groups active in the county and they have recorded some remarkable feats of long-distance flying, some of which are shown on the map. Other notable records are mentioned in the species accounts. In addition, the relatively recent use of coloured plastic darvic rings on larger species, such as gulls and geese, has allowed field observers to play their part in adding to our ever increasing knowledge. Colour ringing schemes, whether of Waxwings in Scotland which are subsequently seen in our county, or the Common Tern scheme within our own county when birds are seen elsewhere, is interesting and exciting. For example, two Common Tern chicks ringed at Little Marlow were recovered in West Africa while a Lesser Black-backed Gull ringed as a chick in Norway was seen at Little Marlow the following year.

Visible Migration

Inland counties are restricted in their opportunities for viewing visible migration. In the case of Buckinghamshire the most reliable sites are on the tops of hills for passerines, water for hirundines and swifts, and muddy margins of lakes for waders. One of the best sites for finding migrant passerines is the section of the Chiltern escarpment near Ivinghoe which includes Ivinghoe Beacon, Steps Hill, Incombe Hole and Pitstone Hill. Another good site is the isolated limestone ridge of the Quainton Hills which is west of Aylesbury. Both sites regularly turn up Northern Wheatears, Common Redstarts and Ring Ouzels, sometimes in good numbers, but the most dramatic movements usually occur over the Ivinghoe Hills. From early October some of these movements can involve hundreds of winter thrushes, finches, buntings and pigeons. On 12 October 1997 at Steps Hill, during a six hour watch, a staggering 18,000 Redwings arrived from the east and passed over towards the south-west. This huge movement was noted throughout the UK and was probably brought on by early and heavy snowfall in Scandinavia which caused a sudden and mass exodus. It is usually from mid to late October that large flocks of Fieldfare arrive. These are then followed by often spectacular movements of Woodpigeons which last until the first week of November.

The Ivinghoe Hills were also the best place in the county to witness the huge, unprecedented passage of Honey-buzzards which took place in the autumn of 2000. Between 22nd and 24th September 25 birds were seen passing over the hills and another five were recorded on 27th. Up to that point there had been only 12 records of Honey-buzzard in the county.

Incombe Hole, a prime site for migrating Ring Ouzels   *David Ferguson*

Visible migration has always captured the enthusiasm of birders but the current quality of optics has been responsible for a growing number of observers spending their time partaking in this addictive aspect of birding. Not only can the vis-miggers, as they are known, see most of what is passing them by, but they can actually identify large numbers too. However much of the time whilst 'vis-migging' your hearing and identification of birds by calls and recognising many birds by 'jizz' is equally important. Sometimes days where the forecast suggests the skies will be full of birds can result in an almost birdless sky. Similarly, the opposite can occur when the forecast would suggest a quiet morning but birds can be streaming overhead; these 'surprise' days somehow always feel better! On the good days the numbers and variety of birds can be amazing, when birds can be flying in large numbers and in all areas of sky. Then identifying and counting them can be seriously demanding. Watching this spectacle from the top of the Chiltern escarpment can be awe inspiring, and should be experienced by all observers in the county at some point in their birding lives. With more observers partaking in this aspect of birding, coordinated counts now take place across the UK on given days each autumn. Buckinghamshire is on this map with counts undertaken at Steps Hill.

Waders represent a different challenge. There are many of them and they can look very similar. They also tend to inhabit areas of distant mud. Buckinghamshire is just south of the direct route between the Bristol Channel and the Wash so wader numbers are usually small. Nevertheless there have been many examples of interesting migration. The skills of some birders are such that, coupled with high quality optics, it is sometimes possible to determine races of waders. For example, 49 Black-tailed Godwits at College Lake on 4 July 2004 were found to be of the Iceland race. The various Dunlin sub-species represent a more difficult challenge. It is suspected that the Iceland and Greenland races pass through Buckinghamshire but at present this has not been confirmed.

A most beautiful race regularly to be seen in Buckinghamshire is the Greenland sub-species of Northern Wheatear *Oenanthe oenanthe leucorhoa.* This bird, which is larger and brighter than the nominate race, is annual in the county. They breed in Canada, Greenland and Iceland and winter in West Africa. This extraordinary route takes them across the North Atlantic in one long sea crossing. They can spend eight months of the year migrating.

Greenland Wheatear   *Mike Wallen*

Weather

Weather patterns, wind direction, clear skies, cold weather and storms can all have an effect on the birds using Buckinghamshire as a flyway from one locality to another. Understanding weather charts and keeping a close eye on weather systems across the UK and into Europe can not only allow one to predict observations that might be forthcoming in the days ahead, but they also allow us to understand some of the avian events which unfold within the county. For example, in autumn as a front crosses the UK and heads into Scandinavia with the winds rotating anti-clockwise, its western edge can become favourable for birds destined for the UK to set off and reach our shores in a tail wind or clear weather window. Likewise birds in Iceland such as Whooper Swans will wait for the right winds and weather interlude to set off and complete their journey in the optimum conditions to save energy and enjoy a safer crossing.

It is well known that at certain times in spring and autumn many terns and waders can be passing over the county, but flying into a fast moving rainstorm can force these birds down to water bodies allowing observers a fleeting view. These freak weather events can be very short lived and sometimes no sooner have the birds dropped in, the weather clears and they are gone again. Arctic Terns can form sizeable flocks in spring and if faced with strong northerly winds, again they can make spectacular viewing, for example on a number of occasions at Calvert in recent Aprils.

It is a common mis-conception that birds will always wait for a tail-wind to assist them. Whilst this may be true of larger birds, such as wildfowl, or strong flyers like waders, many passerines will actually prefer to fly into a slight headwind, so birds moving to the south-west in the UK will fly into a light south-westerly. Whilst a light wind from behind could be favourable it is thought that too strong a wind can affect the bird's rudder (its tail) and cause it to be off balance, with continued correction requiring the use of precious energy reserves.

Cold weather on the continent can force birds westwards reaching Holland and the Low Countries. If the cold weather continues westwards, birds will cross the North Sea into the UK, or fly further south. Some species will sit out these cold spells but others will be forced to move to enable them to feed. For example the winters of 2009-10, and 2010-11 both saw continued cold spells and Woodcocks were noted arriving down the east coast at migration watch points and Bitterns wintered in Britain in record numbers.

Migration Strategies

Movements of a variety of species occur at different times during the migration periods, some flying by day, others by night. Some are observed far more easily and frequently than others, for example waders start moving south in late summer, and due to a high proportion of birders watching gravel pits and other water bodies many are recorded. However the birds actually noted are only a tiny percentage of those flying over the county; many flying over are far too high to see. An indication of what is passing over unnoticed occurred on 16 August 2004 when, during a brief but heavy shower, two Pied Flycatchers landed in the trees by a group of wader-watching birders. This was one of the few multiple occurrence records of this species. Tape lures can help birders to see the true picture. For example on 8 September 1991 at Little Marlow Gravel Pit, a tape lure in apparently birdless skies brought down thousands of House Martins. It was estimated that 20,000 moved through on the day.

Many birds migrate at night and whilst most of these are invisible to us, they can still be witnessed, for example on October nights the contact calls of migrating Redwings can be heard 'zeeping' across our night skies. A study of the prey taken by the Peregrines in Aylesbury has also provided us with an insight to the birds passing over our towns and countryside as we sleep. It is now understood and evidenced both in Aylesbury and elsewhere in the UK that urban Peregrines are able to use the reflective glow of town lights to pick out prey flying above. Of course many birds and animals are darker on their upper sides and lighter on their undersides to allow them some protection from predatory species, but in these urban environments at night this small advantage becomes a distinct disadvantage.

We must not underestimate the numbers of birds involved in some of these movements, or the scale of a departure from one land mass towards the next. If birds are held up by adverse winds or poor weather, significant numbers will build up, particularly if the next stage of the migration is a sea crossing. For example strong southerly or westerly winds in autumn will hold significant numbers of thrushes in Scandinavia that are destined for the UK, but on a change of wind direction they can set off on-masse. These flocks can be so large that they are easily seen on local radar! Of course migrating in a flock has many advantages for the individual bird, not least that its less likely to be predated, but there is clearly a strategy in that younger birds migrate with adults who show them the way, or 'collective' thinking is more likely to ensure that they arrive at the intended destination. Birds communicate to each other during these migrations, whether by day or by night, the contact calls of Redwings mentioned above being a good example.

Changing Seasons

January, February and early March see very little moving, unless, as in recent winters, there is a cold snap. If this lasts for even a few days then a number of species will move in an attempt to escape the cold and find food. Two species with which we usually associate these movements are Lapwing and Skylark.

Over the last few decades spring has definitely started earlier for our migrants and by mid-March the hirundines can be with us and Northern Wheatears passing through. Mid-March to the middle of May sees the bulk of the spring migration. Warm winds from the south, particularly all the way from Africa and Spain, can see a number of continental overshoots. Under these conditions scarcities such as Hoopoe and Glossy Ibis reaching our land-locked county.

However it is not these vagrants that should warrant our attention, but the continual record breaking early arrival dates of our summer visitors and the indication of global warming. The changing fortunes of our breeding migrants, and indeed the invasions of previously scarce breeding southern species will be keenly watched in the coming decades. Spring used to finish at the end of May but the vast majority of passage is now over by mid or even early May. However Arctic bound waders can still be moving North at the end of May and into June. Some of these returning waders can be back in the county by the end of June or the start of July, and this group of birds can leave us wondering where spring migration stops and autumn migration begins.

July and August is very much the time for returning waders, but also in August chats such as Northern Wheatear and Common Redstart can be evident. From the end of August and throughout September, particularly in an easterly wind, drift migrants from Scandinavia can occur in the east of the UK, with birds like Wryneck gracing our county's gardens and open spaces.

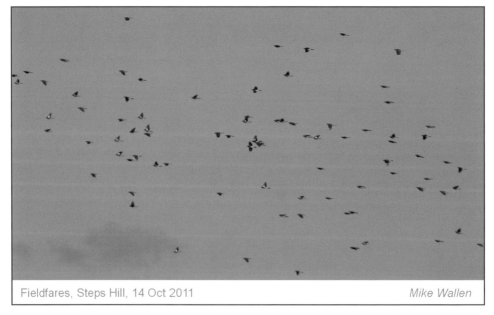

Fieldfares, Steps Hill, 14 Oct 2011   *Mike Wallen*

October sees the largest number of species and quantity of birds passing through, with the stragglers who have spent the summer in the North heading for warmer weather in the south. Early to mid-October is usually best for the majority of finches and thrushes. We are also invaded by birds from the east and the west, whether using the UK as a migration route to the continent, or moving to the county and our shores to seek milder weather compared to that now occurring in their breeding grounds. These movements can be prolonged, over weeks, or sometimes compact into a few days of intense activity. Early November can see large movements of Woodpigeon and some good numbers of later thrushes such as Fieldfare, and if we've enjoyed an Indian summer many species more usually associated with October. These Woodpigeons can travel down through the UK where they are often observed in vast numbers heading out over the English Channel, heading for sunnier climes in France, Spain and Portugal.

December can be very much a month of migrant doldrums with very little on the move, if anything, however as we race towards the year end we are all hoping for a Waxwing invasion to brighten those winter days.

The accompanying map shows some of the more spectacular ringing recoveries involving Buckinghamshire birds. The red lines indicate birds ringed in Buckinghamshire and controlled in Europe while the single yellow line indicates a bird ringed in Finland and controlled in Buckinghamshire. Clockwise, starting with Iceland, the species involved are:

Iceland: Blackbird
Norway: Siskin
Sweden: Fieldfare
Finland: Fieldfare
Finland (yellow): Pochard
Russia: Fieldfare
Russia: Mandarin
Poland: Starling
Germany: Long-eared Owl
Slovenia: Lesser Whitethroat
Lebanon: Lesser Whitethroat
Italy: Wood Warbler
Congo: Swift
Ghana: Garden Warbler
Spain: Grey Heron
Morocco: Reed Warbler
Mauretania: Common Tern

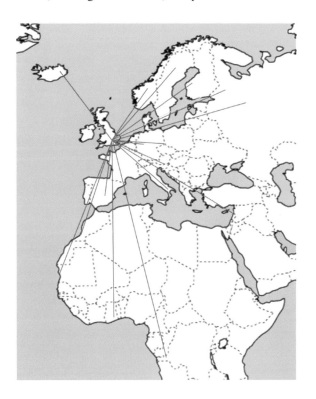

THE MAPS

The breeding atlas 1980 - 1986

When the first national Breeding Atlas (Sharrock 1976) was published, several counties were considering producing maps which would be more meaningful on a local basis. The 10-km squares used by the national survey were at too coarse a scale to show much of interest at the local level although within the county the Sparrowhawk and Hawfinch, for example, were clearly only in the southern half, in the woods of the Chilterns (see Fraser and Youngman 1976).

Starting with Hertfordshire, who did their fieldwork largely coincident with the national atlas 1968-1973, several counties started surveying their counties by tetrads and using the same field methods as the national survey. Buckinghamshire too was considering doing this and fieldwork for the first atlas, which was restricted to breeding species, started in 1980 largely at the instigation of Ron Youngman. Responsibility for the organisation quickly devolved to the Buckinghamshire Bird Club, with Trevor Brooks acting as co-ordinator. Fieldwork continued on a wide scale until the summer of 1985, although there was a limited amount of 'gap-filling' during 1986.

The summer and winter atlases 2007 - 2011

The Club committee had been considering a second atlas when the BTO announced its intention to launch a national atlas starting in 2007. It seemed sensible to integrate fieldwork for a county atlas into the national atlas. The methods were almost the same as before.

Methods Used

The units of distribution were the tetrads (2-km squares) of the National Grid. In the first atlas, observers were asked to record the species they saw or heard in one of three categories of breeding - possible, probable or confirmed. In the second atlas a fourth category was added, present but not breeding. This shows up particularly in the maps for Grey Heron and migrant species such as Northern Wheatear. The winter atlas has only one category - present.

The criteria for the birds to be recorded in each category have been more or less agreed by the European Ornithological Atlas Committee. Possible breeding means simply that the species was seen in possible breeding habitat during the season. Probable breeding means that breeding was deemed likely, for example the species was holding territory, or a pair of birds were seen courting. Confirmed breeding means that a nest was found with eggs or young, parent birds were seen carrying food for their young, etc. These categories are represented on the maps in this book by three different colours, the darker the colour the higher the category. There was one major change between the two atlases. In the first atlas a bird singing on a single date was considered to be in the probable breeding category. In the second atlas this was demoted to possible breeding. Here a bird was required to be singing in the same location for at least a week before it could be considered to be probably breeding. This explains the preponderance of orange dots in the later breeding atlas and the lack of pale green dots in the earlier.

The winter period was deemed to be November to February while the summer period was April to July although records of early and late breeding species outside these months were allowed.

Coverage Achieved

The objective at the start of the surveys was to find all the species breeding in each tetrad in the county and to confirm breeding there. This was not achieved. The maps show the coverage. It should be noted that the first survey only covered these birds breeding within Buckinghamshire while the second survey included all of the boundary tetrads even if part of the tetrad was in a neighbouring county. The reason for this was that the survey results were inputted onto the BTO national atlas which only recognised tetrad boundaries. Thus the number of species recorded in the boundary tetrads was higher in the second survey.

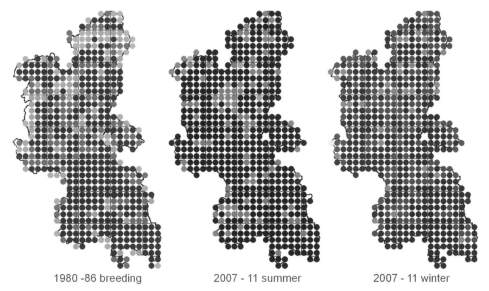

| 1980 -86 breeding | 2007 - 11 summer | 2007 - 11 winter |

pale dots: <20 species per tetrad   mid-coloured dots: 21-40   dark dots: >40

The maps

Tetrad distribution maps for most of the of the regularly occurring species in the county are shown. There may be up to three maps for a species. The map on the left with dots in shades of green are the result of the 1980-1986 breeding survey. The map in the middle with dots of grey and shades of red are the result of the 2007 - 2011 survey while the winter maps have blue dots.

The dot colours on the summer maps represent levels of breeding confidence. They are:

Grey (2007 - 2011 only): present but not breeding
Pale green (1980 - 1986) or orange (2007 - 2011): possible breeding
Mid green (1980 - 1986) or mid red (2007 - 2011): probable breeding
Dark green (1980 - 1986) or dark red (2007 - 2011): confirmed breeding

A certain amount of guessing has gone into the separation of the grey and orange dots. Some of the records have come via the BTO's Birdtrack scheme, which does not use breeding codes. It is thus difficult to separate these from records where it is known that a bird is not breeding - such as Grey Heron. The separation has been done by taking into account date and habitat. Grey dots tend to be noticeable on the maps of summer migrants.

THE SPECIES ACCOUNTS

Scope

This book contains accounts for all bird species that are believed to have occurred in Buckinghamshire. There are four lists:

a) The main group contains those species on the British list which have been confirmed as having occurred in Buckinghamshire. There are currently 294 species in this category.

b) The second list contains species that are known to have been introduced, or are on the British list but are believed to be escapes from captivity. The list does not include escapes of exotic species, of which there have been many.

c) The third list contains those species which have been mentioned in older works on the birds of Buckinghamshire but which are considered to be unsafe by the current records committee. They have been included in order to provide continuity with the older works.

d) The fourth list contains species which have been recorded within the vice-county of Buckinghamshire but outside the present county boundary. There are four species in this category. The discrepancies between the present county boundary and that of the Watsonian vice-county are discussed in the next section.

The county boundary

In 1974 the county boundary was altered. The main change was the transfer of Slough from Buckinghamshire to Berkshire which meant that the ornithologically important sites of Slough Sewage Farm and Wraysbury were lost to the county. As only records occurring within the present county boundary are included on the county list this led to the loss of a number of important records which are listed in an appendix.

The loss of the Slough area has occasionally made the compilation of the species accounts difficult. For instance, the first record in Buckinghamshire for Little Ringed Plover is quoted in the contemporary accounts as Slough SF. Subsequent records which are within the present county boundary are not mentioned, so it has been very difficult to discover where the first record was. The occasional references to sites in the Slough area are an attempt to circumnavigate the problem.

Another problem exists in the Tring Reservoirs area. Parts of Startopsend and Marsworth Reservoirs are in Buckinghamshire, but it has been assumed, unless known otherwise, that records for these sites occurred in Hertfordshire.

Biological recorders use vice-counties, rather than the present counties. The Buckinghamshire vice-county has slightly different boundaries to those currently marked on the maps. The most important changes are both losses: the Slough area has already been mentioned, but New Wavendon Heath, which is part of Brickhill Woods and is now part of Bedfordshire, has interesting birds. Birds which have been recorded in the Buckinghamshire vice-county, but not within the present county are listed separately. Since the publication of the first edition of *The Birds of Buckinghamshire* another small but ornithologically significant change took place. In the far south-east of the county the boundary was redrawn along the M40 which moved Old Slade and Colnbrook into Berkshire. This accounts for the difference in the map outline in this area between the first atlas maps and the subsequent maps.

Taxonomy and names

The species accounts order and the scientific names are those used by the BOU. The common names are mostly those used in the first edition. The exceptions are those species where there may be some ambiguity in the Buckinghamshire list such as European Teal and Green-winged Teal.

Time period

The species accounts begin with the earliest available records. Occasionally these are from the invaluable 18th century records of Dinton Hall, but more often it is Clark Kennedy's book of 1865 that provides the first comments. It must be stated, though, that this remarkable book contains some unsubstantiated and doubtful records. It also includes many Berkshire records which have been incorporated into global statements for both counties. The records end on 31 December 2011.

Rarities

No records of national rarities after 1958 have been included without acceptance by the British Birds Rarities Committee. Before 1958, when the BBRC did not exist, it is assumed that the records were subjected to some kind of local vetting process.

Extreme rarities have their records listed in full. Those species which are still sufficiently rare to have their records listed individually in the annual report of the Buckinghamshire Bird Club usually have their records since 1972 shown by two graphs. The numbers of records and individual birds are then given. Dividing the second figure by the first gives the average flock size. This has been done to compensate for the fact that the graphs do not take into account flock size. The records are then divided into three regions: north, middle, and south. The county is 80 km from north to south but on average only 30 km wide. If there are any differences in the distribution of a species within the county they are likely to be on a north south axis. Finally, details of the largest flocks and of any significant ringing recoveries are given.

The graphs

The graphs for scarce species are shown in pale blue and are in pairs. One graph shows the number of birds recorded each year, while the other shows the number of birds recorded each week. No differentiation is made between a flock of x birds and x individual birds arriving on the same day. The date of the record is taken as the date the bird was first recorded, and no account is taken of duration of stay or of changes in location. This accords with the methodology of the graphs in *Rare Birds in Britain and Ireland* (Dymond et al 1989).

The graphs showing wildfowl count data are shown in green and are also in pairs. The first graph shows the average total numbers for each month of the survey period (September to March) while the second shows the average total numbers for each of the 20 years between the winters of 1972/73 and 2010/11. For a few species, counting did not begin until 1982. In these cases the period shown is from this date. It should be emphasised that the graphs display *average* counts and that numbers can vary considerably from year to year. No account is taken of missed counts, though this is believed to be insignificant.

The graphs showing the percentage of occupied gardens are shown in light brown. The data is taken from the BBC garden bird survey. More details about the survey are provided on page 353.

Abbreviations

The following abbreviations are used:

BBC	Buckinghamshire Bird Club
BBRC	British Birds Rarities Committee
BBS	Breeding Birds Survey (of the BTO)
Breeding Atlas	Sharrock, J.T.R. 1976. The Atlas of Breeding Birds in Britain and Ireland. Poyser, Berkhamsted.
BTO	British Trust for Ornithology
BWP	Cramp, S. and K.E.L. Simmons 197?-1992. The Birds of the Western Palaearctic, vols 1-7. University Press, Oxford.
CBC	Common Birds Census (of the BTO)
F & Y	Fraser A.C. and R.E.Youngman. 1976. The Birds of Buckinghamshire and East Berkshire. Middle Thames Natural History Society, Slough.
GBS	BBC Garden Birds Survey.
GP	Gravel Pit
Handbook	Witherby H.F, F.C.R.Jourdain, N.F.Ticehurst, and B.W.Tucker. 1938-1941. The Handbook of British Birds, vols 1-5. Witherby, London.
H & J	Hartert E., and F.C.R.Jourdain. 1920. The Birds of Buckinghamshire and the Tring Reservoirs.
H & R	Hartert E., and W.Rothschild. 1905. Birds pp 128-152 in A History of Buckingham (ed W.Page). Constable & Co., London.
L & F	Lack P., and D. Ferguson. 1993. The Birds of Buckinghamshire. Buckinghamshire Bird Club.
Migration Atlas	Wernham C., Toms M., Marchant J., Clark J., Striwardena G. & Baillie S. The Migration Atlas. 2002. Poyser.
MTNHS	Middle Thames Natural History Society
New Atlas	Gibbons, D.W., J.B.Reid, R.A.Chapman. The New Atlas of Breeding Birds in Britain and Ireland: 1988 - 1001. 1993. Poyser.
NBBR	North Bucks Bird Report
NR	Nature Reserve
OOS	Oxford Ornithological Society
Res	Reservoir
SF	Sewage Farm
STW	Sewage Treatment Works
WAGBI	Wildfowlers Association of Great Britain and Ireland (now British Association for Shooting and Conservation)
Winter Atlas	Lack P.C. 1986. The Atlas of Wintering Birds in Britain and Ireland. Poyser, Calton.

Mute Swan
Cygnus olor

Local resident.

The early accounts suggest that Mute Swans were regarded not as a wild species, but as royal birds. Clark Kennedy mentions that Eton College had long held the right to keep swans on the River Thames, and quotes Yarrell regarding the College 'Swan mark' which represented 'the armed point and the feathered head of an arrow'.

Little Marlow, 27 May 2005   *David Ferguson*

Mute Swans are indigenous to E England. They were semi-domesticated in mediaeval times for their culinary worth and were kept on many rivers and lakes. Later, when they faded from the gastronomic scene, they reverted to the nominal wild state they occupy today.

There is some evidence of an increase this century with a decline during the Second World War. After the war the population increased although hard winters affected numbers (Campbell 1960, Ogilvie 1967). The annual counts graph shows an increase in the county since the mid 1970s when around 50 birds were recorded during the winter to 350 in 2008 and 2009. This increase has been assisted by the increase in waters available through gravel extraction (Morgan 1980, Knight & Stone 1986). Numbers on the River Thames were affected by lead poisoning, but this had not affected the Vale of Aylesbury and the Ouse Valley areas as lead weights and shot tend to settle and sink in the mud rather than mix with the gravel as elsewhere (Brown & Stone 1990). Lead fishing weights were banned from 1 Jan 1987.

The rapid increase in numbers of Canada and Greylag Geese in Buckinghamshire may affect swan breeding. Although Mute Swans are dominant, the sheer pressure of numbers of geese on some of the breeding sites, and the shorter breeding cycle of the geese, which means that fledged goslings are augmenting goose numbers when the cygnets are still in down, can cause nesting failures.

Non-breeding birds herd together on open waters in summer and also form flocks in the winter. The summering flock at Willen often reaches over 100 birds; there were 253 present on 26 Jul 2004. The largest recorded wintering flock was at the same site: 197 birds in Nov 1987.

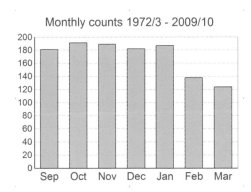
Monthly counts 1972/3 - 2009/10

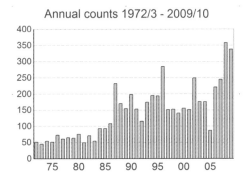
Annual counts 1972/3 - 2009/10

There are two ringing records of interest. A bird ringed at Spade Oak on 1 Sep 1986 was recovered on 18 Jul 1987 at Whitcombe Reservoir, Gloucestershire, while a breeding bird ringed at Linford on 20 May 1973 was found dead at the same locality on 15 May 1991, 18 years later.

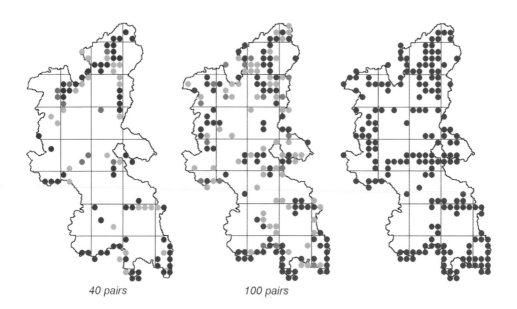

40 pairs   100 pairs

NHFS

Bewick's Swan
Cygnus columbianus

Scarce winter visitor and migrant.

Early records of this species cannot always be relied on because of confusion with the Whooper Swan. The first certain record is of three or four at Olney in March 1942, but it was very rare until 1955 when a flock of 10 birds appeared at the same site on 10th March. The numbers built to a maximum of 17 birds on the 15th. This site - meadows by the River Ouse - was used in the early part of the year until 1957. There was a maximum of 40 birds on 10 Mar 1956. Birds reappeared at this site in 1964 and 1965.

Calvert, 4 Jan 2010   *Tim Watts*

Away from Olney there were no records until 1961, after which there were 15 records of 191 birds to 1971, including a flock of 60 birds in the Olney/Emberton area on 1 Feb 1971. Records from 1972 are shown on the graphs. Of the 1338 birds recorded, 1017 were seen in the north, 224 in the middle, and 97 in the south.

Visits to Buckinghamshire by Bewick's Swans are usually short stops on passage or the result of bad weather movements, the birds usually occurring on lakes in the north of the county. As with Whooper Swans, longer stops are dependent on suitable grazing near water. Since 2001 flocks have become very scarce. Birds have been recorded in only five of the nine years with no flock exceeding 10 birds. This is part of a national decrease and appears to be caused by poor breeding success in Arctic Siberia.

Whereas Whoopers tend to move as family parties, Bewick's are more often encountered in small flocks. The largest group reported is of 46 seen together at Willen on 30 Oct 1974. They can be expected from early October onwards, having left their Siberian breeding quarters and migrated through N Europe, but they are more often recorded from January to March than in the autumn. Some birds show signs of shot sustained during their long passage over land.

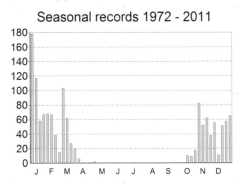
Seasonal records 1972 - 2011

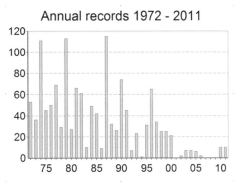
Annual records 1972 - 2011

NHFS

Whooper Swan
Cygnus cygnus

Scarce winter visitor and migrant.

As it was not until 1830 that the distinction between Whooper and Bewick's Swans was made, all early records refer simply to 'wild swans'. They should therefore be used with extreme caution unless the actual specimen can be verified. Clark Kennedy noted several occurrences, but as he made no mention of Bewick's, these could refer to either species or both. Mistaken identification, even by generally competent observers, can still not be discounted entirely.

Latimer Park, 1 Oct 2009   Ashley Stow

Clark Kennedy provided a cautionary anecdote, albeit from outside the county: 'I received the following letter from a Windsor lad of 1831: " - I remember about twenty-five years back a Mr. Hughes, connected with the Royal household, and well-known in Windsor as 'old Buffy Hughes, shooting in the neighbourhood of Clewer Point, Windsor, a couple of Whoopers or Wild Swans; and I well remember that one was converted into soup, and most of the people who partook of it were very much disturbed in their internal economy".'

There were no post-war records until 1959 when 23 flew over Dorney. This was followed by six records of 13 birds between 1960 and 1971. The records from 1972 are shown on the graphs. During this period about 468 birds were recorded. 376 were seen in the north, 57 in the middle, and 95 in the south. The last figure includes a flock of 90-100 seen flying in formation SW over West Wycombe, on 28 Dec 1979, the largest flock recorded in the county.

A small family group wintered regularly along the River Ouse between Deanshanger and Buckingham. The birds usually arrived about mid November and departed during March. They often associated with, but did not mix with, a herd of Mute Swans on the meadows. Rust stains on the head feathers seemed to indicate that the Whooper Swans were part of the Icelandic population. The Whooper spends more time grazing than our other swans, returning to water to drink and bathe as well as for protection. All the wild swans depend on sufficient grazing near water, and ploughing of this family's favourite meadows along the Ouse meant that the visits ceased.

Up to seven that roosted at Calvert from 13 Jan to 17 Feb 2001, three that were present at Hillesden from 5 Jan to 8 Mar 2008 and two at Wotton Lakes from 18 Jan to 2 Mar 2009 are the only birds that have stayed for more than a month this century. A feral group has been present in the Tring-College Lake area since about 2002.

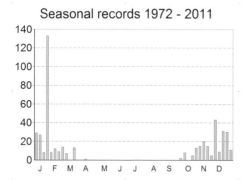

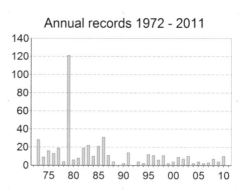

NHFS

Bean Goose
Anser fabalis

Rare vagrant. All records are given.

Clark Kennedy gives undated records for Slapton and Chesham, and both Clark Kennedy and H & R mention records from the R. Thames.

1947: 1 in Jan, Calvert, perhaps same bird later recorded as Pink-footed Goose on 2 Feb at Waddesdon.

College Lake, 28 Jan 2006   *Rob Andrews*

1982: 1 from 1 to 11 May, Stony Stratford NR, joined by a second bird on 6th. In view of the date, the birds were almost certainly feral.

1985: 1 on 9 Feb by Wilstone Res. The bird was present in Hertfordshire from 9 Feb to 23 Mar.

1989: 1 on 30 Apr, Willen was also reported at Linford.

1996: 1 *fabalis* from 29 Feb to 2 Mar, Linford was probably an escape.

1996: 2 *rossicus* from 13 to 14 Dec, Dorney Common.

1996: 2 *rossicus* from 26 to 30 Dec, College Lake.

2000: 1 *rossicus* on 9 Apr, Willen.

2003: 1 *rossicus* 23 Feb, Linford was probably a wild bird.

2005: 1 *rossicus* from 9 to 12 Mar, Newport Pagnell, from 20 to 31 Mar, Gayhurst Quarry.

2006: 14 *rossicus*, from 27 Jan to 4 Feb, College Lake.

2009: 4 *rossicus* on 7 Jan, Wotton Lakes.

2011: 2 *rossicus* on 13 Nov, Gayhurst Quarry.

Birders became aware of the two distinctive subspecies in the mid-90s and since then all records have been assigned to either *A.f.fabalis* (Taiga Bean Goose) or *A.f.rossicus* (Tundra Bean Goose). The 1996 *rossicus* records were part of a small influx into England are were probably the first wild birds to be recorded in the county.

Pink-footed Goose
Anser brachyrhynchus

Scarce migrant.

Prior to 1982 there were eight records:

1947: 1 on 2 Feb, Waddesdon (see above under Bean Goose).

1963: 1 from 13 Feb to 10 Mar on Thames between Marlow and Bourne End.

1965: 6 on 30 Jan, Iver GPs.

1966: 60-70 on 6 Mar, Mentmore flying in moonlight.

1968: 30 flying NW on 31 Dec, High Wycombe.

1977: 1 on 2 Apr, Marsworth Res.

1978: 1 from 12 Feb to 13 May, Linford.

1979: 70 on 28 Jan flying W over Concord, The Lee.

Since 1982 there have been records of one or two birds almost every year. It is likely that the above records referring to single birds were feral birds. The preponderance of records in the early part of the year is strange, however.

White-fronted Goose
Anser albifrons

Scarce migrant and rare winter visitor.

There are about 27 records prior to 1973. The first is an undated record from Olney in H & R. Between 1920 and 1939 there were about six records, with the largest flock 24 birds on 7 Jan 1938 near Olney. Between 1940 and 1959 there were five

Jubilee River, 3 Feb 2011   David Ferguson

records, with the largest flock 89 birds on the River Thames at Boveney on 18 Feb 1940. After 1960 there was a considerable increase in the number of records. Between 1960 and 1972 there were 16 records with c200 birds seen on 25 Jan 1970 at Boarstall.

The records since 1973 are shown on the graphs. The largest flock during this period was 86 birds flying north over Grendon Underwood on 9 Mar 1975, and 110 birds in three skeins were seen on 12 Jan 1985 flying east over Willen.

There have been two instances of large flocks wintering. A flock of over 70 birds commuted between Little Marlow and Cockmarsh, Berks between 4 Dec 1998 and 9 Mar 1999. A flock of 18 fed in a field by the Jubilee River from 18 Dec 2010 to 17 Jan 2011.

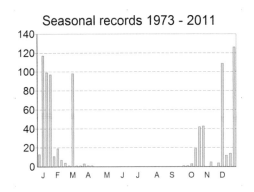

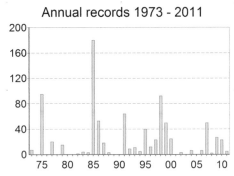

Greylag Goose
Anser anser

Introduced local resident.

Little Marlow, 11 May 2010 — David Ferguson

The early history of the Greylag Goose in Buckinghamshire is very shadowy. Clark Kennedy mentions that flocks sometimes landed in winter on flooded meadows near Hulcott and Aston Clinton. H & R report that, according to Mr Wigglesworth, they were sometimes seen near Castlethorpe on the River Ouse. An individual shot in September 1886, singles seen on 18 Mar 1927 and 13 Oct 1942 at Tring Reservoirs (Hayward 1947), and a pair at Weston Turville Res in July 1938, are all suspected of being 'escapes'. Free-flying birds from Whipsnade also visited the Tring Reservoirs after the Second World War. In 1959 WAGBI (as it was then) turned its attention to the Greylag in a translocation scheme that aimed 'to try to re-establish the Grey Lag as a wild nesting bird in England' - something that had been lost to England since the draining of the Fens in the seventeenth and eighteenth centuries. Sixteen birds were released at Linford in 1972, the year which saw the beginning of the Canada Goose influx at that site. From this small group the Greylag population increased slowly until the mid 1980s. The first atlas survey, carried around this time, shows the species to be still virtually confined to the north of the county. After this the population suddenly expanded to reach a plateau in the early 1990s. The second survey shows birds occupying most of the large waters in the north of the county and along the Thames

Valley. It is likely that the southern birds have originated from the free flying flock that was released in Windsor Great Park in the late 1960s.

Greylags in Buckinghamshire associate with Canada Geese, grazing on arable farmland and improved pasture. In the north of the county, where such pasture is limited, the birds will graze on autumn-sown cereals and other crops. This has not endeared them to farmers, and a certain amount of persecution has ensued. Yet, despite fluctuations, the overall increase in numbers has not been affected. The habit of feeding away from water has made the wildfowl counts somewhat unreliable as they are restricted to wetland sites. The largest flocks recorded are 597 at Gayhurst Quarry in February 2009, 595 at the same site in March 2006, 569 at Newport Pagnell Gps in December 1996 and 558 at Emberton in Sep 1997. It is noteworthy that all these sites are in the far north of the county.

There is competition with Canada Geese and Mute Swans for breeding sites, especially on islands. Greylag often nest farther away from water, but whether this makes it harder for predators to find the nests is difficult to establish (Wright and Giles 1988). Competition between the three species may eventually lead to stabilisation of numbers.

The Greylag's normal breeding range in Eurasia extends from the low tundra to the temperate zone, and, unlike its relatives it often remains in its breeding area throughout the year. Thus, once established in an area, feral populations tend to spread outwards from the centre as densities increase. The normal wintering range for W European birds is the Mediterranean area including N Africa, but it seems very unlikely that the birds in Buckinghamshire will ever develop a migratory pattern. One ringed at Slimbridge on about 15 Jul 1956 was, however, shot at Ickford on about 1 Feb 1960.

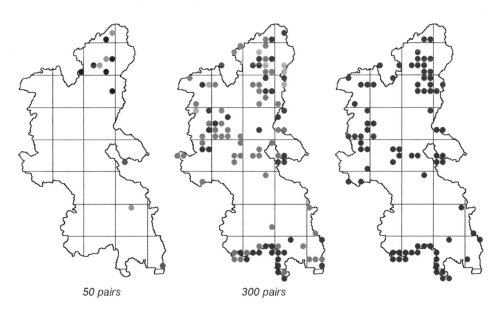

50 pairs   300 pairs

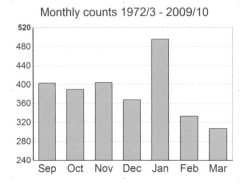

Monthly counts 1972/3 - 2009/10

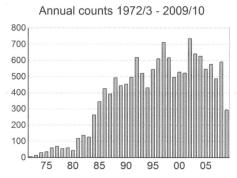

Annual counts 1972/3 - 2009/10

NHFS

Canada Goose
Branta canadensis

Introduced resident.

The Canada Goose was probably ignored by commentators in the nineteenth and early twentieth century as an ornamental fowl on private waters and an `escape' on others. In the 1950s and 1960s, and in Buckinghamshire as late as the early 1970s (Giles and Wright 1986), populations were being established in suitable habitat throughout the country. Some populations were the result of introductions to provide shooting, others were the result of expansion from established colonies. Deliberate introductions may have been a mistaken policy as the Canada Goose has responded with an unprecedented population explosion and has become a nuisance in many areas. In Buckinghamshire it is causing concern among farmers in the north of the county.

Little Marlow, 3 May 2006   *David Ferguson*

   Canada Geese began to colonise the Linford Pits in 1972 at the time that gravel extraction was nearing completion. An examination of the Wildfowl Count returns shows a moderate increase in the early years, accelerating to rapid growth in the 1970s. Richardson (1982) gives an account of the Canada Goose in Northamptonshire, particularly its establishment and spread. It is logical to surmise that an overflow from the Nene Valley gravel pits population provided the nucleus for the present stock in N Buckinghamshire, although Ogilvie (1977) suggests a link from the west in Oxfordshire. The rapid increase continued until the mid 1990s when it seems to have peaked. Possibly birds have now occupied all suitable breeding habitat.

   An attempt was made at Willen in 1993 to reduce the population by destroying 1300 eggs. This seems to have been unsuccessful as flocks of over 600 were recorded at Linford and Emberton in the late 1990s while Emberton hosted 880 birds in October 2002. Since then flock sizes have decreased; the only flock in the north of the county to exceed 300 birds was in the autumn of 2009 at Foxcote. This reduction in numbers has been compensated by huge flocks appearing at College Lake, possibly as a result of shooting at nearby Wilstone. In October 2005 the flock size peaked at 973 birds. Even this was eclipsed by a count of 1166 birds at Dorney in October 2008.

The Canada Goose feeds mostly by grazing and can therefore come into direct competition with grazing livestock, particularly sheep. The geese also eat roots and tubers and could be in competition with grey geese. In mitigation, their digestive system is so inefficient that they return nearly as much to the land in droppings as they crop.

Their nesting preference is for quiet waters with plenty of marginal growth. The site itself is by choice an island, as in their original habitat, though the birds have fewer predators to cope with here. In their study, Giles and Wright (1988) found that although nesting success was high for both Canada and Greylag, gosling mortality was higher in the former. The earlier nesting of Canada was suggested as a reason. There is competition for nesting sites with Mute Swans, the swans usually establishing a territory after some show of force. Occasional hybridisation of Canadas with Greylags occurs.

Individuals of the smaller subspecies are occasionally recorded. All are presumably of captive origin. A bird ringed as a gosling at Tamworth, Staffs in June 1998 was seen at Linford in August 2000.

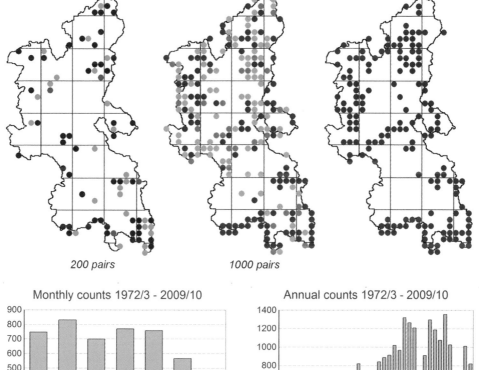

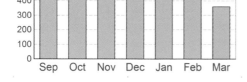
200 pairs   1000 pairs

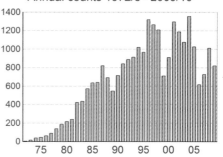

NHFS

Barnacle Goose
Branta leucopsis

Aylesbury, 8 Jan 2006   Mike Wallen

Introduced resident.

The flock in neighbouring Bedfordshire was deemed in 2005 to be self-sustaining and was thus promoted to category C2, the same as Canada Goose. Colour-ringed birds from this flock were seen in the county in 2007 so the species has been added to the county list. Feral birds breed at Emberton and Olney and flocks of up to 240 birds have been seen in this area. Small numbers of clearly feral birds are regularly seen elsewhere in the county. On 27 Dec 1991 about 50 flew over Drayton Parslow on a day when many geese were on the move. Even so, these birds cannot definitely be considered as wild.

Brent Goose
Branta bernicla

Furzton, 15 Jan 2006   Mike Wallen

Scarce migrant.

The first record within the present county boundary was:

1965: 1 dark-bellied on 4 Oct, Foxcote.

There were no more records until 1981. Since then about 187 birds have been recorded, occasionally in large flocks, the largest of which are c50 over Stokenchurch on 16 Feb 1994, 29 flying over College Lake on 19 Mar 2005 and 20 flying W over the Thames Valley at Little Marlow on 17 Nov 1991. Only one bird, at Willen from 29-30 Mar 1982, showed the characters of the light-bellied *B.b.hrota*.

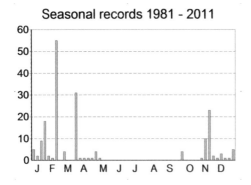

Seasonal records 1981 - 2011

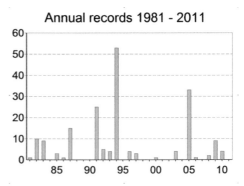

Annual records 1981 - 2011

Egyptian Goose
Alopochen aegyptiaca

Introduced local resident.

H & R noted a report by J W Owen in *The Field* of 19 Nov 1859 that 'A fine specimen was shot on November 1 at Marlow' and commented that 'It is supposed to have been driven there during preceding gales, as it presented no appearance of ever having been in confinement. We are inclined to think that it must have escaped from some pond.'

Little Marlow, 22 Apr 2010   *David Ferguson*

Up to 1990 there were just a further five records:

1867: 1 at Dorney Common.
1972: 1 on 4 Jul, Foxcote.
1983: 1 from 15 Apr-4 May, Haversham, Linford, Cosgrove.
1985: 1 on 5 May, Pitstone.
1989: 2 on 19 Feb, Willen.

From 1991 to 1996 singles or pairs were recorded in scattered locations for every year except 1994. The first known successful breeding took place at Amerden Lake in 1996. After this numbers increased rapidly with Little Marlow becoming the centre for late summer and autumn flocks. The first double figure flock was 14 on 17 Aug 1998 after which numbers rose steadily year by year to a maximum of 107 on 26 Aug 2005. During this period birds bred at Langley Park, Taplow, Denham and Linford . The maps show the range expansion since then. The increase seems to be due to escapes from collections outside the county and a northwards expansion from east Berkshire: breeding there was confirmed in 55 tetrads during the second survey. The rapidity of the population increase is remarkable.

DMF

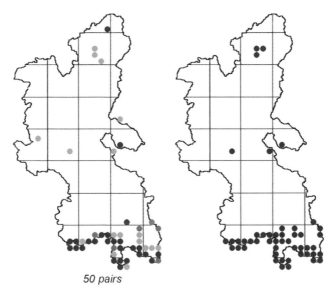

50 pairs

Shelduck
Tadorna tadorna

Scarce resident and regular migrant.

The Shelduck was first noted in Buckinghamshire in March 1780 when a male was shot in the Tring neighbourhood (illustration in Dinton Hall MS). Price noted that `since 1920 it has been

Little Marlow, 28 Mar 2011   *David Ferguson*

recorded many times at the Slough Sewage Farm, several times near Olney and occasionally elsewhere, in every month but July, though most frequently in April, May, August, and September. The largest number seen together was seven near Olney in March 1942.' Hayward (1947) attributed many of the early records to escapes but noted `a party of eleven which visited Wilstone for about twenty minutes before flying off to the west, on August 30, 1925.'

Since the Second World War numbers and visits have increased. Breeding first took place in the county at Linford in 1975 and successful breeding occurred at this site in four of the next thirteen years. This was the only breeding site in the county until 1994 when a pair successfully raised eight young at Littleworth Common. Thus began a trend to breed away from the usual large lakes with pairs raising young at Langley Park, Old Wolverton, Fulmer and Dorney. There is a suspicion that some of these birds were of feral origin. Away from the breeding season birds have been recorded on most large waters of the county, always in small numbers.

The spread of the Shelduck inland seems to have coincided with the range expansion of the small snail *Potamopyrgus jenkinsii* from brackish to fresh water since the end of the nineteenth century. This snail is parthenogenetic, in fact no male has ever been found; also it does not appear to suffer from any flat-worm endoparasites and is altogether one of those intriguing mysteries of evolution. This snail, together with its saltwater counterpart *Hydrobia ulvae*, constitutes a considerable part of the Shelduck's diet, being sifted out of the soft mud. Its presence or non-presence may therefore be a deciding factor in the Shelduck's inland distribution. The small but increasing number of breeding Shelduck in Buckinghamshire provides some evidence for this. If the water is shallow enough and with soft mud, and if *Potamopyrgus jenkinsii* is*jenkinsii* is present, then sooner or later Shelduck will occur.

Shelduck were - and still are where possible - burrow nesters, favouring rabbit warrens. However, the spread of myxomatosis, plus the post-myxomatosis habit of some does to give birth above ground rather than in special breeding stops, has forced Shelducks themselves to breed more often above ground as they most likely did before the rabbit was introduced to Britain. This change of habit might be a causal factor in the spread of the Shelduck away from sandy coastal dunes.

It has long been known that non-breeding Shelduck migrate to certain areas where they congregate for the annual moult. For many years it was thought that they all used the Wadden Sea area of the German coast, but it is now known that several smaller areas are also used for this purpose. The nearest to Buckinghamshire is on the Wash and may be the one used by such birds as occur in the county. However, the numbers which actually breed are insufficient for a crèche system to develop as happens on the coast, and the Buckinghamshire breeding birds probably therefore moult on the breeding site.

NHFS

Mandarin
Aix galericulata

Introduced local resident.

Mandarins have long been a component of wildfowl collections in Great Britain. They seem to have been imported into this country in the 18th century, but only in small numbers as the Chinese were reluctant to allow their export. By the 19th century, however, they were being frequently imported and no major collection was without some specimens.

Hedgerley, 23 Mar 2012 — David Ferguson

Our local birds probably originated from two sources. In 1928 Mr Alfred Ezra added six pairs of Mandarins to his wildfowl collection at Foxwarren Park in Surrey. These birds found the conditions so congenial that within four years the species had escaped and was breeding in Windsor Great Park and Virginia Water. They have been spreading from this source ever since until there are now over 500 pairs breeding in Surrey and E Berkshire.

The second source is the origin of so many of Britain's exotic fauna. The 11th Duke of Bedford had some Mandarins in his great collection of wildfowl at Woburn, where they soon began to breed around the estate, favouring the rhododendron thickets around the lakes. Birds have spread outwards from the estate in small numbers.

The first record within the present county boundary was of a pair seen at Littleworth Common from 6-11 Apr 1955. On 15 Jun 1955 a female with young was seen at nearby Dropmore; it is not known if the same birds were involved. The next record was in the north of the county. A female was seen on the River Ousel near Linslade at the end of June or early July 1964. After this, there were one or two records per year until 1978 when birds were recorded at five sites. Pairs bred at Stoke Hammond in 1982, at Cliveden in 1984, and at Wooburn Common in 1985.

There was a considerable increase in the number of records in 1987. Single pairs bred at Three Locks, Cliveden, and Boveney, while two pairs bred in specially designed nestboxes at Taplow Court. 20 birds were seen at this site in Oct, while 30 were seen at Hedsor in the same month. The birds have continued to increase until by 1990 Taplow Court had 14 breeding pairs, a pair bred in a nestbox at Wooburn Common, and two broods were seen near Three Locks. On 7 Oct 1990, 44 birds were seen at Taplow Court.

During 1992 a radio-tracking and colour ringing project was started at Taplow Court. 487 birds were trapped and ringed on the backwater between 1992 and 1995, with 193 of these trapped during the autumn and winter of 1993/94. Some of the tagged females bred in the local woods and were seen leading their young to the Thames and the Taplow Court backwater shortly after they had left the nest. These included broods from the Dropmore estate and Wooburn Common area where birds would have had to travel a considerable distance (at least 1 Km) over land to reach the Thames. Once on the Thames small ducklings appeared to feed mainly on insects caught over water but larger ducklings were also seen taking bread. The Slow Grove Island area at Cliveden is a favoured area in late summer where people in boats often feed Mandarin and other ducks. The largest broods were all recorded in this area and 45 young were seen there in June 1997.

During the autumn and winter birds appear to be dependent on food provided at local duck shoots. Flocks were regularly recorded visiting feeding ponds with over 70 recorded at a shoot in 1993. The flood meadows at White Brook on the Berkshire side of the Thames opposite Cliveden reach used hold large numbers of birds during periods of winter flooding but this was before the flood relief channel was constructed.

Mandarins roost communally, both at night and during the day, with the largest gatherings recorded during autumn and winter evenings. Radio tracking enabled roosts of over 30 birds to be found along the Thames at Taplow Court, Cliveden Islands, Formosa and Hedsor Wharf but the largest roost was found on the Dropmore estate where approx 140 birds were recorded roosting in Rhododendron overhanging a small pond near Cabrook on the south side of the estate on 10 Aug 1992.

1 pair   80 pairs

The maps clearly show a considerable increase in the breeding distribution within the county. Birds have spread from the Cliveden-Taplow area along the Thames Valley as far west as Medmenham and as far north as Shardeloes. The region around Three Locks and Stockgrove, which did not register on the earlier map, shows a healthy distribution while a new enclave centred around Weston Turville and Broughton, Aylesbury has appeared. It would seem from the winter map that Mandarins vacate many of their breeding sites in the winter.

The increase in numbers within Buckinghamshire is part of a general increase in the British population, but is also helped by the nestbox scheme in the south of the county. The British population in 1990 was around 7000 individuals, and is significant on a world scale, where Mandarin numbers in China, Japan, and Russia may be less than 20,000 birds.

There is have been three long-distance ringing recoveries. An adult female ringed at Taplow on 3 Jun 1989 was recovered at Southgate, Greater London on 16 Feb 1991. A bird ringed at Taplow was recovered in the Netherlands 42 days later. A female ringed at Taplow on 19 Nov 1995 was found dead at Aleksandrov, Vladimir, USSR on 5 Oct 2001 having travelled 2643 kms.

NHFS & PJS

Wigeon
Anas penelope

Regular winter visitor.

Historically, the Wigeon appears to have been a bird of coastal marshes and saltings, but more recently it has increasingly moved inland. A major reason for this was probably the virtual disappearance, through disease, of eel-grass from the coastal shallows in the 1930s. Another factor was the increase of lowland water through gravel and other extraction, particularly where suitable grazing and loafing areas were available close to the water. This would seem to be the case in Buckinghamshire, with Weston Turville Res attracting large numbers of birds in the nineteenth century.

Foxcote, 10 Dec 2007   Mike Wallen

In the early years of Willen and Caldecotte Lakes, Wigeon were numerous winter visitors but increasing urbanisation has caused their numbers to decline. This has been compensated by increasing numbers at Foxcote where 984 were recorded in Nov 2005. Further south, College Lake has proved to be a favourable site for Wigeon, particularly as a refuge when shooting takes place at nearby Wilstone Reservoir. Thus on 12 Jan 2005 about 1900 birds were recorded, a figure only surpassed by the

2200 present on 28 Jan 2006. These figures, to some extent, account for the increasing numbers shown on the graph.

Wigeon graze in compact flocks, feeding on fine grasses, roots and stolons. Some seeds are also taken. They will associate with Mallard on autumn stubble, but nowadays this is often ploughed in before it can be utilised. The birds compensate for this by feeding on newly-sprouted winter cereals. There is some competition with sheep, as both prefer the finer grasses. Wigeon feed by day and night, but where there is disturbance their feeding is restricted to night-time.

Single birds and the odd pair are reported occasionally during the summer months in Buckinghamshire. Though well outside the normal breeding range, sporadic nesting does occur in SE England and may yet be seen in the county.

A few birds appear as early as August, but these may be birds dispersing from breeding grounds elsewhere in Britain. Most start to arrive from October onwards, some from Iceland but the majority from Scandinavia and the USSR, fleeing severe weather on the continent.

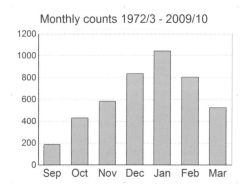

Monthly counts 1972/3 - 2009/10

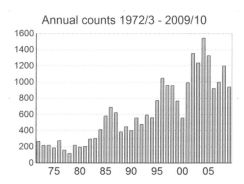

Annual counts 1972/3 - 2009/10

NHFS

Gadwall
Anas strepera

Local resident and regular winter visitor.

The Gadwall, on the extreme edge of its range in Britain, owes its position as a breeding bird in Britain to the release of two pinioned birds at Narford in Norfolk in 1850, these birds having previously been caught at Dersingham Decoy. Prior to this it had not been known to breed, although it was a regular winter visitor in small numbers. Clark Kennedy says that it

Shardeloes, 15 Mar 2012   David Ferguson

was 'uncommon' and only included it 'on the authority of the Rev. H. Harpur Crewe of Drayton Beauchamp', who reported that birds of this species had occasionally been killed on the reservoirs at Marsworth and Wilstone. H & J reported that they had no definite record for Buckinghamshire apart from the above. Price reported one killed at Boarstall

Decoy about the beginning of February 1932, described as a new record for the county. Sporadic occurrences were considered noteworthy until the 1950s, when numbers started to increase. Birds first bred in the county at Willen in 1985. A female with two young were seen in the county on the River Colne at Denham, but they may have bred in Hertfordshire. A nest was found at Drayton Beauchamp in 1989, and a pair bred at College Lake in 1990. Since then the range has slowly expanded so that the latest breeding map shows sites scattered across the county. However, it still remains a scarce breeding species.

A predominantly freshwater species, the Gadwall is found on the county's shallow waters, though it is not so dependent on gravel pits as some other ducks. It has a mainly vegetarian diet, feeding mostly on floating and submerged plants. Feeding is generally from the surface of the water, with a small amount of dabbling; diving is rare. The Gadwall is also a kleptoparasite, mainly on Coot, but other ducks that bring vegetation to the surface are also parasitised. Nesting is in rank vegetation close to water, though tending to be in rather drier areas than Mallard.

It would appear that general colonisation of Buckinghamshire did not take place until the late 1970s. The Wildfowl Counts from 1961-83 showed only odd birds in the early years, scattered over a number of sites; but by 1978 double figures began to appear, and some sites seemed to be more favoured than others. Good numbers were 22 at Linford on 12 Feb 1978 and 16 at Willen on 17 Dec 1982 although, around this period, Old Slade, which was then part of Buckinghamshire, held 26 on 15 Jan 1978 and 84 on 17 Feb 1980. However, a count of 154 at Willen in January 1988 shows how rapidly the position changed. The graph shows that the winter population increased dramatically between the mid 1980s and the mid 1990s and then stabilised. From an examination of both the Breeding Atlas and the Winter Atlas it would seem that the colonisation of the county had two separate sources: that in the south being from the London area, and that in the north being from the East Midlands. Birds raised in Britain are mostly sedentary, though a few ringed in East Anglia have been recovered abroad, mainly in locations to the south-west. This could be a case of abmigration, as wintering and passage birds come from NE Europe.

The main breeding range of the Gadwall in Europe is east of 20° E longitude, with scattered populations to the west. Climatic changes may be responsible for the expansion of its range westward from a continental climate to a more maritime one (mirrored by an eastward spread in N America), but there can be little doubt that the establishment of feral populations in W Europe including the British Isles has accelerated the process.

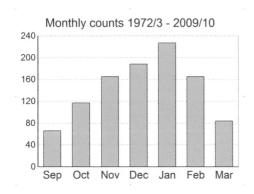

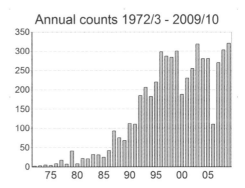

10 pairs

NHFS

Eurasian Teal
Anas crecca

Regular winter visitor. Has bred.

With the increase in the water area in Buckinghamshire over the last few decades, notably in the north of the county, the numbers of Teal present in winter have grown. Against this, increased drainage has reduced suitable breeding sites, and the presence of Teal (particularly single males) in summer should not be taken as an

4 Mar 2012, Little Marlow   *Jim Rose*

indication of breeding. Non-breeding birds occasionally spend the summer in the county and the males later disperse for moulting.

Clark Kennedy mentions that 'in the summer of 1861 two nests ... were discovered among some moss and rank herbage growing by the side of a pond near Burnham: it is probable that the birds had bred there previously'. He also states that 'the Rev. H. Harpur Crewe had taken the nest of this bird by the banks of the Wilstone and Marsworth reservoirs, where this species breeds in limited numbers every season.' According to H & J, they continued to do so until 1887. No further breeding was noted until 1918 when a brood was hatched at Marsworth Reservoir. H & J also reported that the late Lionel Wigglesworth had found the species breeding in small numbers near Castlethorpe. Teal continued to breed regularly on Marsworth and Wilstone Reservoirs until 1934. Mallard were artificially reared on these reservoirs from about 1890 to 1914 and again from 1933 to 1939, and this may have had some influence on Teal breeding. Since then it has only bred rather sporadically.

The habitat requirements of the species rather limit its distribution in Buckinghamshire. Teal come midway between Mallard and Shoveler in feeding specialisation. They prefer shallow water, not more that 25 cm in depth, over a muddy bottom. They feed by walking, slowly filtering mud through their bills, occasionally up-ending and very rarely diving. Though they are omnivorous, in autumn and winter their diet consists mainly of seeds, and they occasionally join Mallard on stubble grain. They feed both by day and night. For nesting they require thick marginal vegetation or cover such as an overhanging willow or bank. Breeding can be difficult to establish as the female and young tend to keep to cover rather than swim in open water. During the first survey period confirmed breeding was obtained only on the River Chess, while breeding was considered probable at Little Marlow. On 17 Aug 1992 three not fully fledged juveniles were seen at Little Marlow. Since then there has been no confirmed breeding. The second survey showed probable breeding at four sites but it is likely that these were summering non-breeders.

Teal start to appear in moderate numbers in autumn although an exceptionally high number of 211 appeared at Willen on 12 Sep 1976. A rapid increase in wintering numbers began in 1994 when the new reserve of College Lake proved to be very congenial to the birds while Little Marlow also became more suitable around this time. Winter peaks have been 468 at College Lake in Jan 2005, 368 at the same site on 11 Jan 2006, and 340 at Foxcote in February 2009. An early record of 385 at Boarstall Decoy on 17 Nov 1971 was exceptional for the time. The birds seen in winter in Buckinghamshire are probably all immigrants from NW Europe. Being small they are susceptible to bad weather, and in sustained cold spells the majority may move south-west as far as S France and the Iberian peninsula.

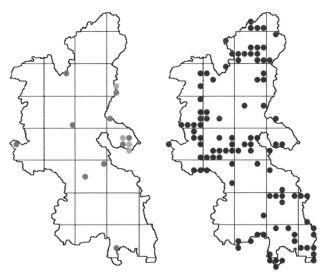

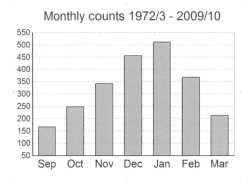

Monthly counts 1972/3 - 2009/10

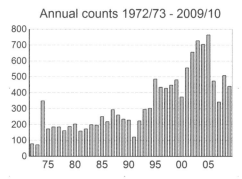

Annual counts 1972/73 - 2009/10

NHFS

Green-winged Teal
Anas carolinensis

Very rare vagrant. All records are given.

1994: male from 14 to 20 Nov, Willen.
1996: male on 31 Mar, Linford.
2000: male from 12 to 24 Apr, Linford.
2004: male from 11 to 16 Jan, Linford.
2010: male on 24 Mar, Linford.

These are typical dates for this North American vagrant. It is not obvious why Linford is so favoured.

Garganey
Anas querquedula

Scarce migrant and summer visitor.

The first record of Garganey within the present county boundary was not until 1937 when birds were recorded at Olney from 11-20 May 1937. Since then it has become a rare but annual passage migrant and summer visitor. It is our only summer

Linford, 14 Apr 2012   Jason Chalk

visitor among the ducks, usually first appearing in April and leaving in October.

Between 1946 and 1971 there were 19 records of 41 birds, while between 1972 and 2011there were 227 records of 286 birds. 176 birds were found in the north of the county, 55 in the middle, and 55 in the south. These later records are shown on the graphs. The largest flock was eight at Dorney Common on 26 Aug 2000. It is likely that the increase is due to increasing observer awareness of the difficulties in identifying the birds in their long-lasting eclipse plumage as well as the larger number of observers in more recent years.

Although pairs of Garganeys have frequently been seen in suitable breeding habitat in the spring the species has never been proven to have bred in Buckinghamshire. It is opportunist in its summer quarters, preferring ditches and other drainage channels, small pools, or larger waters well broken up with plenty of cover. It is very elusive at this time, and proof of breeding is difficult to obtain. During the period of the first atlas survey birds were recorded in two tetrads - SP84Q and SP80U. In the second atlas survey birds were recorded in seven tetrads. Although these records included several pairs there was no indication of breeding.

The graphs show that the spring migration peaks at the end of April, while the smaller autumn migration peaks in mid-August. The earliest record is of a pair on 9 Mar 1969 on the Wendover Canal, although there is a record of a female which wintered at Willen, not leaving until 15 Apr 1984.

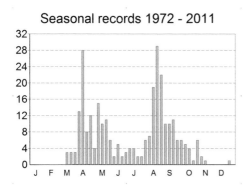

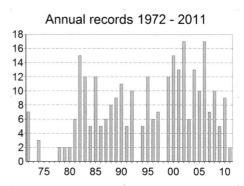

NHFS

Mallard
Anas platyrhynchos

Common resident and winter visitor.

Mallards are by far the commonest ducks in the county, and have been since records began. They are likely to breed anywhere that has water, from pollarded willows by a ditch and small tree-fringed field ponds to large lakes and rivers. The maps show that they breed throughout the county,

Gerrards Cross, 8 Apr 2009   *David Ferguson*

except for parts of the Chilterns which are without surface water, and some areas of the north. It is likely that the apparent expansion into the north-west is probably due to under-recording during the first atlas.

The graph of annual counts shows a population decrease in the early 1990s which may be due to the reduction in the large-scale releases for shooting which have been a feature at the nearby Tring reservoirs.

The graph of monthly counts shows that numbers remain fairly constant between September and January then fall off rapidly. The largest monthly count is one of 2816 birds in Nov 1980 while the largest count at a single site is 840 birds at Linford in December 1980. Recently, numbers at Linford rarely reach three figures.

More than 90% of ringing recoveries of birds ringed in the county have been made in S England, half of which have been within 100 km. The longest distance travelled involved a bird ringed in the county on 3 Jul 1965 which was recovered in Cornwall on 9 Dec 1967. There has been one foreign ringing recovery: a bird ringed at Boarstall Duck Decoy on 6 Nov 1985 was recovered near Calais on 12 Oct 1986.

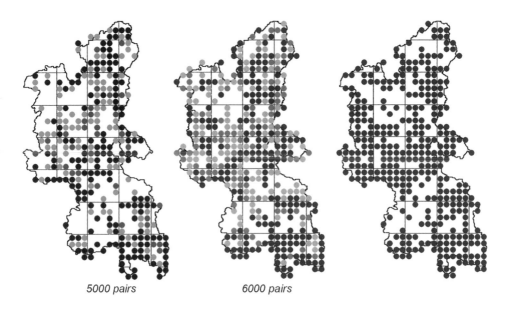

5000 pairs   *6000 pairs*

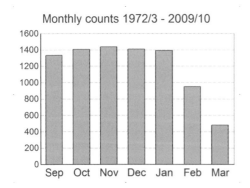

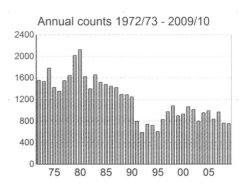

NHFS

Pintail
Anas acuta

Uncommon migrant and winter visitor.

The earliest record is that noted by Clark Kennedy of one 'shot on a sheet of ice in Stoke Parke by a man named Gregory in the winter of 1863'. H & J, writing in 1920, did not record any within the county, though in 1947 Price stated that the species was 'an uncommon winter visitor'.

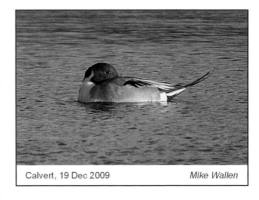

Calvert, 19 Dec 2009   Mike Wallen

Between 1946 and 1959 21 birds were recorded, but between 1960 and 1969 this had increased to 222 birds. In the early 1970s a number of wing-tagged birds were released at Linford GPs by the Game Conservancy, but although some were present for several years they did not become established. They did, however, succeed in confusing the status of the species in the county.

Birds have been recorded annually since 1954, except for 1962. Flock sizes have usually been in single figures, but occasional large gatherings are seen. The largest flock recorded is one of 57 birds seen flying SW into Bucks from Wilstone Res on 31 Jan 1985. The next largest flock is one of 40 birds seen at Foxcote Res on 1 Mar 1964. On 16 Jan 1972, 26 were seen on Foxcote Res at the same time that 10 flew over. Since then there have only been two flocks recorded with more than twenty birds: 26 at Little Marlow on 18 Jan 2003 and 22 at Linford on 4 Jan 2003.

Birds have been seen at all the major waters in the county, with no one site dominating. They have occasionally been seen on floodwater. The earliest birds are sometimes found in September and occasionally in late August, but numbers do not peak until the early months of the year. By the end of March the birds are gone, but a male was seen at Willen on 9 May 1976.

NHFS

Shoveler
Anas clypeata

Scarce resident, local migrant and winter visitor.

The Shoveler, a duck of southerly distribution, has shown a huge population increase in Great Britain and W Europe over the last hundred years (Alexander and Lack 1944, Parslow 1973), though the latter suggests that the increase may have slowed down since the 1950s. This expansion may be related to an

Willen, 14 Nov 2009   Keith O'Hagen

improvement of the climate following the `little ice age' from the seventeenth century to the first half of the nineteenth.

The Shoveler makes very poor eating, its flesh being rank and is therefore not a target for fowlers. There is, however, a record of one shot near Dinton Hall on 10 Sep 1774 and another of four present on 29 Aug 1800, of which one was shot. Clark Kennedy indicated that it was a winter visitor to Buckinghamshire, but not a common one. H & J noted that in June 1918 Hartert came across a female leading eight ducklings along a ditch leading to Wilstone Reservoir; they also reported that Shoveler had been breeding there from at least 1905. Hayward (1947), however, states that they were breeding regularly by 1887 but declined after that. Breeding occurred again from 1914 to 1934, after which the next record was in 1943. These gaps in breeding coincide with the artificial breeding of Mallard on the reservoirs, which obviously limited breeding sites.

Breeding was almost annual at Willen until 1987 when there was a gap until 1996 when two pairs were successful. A pair bred for the first time at Linford in 1991, again in 1992, and two pairs bred in 1995. Since then there has only been two reports of successful breeding: in 2001 at Shardeloes and in 2006 at Gayhurst Quarry. In 2005 five Shoveler x Mallard hybrid ducklings were seen at College Lake.

Although there has been an increase in water area in the county, not much of it is suitable for this species. Shovelers require large areas of shallow, mud-based water. Of the newly created waters only the marsh at College Lake is suitable.

In spite of this, there has been a steady rise in wintering numbers. Three-figure flocks are unusual but they have been reported from Willen, Tongwell and College Lake. The largest flock recorded is one of 225 birds at Willen on 29 Aug 1988. 220 were recorded at the same site in Nov 1994. It would appear that summering birds in Britain move out in the autumn to S France and Spain, to be replaced by other birds from Europe which in turn move down to winter quarters in the south. Up to the 1950s and early 1960s there was also a peak in February and early March, presumably a stop-off on the return migration. Since then the pattern seems to have altered, and birds by-pass Britain on the return. This may again be due to climatic change, allowing a single movement from winter to summer quarters. It is interesting to speculate whether, if conditions changed again, Shoveler would revert to their earlier migration pattern, and if so how often this may have happened in the past.

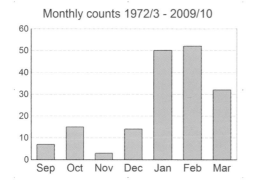

Monthly counts 1972/3 - 2009/10

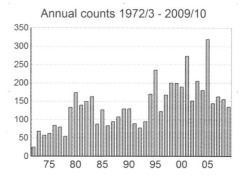

Annual counts 1972/3 - 2009/10

NHFS

Red-crested Pochard
Netta rufina

Uncommon vagrant, most of which are probably feral.

1918: 1 at Weston Turville Res, perhaps escaped from Woburn.
1920: 1 at Weston Turville Res, perhaps escaped from Woburn.
1961: female on 6 Apr, Little Marlow.
1971: female on 10 and 17 Oct, Little Marlow. Exceptional numbers occurred in SE England and this may well have been a wild bird.

Caldecotte, 1 Nov 2010   *Keith O'Hagen*

Since 1972, 348 birds have been recorded. Numbers remained low until 2007 when there was a sudden increase followed by a stabilisation. The increase is probably related to the increase in the feral population in places such as the Cotswold Water Park. Most birds are found in the north of the county but they may be encountered on any large water in the county. There is some evidence of a small autumn passage but it is likely that most are feral birds engaged in post-breeding dispersal. Only a few birds have shown signs of a wild origin.

The map, which is the result of four winters' surveying, exaggerates the status of the species.

Seasonal records 1972 - 2011

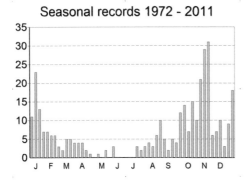

Annual records 1972 - 2011

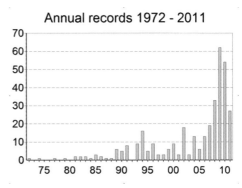

Common Pochard
Aythya ferina

Scarce resident, but common winter visitor and passage migrant.

The first record of Pochard in the county is of one shot at Dinton Hall on 16 Jun 1825. According to Clark Kennedy, the Rev. Harpur Crewe stated that this duck was 'a common winter visitor to the reservoirs near Drayton Beauchamp', but that it was 'rare on the rivers'. He also noted that it had bred on two occasions at Marsworth

Little Marlow, 4 Mar 2011   *David Ferguson*

and Wilstone reservoirs in the 1850s. It would appear to have increased in the county during the latter part of the nineteenth century, as H & J reported that it 'breeds numerously at the Halton and Tring Reservoirs'. Two pairs nested on a pond at Burnham Beeches in 1916 (H & J); and E O Höhn (1943) said that the bird had bred annually on a pond in Buckinghamshire since the beginning of the century.

The Pochard has a more southerly distribution than the Tufted Duck. In common with most of Europe, the British population has increased markedly during the present century, probably for the same reasons that apply to the Tufted Duck (qv). There has, however, been some decline since the early 1970s when there were very high numbers in Britain. This is particularly marked in SE England, where most of the country's Pochard breed. In Buckinghamshire this decline is offset (or masked) by the availability of additional waters favourable to the species. Poor breeding success or climatic change may account for what is probably a temporary dip in numbers.

In Buckinghamshire the Pochard is still an uncommon breeding bird; birds seen in summer are usually non-breeders. The bird prefers shallower water than the Tufted Duck. Its dives are only up to 3 m and are of shorter duration. Occasionally it feeds by up-ending. Though it feeds by day as well as at night, it is most often seen in daytime sleeping on the water. The preferred food is vegetable matter, but some animal material is taken. For breeding, the female prefers undisturbed waters with plenty of marginal vegetation. The nest is constructed close to the water's edge. Weston Turville Res was the only regular breeding site in the county where up to five pairs bred. The last recorded

78

breeding at this site was in 1995. Between 1993 and 2005, pairs bred almost annually at Shardeloes. The only other sites where they are known to have bred are Linford and Tilehouse. It may be that the species is under-recorded as a breeding bird in the county, especially in the north where there are a number of apparently suitable sites.

The build-up of numbers starts about the middle of August when post-moult birds arrive to join those which have summered, and by the middle of winter large numbers can be present on some waters. In the winter of 1977-78 Shardeloes Lake held over 300, Great Linford 497 on 13 Nov 1977, and Willen 655 a few weeks later on 18 Dec. Other large flocks include 605 at College Lake in Dec 1995, 579 at Willen in Oct 1994 and 517 at Linford in Oct 2004.

There is some evidence that females travel further south than males, which may account for the high proportion of males in winter flocks in Britain. The larger male may be more adapted to withstand cold, and the separation of the sexes in winter could have survival benefits. Ringing recoveries in Buckinghamshire appear to indicate east to west movements in winter. A bird ringed on 13 Jun 1933 in Helsinki, Finland was recovered in the county on 22 Dec 1937
(the first record of a Pochard ringed abroad and recovered in the UK); one ringed at Lake Engare, Latvia on 6 Jun 1964 was shot at Iver on 12 Dec 1966; and one ringed in Czechoslovakia on 12 Dec 1966 was recovered at Latimer on 30 Dec 1967. There is also a record of a bird ringed on the North Slob, Co. Wexford on 18 Jan 1979 being shot at Stone almost exactly eight years later on 14 Jan 1987.

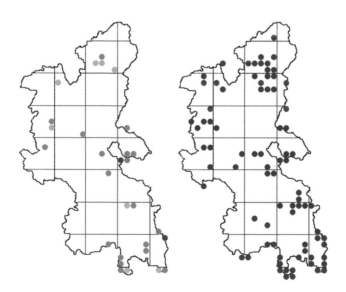

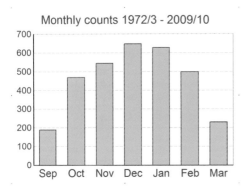

Monthly counts 1972/3 - 2009/10

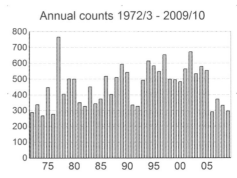

Annual counts 1972/3 - 2009/10

NHFS

Ring-necked Duck
Aythya collaris

Very rare vagrant. All records are given.

Foxcote, 4 Mar 2004   Rob Andrews

1971: male from 14 Feb to 10 Apr, returning from 14 Nov-30 Mar 1972, 17 Dec 1972-15 Jul 1973, and 16 Dec 1973 to 17 Apr 1974, Little Marlow.

1979: male from 7 to 16 Mar, Willen.

1989: female from 14 Jan to 2 May, Yiewsley GP, Iver.

1991: male on 12 May, Willen.

1994: male from 26 Sep to 3 Oct, Willen.

1996: male on 23 Feb, Willen.

2004: male from 14 Feb to 2 Apr, returning from 16 Mar to 5 Apr 2005, 4 to 12 Apr 2006, 9 Dec 2006 to 18 Feb 2007, 25 Mar to 1 Apr 2007, 10 Nov 2007 to 15 Apr 2008, 21 Oct 2008 to 3 Mar 2009, 11 Oct 2009 to 4 Apr 2010 and 18 Oct to 26 Nov 2010, Foxcote.

Long-staying individuals are a feature of this species, though the Little Marlow and Foxcote birds are exceptional.

Ferruginous Duck
Aythya nyroca

Rare vagrant. All records, with the exception of obvious feral birds, are given.

1974: male from 24 Feb to 12 Apr then throughout Oct, Newton Longville.
1976: male on 15 Feb, Eythrope.
1989: female from 3 to 4 Dec, Little Marlow.
1995: female intermittently from 3 Nov to 9 Dec, College Lake. It spent most of its stay on Wilstone Res.
1996: male from 19 to 26 Oct, Little Marlow.
1997: male 23 Dec, Calvert.
1997: male from 22 Feb to 2 Mar, Taplow Lake.
1999: male from 30 to 31 Jan, Little Marlow.
2008: male from 29 Sep to 12 Nov, Calvert which was at Foxcote on 2 Oct.
2009: male on 14 Oct, Calvert. This may be the same bird seen in 2008.

Calvert, 14 Oct 2008   *Tim Watts*

In addition, several possible 'Paget's Pochards' (hybrid Ferruginous Duck x Pochard) have been reported. The status of all records is problematical. It is possible they were all feral, although the dates seem to indicate wild birds.

Tufted Duck
Aythya fuligula

Common resident, passage migrant and winter visitor.

A bird of more northerly distribution than the Pochard, the Tufted Duck has shown a dramatic increase in both its range and numbers in W Europe since the end of the 19th century. This has been linked to climatic changes, particularly to the drier

Hedgerley, 20 Apr 2009   *David Ferguson*

conditions in SW Asia which have resulted in losses of breeding habitat there. It is now the most familiar diving duck in Buckinghamshire, found on most waters with a depth of more than one metre. Undoubtedly the increased availability of suitable sites this century, due in large measure to gravel and mineral extraction, has contributed significantly to this spread.

Clark Kennedy described the Tufted Duck as a common winter visitor to the Marsworth and Wilstone reservoirs, but noted that it did not often occur on the rivers. By 1920 it was already nesting on the Tring and Weston Turville reservoirs (H & J). Since then it has continued to increase in numbers, particularly in winter, wherever there are suitable waters. In recent years the creation of flood balancing lakes as part of the development of Milton Keynes has augmented the number of favourable sites.

81

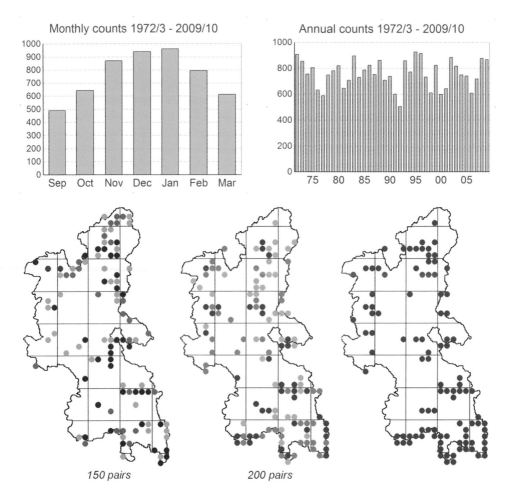

Monthly counts 1972/3 - 2009/10

Annual counts 1972/3 - 2009/10

150 pairs *200 pairs*

The diet of the Tufted Duck consists of about 80% animal material, with molluscs predominating, and the rest insects. Vegetable food is usually in the form of seeds. This food is normally obtained by diving, but upending is sometimes resorted to in shallow water. Dives can be up to 5 m but are generally about half that and average 15-20 seconds in duration. Males tend to dive to greater depths than females, and this probably accounts for some separation out of the breeding season. The males start to flock and begin their moult while the females are still on the nest. Later, the males congregate on the slightly deeper waters, leaving the shallower waters for the females. This may have some survival value, but there may be other factors involved (see Pochard).

This is one of the last duck species to nest, often as late as June or July. The nest is usually close to the water, well concealed in tussock or rushes. In Buckinghamshire, breeding is restricted to waters of moderate size. The birds prefer to use small islands, though these are not always a safeguard from predators; foxes have been known to swim out and search them for sitting birds. The recorded sites follow the line of the river valleys where gravel is worked. Both Willen and Great Linford regularly report over 100 ducklings, but nesting is probably under-reported in the county.

The wintering population builds up from October onwards. Post-moulting flocks are swelled by birds from more northerly parts of Britain as well as from NW Europe and Iceland. It may be that the majority that arrive in Buckinghamshire are from Europe, crossing the North Sea and spreading inland from the Wash. The largest flocks recorded are 603 at Little Marlow in Jan 1997, 558 at the same site in December 1990 and 478 at Great Linford on 12 Dec 1976. Wintering flocks start to disperse about the middle of March. In very bad weather, when the waters are completely frozen over, the birds may desert the county for larger waters elsewhere, such as Stewartby (Bedfordshire) or Grafham (Cambridgeshire), or even the coast, only returning as conditions improve.

Ringing recoveries mainly involve birds ringed in eastern counties of England in autumn or spring being found in Buckinghamshire during the winter. An interesting record is of a nasal saddled bird which was ringed at St Philbert de Grand Lieu just south of Nantes on 1 Dec 2010 seen at LMGP on 26 Oct 2011 and again in March 2012.

NHFS

Scaup
Aythya marila

Scarce migrant and winter visitor.

There are seven records prior to 1973:

1855: 1 female on 26 Jan, on River Chess, Latimer.
1923: 1 on 4 Nov, Weston Turville Res.
1928: 1 on 28 Oct, Weston Turville Res.
1950: 2 females or imms 29 Oct, Weston Turville Res.
1958: male on 16 Mar, Foxcote.
1958: male from 30 Mar to13 Apr, Hartigan's GP.
1960: female from 30 Nov to16 Dec, near Foxcote.

Caldecotte, 9 Dec 2010   Mike Wallen

There are 92 records of 130 birds since 1973. They are shown on the graphs. 57 birds were seen in the north of the county, 16 in the middle, and 37 in the south. The largest flocks were both of six birds: from 10 to 11 Feb 1991 at Boveney Lock, and Tilehouse on 19 Jan 1985 and 10 Jan 1997. Curiously, the two Tilehouse records concerned flocks of circling birds.

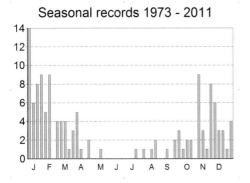

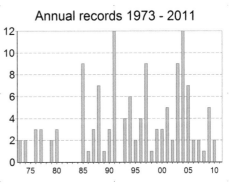

Eider
Somateria mollissima

Very rare vagrant. All records are given.

1988: 2 females on 5 Apr, Weston Turville Res.
1993: adult male and a female/imm, from 31 Oct to 18 Nov, Linford.
1993: female/imm on 6 Nov, Hyde Lane.

The 1993 birds were part of a large influx into the English Midlands. An earlier record of a male at Foxcote on 11 Feb 1961 was unreported at the time and cannot now be substantiated.

Long-tailed Duck
Clangula hyemalis

Rare vagrant and winter visitor. All records
are given.

Calvert, 7 Jun 2009   Mike Wallen

1957: 1 from 18 to 19 Nov, Weston Turville Res.
1959: male from 17 to 19 Nov, Foxcote.
1966: male and 2 females on 11 Apr, Marlow GP.
1969: female/immature on 15 Feb, Shardeloes, during severe weather.
1970: immature from 29 Oct to 13 Jan 1971, Calvert.
1973: male from 18 Feb to 18 Mar, Calvert.
1979: female from 17 Nov to 18 Dec, Willen.
1979: immature from 31 Dec 1979 to 19 Jan 1980, Startopsend Res., typically along Bucks edge.
1981: female on 9 Dec, Willen.
1982: fem or imm from 19 Nov-26 Dec, Stony Stratford.
1983: imm male on 4 Mar, Blue Lagoon, Milton Keynes.
1988: 1 from 23 Oct to early Jun 1989, Startopsend Res, Hertfordshire, was often seen in the Buckinghamshire section.
1990: immature male and female from 16 Dec-13 Jan 1991, Weston Turville Res.
1991: 2 from 2 Nov to 10 Dec, Willen.
1993: female from 10 Jan to 3 May, 30 Oct to 17 Apr 1994, 29 Oct to 2 Apr 1995, 6 Jan and 17 Mar 1996, Jan to 9 Mar 1997, 28 Feb to 10 Apr 1998, 14 Nov to 10 Jan 1999, 27 Jan 2000, Tilehouse.
1996: 1 from 2 Dec to 19 Dec, Caldecotte.
1999: 1 on 4 Apr, Tilehouse. A different bird to the regular female.
2002: imm male from 20 to 28 Apr, Foxcote,
2005: 1st-winter male from 17 Nov to 15 Apr 2006, Calvert.
2006: imm male from 28 May to 11 June, College Lake, previously at Wilstone Res, Hertfordshire.
2009: male in summer plumage from 3 to 7 Jun, Calvert.

The eight winters that a female spent at Tilehouse and nearby Broadwater, Middlesex is exceptional. The last two records were very unseasonal.

Common Scoter
Melanitta nigra

Scarce migrant.

There were nine records prior to 1974:

1893: young male on 18 Dec was shot at Deadmere, Great Marlow.
1910: 11 on 10 Apr, Weston Turville Res.
1913: 1 on 19 Jul, Weston Turville Res.
1957: pair on 4 Apr, Weston Turville Res.
1957: pair and a female on 15 Apr, Weston Turville Res.
1958: male on 31 Mar, Weston Turville Res.
1958: female from 18 to 20 Oct, Shardeloes, after severe gales.
1960: 2 females on 25 Oct, Foxcote.
1971: 1 in Mar, Stowe.

Dorney Lake, 7 Dec 2008   *David Ferguson*

Since 1974 then there have been 166 records of 398 birds. They are shown on the graphs. 274 birds were seen in the north of the county, 92 in the middle and 32 in the south. The largest flocks recorded are of 35 on 7 Apr 1996 at Foxcote, 28 on 1 Apr 2005 at Calvert and 25 on 31 Mar 2005 at Linford. The last two flocks contained different sex ratios and were thus different.

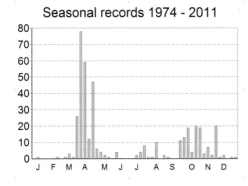

Seasonal records 1974 - 2011

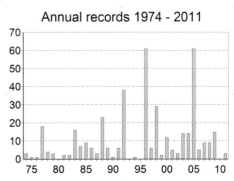

Annual records 1974 - 2011

Velvet Scoter
Melanitta fusca

Very rare vagrant. All records are given.

1890: 1 killed 27 Oct, Linford.
1948: male from 12 to13 Dec, near Iver.
1982: 11 on 9 Jan, Willen.
2006: first-winter male on 2 Feb, Willen.

Bufflehead
Bucephala albeola

Very rare vagrant. There has been one record.

1961: male from 28 Feb to 9 Mar, Foxcote Res.

This was the sixth British record of this North American bird.

Goldeneye
Bucephala clangula

Local winter visitor.

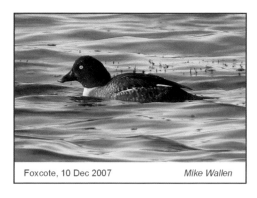

Foxcote, 10 Dec 2007   *Mike Wallen*

Clark Kennedy refers to this duck as being `A winter visitant, but never appearing in great numbers'. H & R, however, talk of `an irregular winter visitor, often appearing in great numbers on the Tring Reservoirs in very cold weather'. H & J only speak of `small flocks'. The Rev. J. Williams stated in 1849 that `small flocks visited the Tring Reservoirs annually, arriving at the end of October and staying until driven away by frost,' and that `nearly all were females or birds of the year'.

Mainly a sea duck, the Goldeneye prefers large open waters such as estuaries. Inland it will frequent larger waters of reasonable depth. Dives are up to seven metres, the food being mainly of an animal nature. The increase in the number of suitable waters in Buckinghamshire, particularly in the north, plus the increased number of observers, has meant that more are reported; but it is still possible to overlook `redheads' among other diving ducks.

The annual graph shows a steady increase to a peak in 2002 and then a more rapid decline. The reasons for this are not known.

Goldeneye tend to arrive in October and begin to disperse in late March. Willen and Foxcote can regularly be relied upon to produce double figures in suitable weather in winter. The largest flock recorded in the county was at Willen, 40 in Feb 2009. The earliest record for the county, 10 Aug 1998, was of a `redhead' (possibly a juvenile) at Stony Stratford NR. There have been several years when birds have summered. A female, possibly the same bird, summered at Linford from 1989 to 1992. A male summered at Little Marlow in 1998 - it was presumed to be injured. Two immatures were seen at Little Marlow on 18 July. A female was present at Linford from 27 Jul to 4 Aug.

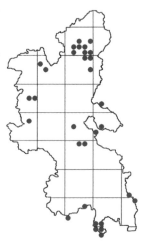

There is a tendency for more `redheads' to be seen on Buckinghamshire waters in winter. This has more to do with females moving further south than males, rather than segregation of the sexes as such, and, of course, the dispersal of juveniles.

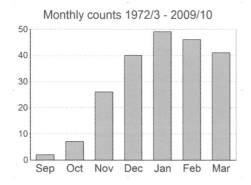

Monthly counts 1972/3 - 2009/10

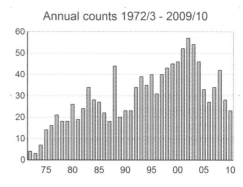

Annual counts 1972/3 - 2009/10

NHFS

Smew
Mergellus albellus

Scarce winter visitor.

The first county record is of a female shot at Dinton Hall on 23 Nov 1774. There were seven records between 1920 and 1947, mostly at Weston Turville Res. Between 1947 and 1968 birds failed to be recorded in only four years, but there followed nine blank years until birds began to be recorded regularly from 1978.

Calvert, 21 Jan 2006   *Tim Watts*

The main wintering area in Britain is SE England and E Anglia. This is reflected in the local records, which indicate that Tilehouse GPs were the most regular site in the county before the recent decrease.

Before 1978 there was one major influx. In February 1963, during severe weather conditions when most waters were frozen, birds appeared on the River Thames. A flock of 19 birds was seen at Cliveden Reach on the 4th, and a flock of 15 birds at Medmenham on the 7th, but the largest recorded flock is one of 26 birds which was seen flying round Marlow GPs on 26 Jan 1992 at a time when many waters were frozen.

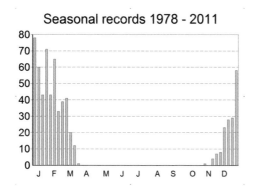

Seasonal records 1978 - 2011

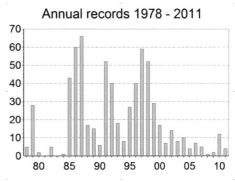

Annual records 1978 - 2011

87

The graph shows a sharp decline since a peak in 1997 when birds were found on waters throughout the county. This decline may be in part due a decrease in the Russian population.

An injured female summered at Linford in 1997. The earliest date is of a redhead at Weston Turville Res on 28 Sep 1951. This is so early that some doubt must be cast on the record, especially as it is not commented on in the MTHNS report. The next earliest date is of two redheads at Calvert on 18 Nov 1989. The latest date involves a male which stayed at Willen until 28 Mar 1985.

NHFS

Goosander
Mergus merganser

Local winter visitor. Has bred twice.

Caldecotte, 21 Jan 2012   Keith O'Hagen

Unlike the Red-breasted Merganser, the Goosander is mainly a bird of inland waters in winter. The earliest extant record for the county is of a female shot at Dinton Hall on 26 Nov 1774. It has increased its range considerably in recent years. Today it is recorded in all months from November to March, and occasionally birds stay later. In contrast to the Red-breasted Merganser, the Goosander will remain on suitable waters for a considerable time. Slightly different feeding techniques may give it an advantage; it has a deeper bill with a more pronounced hook at the tip, which may assist it when searching among stones on the bottom. In common with the other sawbills, adult males arrive later than the `redheads'. It is also possible that `redheads' winter further south than the adult males.

There are three regular wintering sites in the county: Foxcote, Caldecotte Lake, and Linford. Record numbers arrived in January 1997 when the largest flocks recorded were 115 at Linford on 23rd, 59 at Thorney on 5th, 45 at Caldecotte on 6th. Prior to this the record flock was 49 in Linford in December 1986. The other large waters record the bird irregularly, usually in single figures.

In May 2007 a female with about 12 ducklings was found on the River Ouse at Gayhurst. This astonishing record was repeated in July 2010 when a female with six

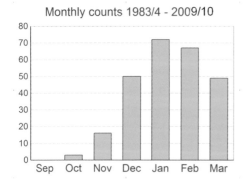

Monthly counts 1983/4 - 2009/10

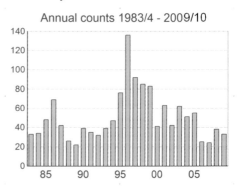

Annual counts 1983/4 - 2009/10

ducklings was seen at Olney Mill. This may be part of the gradual increase in the UK breeding population whose range has slowly moved south from its stronghold in northern England and Scotland.

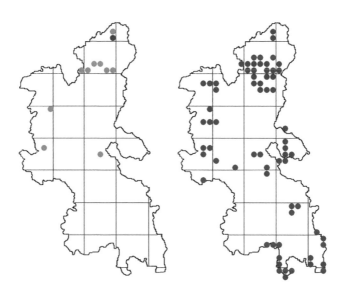

NHFS

Red-breasted Merganser
Mergus serrator

Rare vagrant and winter visitor.

Clark Kennedy stated that 'individuals were occasionally shot on the Thames', but the first dated record is:

1973: redhead 1 & 3 Nov, Weston Turville.

Since 1973 there have been 54 records of 83 birds. They are shown on the graphs. 41

Willen, 21 Dec 2008   Mike Wallen

of the birds were seen in the north of the county, 18 in the middle, and 24 in the south.

The February peak may be the result of cold weather movements. In Feb 1979, when 12 birds were seen in the county, 420 birds were reported in inland Britain, an event that was due to severe weather conditions on the Baltic and North Sea coasts (Chandler 1981).

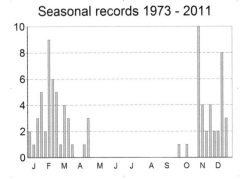

Seasonal records 1973 - 2011

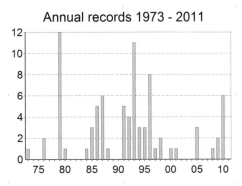

Annual records 1973 - 2011

Ruddy Duck
Oxyura jamaicensis

Formerly a very local resident and migrant, now extirpated.

Ruddy Ducks are a North American species where they breed in the marginal vegetation of small reed-fringed ponds and lakes. At least 70 juveniles escaped from the wildfowl collection at Slimbridge between 1952 and 1973 and were first recorded breeding in the wild at Chew Valley Lake, Avon in 1960. The

Shardeloes, 16 Aug 2004   *Mike Wallen*

population remained fairly constant for a few years then rapidly expanded, breeding as far away as Scotland and Northern Ireland. In 2000 the UK population was estimated at c6000 birds. Ruddy Ducks were first recorded at Tring Reservoirs in 1960 and first bred there in 1965 (Gladwin & Sage 1986). The small Buckinghamshire population presumably originated from there.

The increasing UK population was reflected by increasing numbers appearing in the near Continent and eventually Spain where a few hybridised with the endangered White-headed Duck *Oxyura leucocephala*. The threat to the Spanish White-headed Duck population was such that the Wildlife and Wetlands Trust began a trial cull of the UK's Ruddy Ducks in 1993 using shotguns and rifles. The trial increased in intensity between 1999 and 2005 when 700 - 900 birds were killed annually. Since 2005, culling took place at 110 sites throughout the UK with 6200 birds being killed (Henderson, 2009). By March 2011 the UK population was estimated to be less than 100 birds.

The following account describes the history of the Ruddy Duck in Buckinghamshire. Since the mid-2000s many of the county's birders deliberately withheld records of Ruddy Ducks to prevent the cullers knowing where the birds were. Thus the later years are somewhat vague. Prior to 1980 there were just seven records:

1960: female 1 Jan-23 Apr, then 7 Sep-12 Nov, Foxcote Res.
1974: female 29 Dec-3 Jan 1975, Foxcote Res.
1975: male 28 Aug-25 Oct, Weston Turville Res.
1976: male 7 Jun, Wotton Lake.

1976: female 23-31 Oct, Weston Turville Res.
1977: male 23-29 Aug, Weston Turville Res.
1979: male 25 Feb, Willen.

In 1980 two pairs bred successfully at Weston Turville Res, and at least six other birds were seen in the county. Subsequently the species attempted to breed every year at Weston Turville until 1993. A juvenile was seen in 2005. Display took place at Wotton Lake in 1982 although breeding was not proved. In 1987 there were two pairs at Shardeloes, one pair in 1988, and two broods were raised in 1990. The drastic reduction in the mean flow rate of the River Misbourne for several years made this site unsuitable for water birds but three broods were raised in 1994, one in 1995, one in 1996, two in 1999, one in 2000, two in 2001, three in 2002, two in 2003, two in 2004 and one in 2008. In 1989 they were thought to have bred at Linford. Two broods were raised at this site in 1992 and again in 1993 although these failed to survive. Successful breeding took place in 2006. A pair bred at College Lake for the first time in 1996 raising six young, and again in 1997, 1998, 2000, 2001 and 2003. In 2004 juveniles were seen at two new sites, Marlow and Fulmer.

Ruddy Ducks can be rather secretive during the breeding season as they tend to stay in the reed beds that they require and may be overlooked. They are best located when they give their spectacular and noisy display, which often takes place at night.

Birds were regularly seen throughout the year at most of the major waters in the county, though usually only in very small numbers. The largest flock recorded was 16 at Thorney on 11 Jan 1997.

There were few places in the county that met the requirements of Ruddy Ducks. It is likely that they were all colonised and that the local population had reached a stable maximum.

DMF

Red-legged Partridge
Alectoris rufa

Fairly common introduced resident.

Hedgerley, 3 Jan 2011   *David Ferguson*

The first recorded introduction of this bird from south-west Europe was in 1673 when birds were released in Windsor Great Park. After 1830 a large number of releases were made. By 1835 they were established at Stokenchurch and by 1920 they had increased sufficiently for H & J to describe them as 'locally common'.

During the 1950s the population declined but this decrease was masked by the release of birds bred in game farms. The decline can be attributed in part to the reduction in the amount of cover required for nesting. Red-legged Partridges leave their eggs uncovered during laying, so they need to build their nests in cover if they are not to be predated. The amount of suitable cover has been reduced because of hedge removal and changes in cropping patterns. Another factor in the decline in numbers is the increased use of insecticides and herbicides which has reduced the numbers of insects available for the young, although this is less of a requirement than it is with Grey Partridges. The recent method of leaving wide unploughed, unsprayed field boundaries is beneficial to the species.

The two breeding maps show some differences. Red-legged Partridges have been virtually eliminated from the Milton Keynes area but have increased in the south of the county, probably due to releases.

Unusual nest sites have included an 18 foot high straw stack at Loughton in 1899, and one next to a Barn Owl's nest at Beaconsfield in the 1960s. Roosting under house eaves has been recorded at Mentmore (Knox), and Buckland Common (Dowson, pers comm), while males calling from the tops of barns is not uncommon, for example, at The Lee, as is calling in the night in the breeding season. A strange record is of a bird which frequented the compound of Aylesbury Prison in 1986. They also use the Wycombe Wanderers football ground to feed and have occasionally been seen running along the touch lines during matches. At least one has flown into the lap of a spectator. 40+ were seen in the car park on 24 Aug 2000. Other large coveys were 40 on Steps Hill on 27 Oct 2003 and at Quarryhall, Milton Keynes on 2 December 2008, 30 birds at Pitstone on 1 Dec 1984 and Dorney Common on 3 Nov 1985. Large coveys have also been recorded at Oakley, Marlow, Hedgerley, North Crawley and Wing. Late breeding was recorded at Hughenden in September 1989 when broods of downy young were seen.

The birds are considered to give poor sport compared to Grey Partridges. They tend to run rather than fly, and, when they decide to fly, to explode in different directions, unlike Grey Partridges, whose coveys pack together.

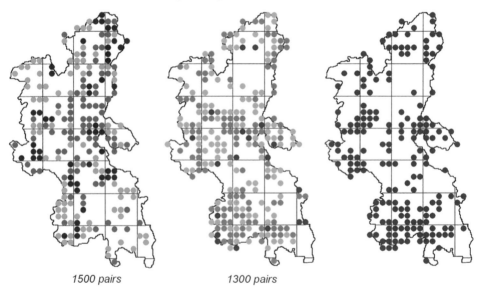

1500 pairs   1300 pairs

SC & DMF

92

Grey Partridge
Perdix perdix

Kimblewick, 17 June 2011   *Richard Billyard*

Uncommon and decreasing resident.

It is evident from the numbers recorded in the game books of country estates that Grey Partridges were much commoner in the 19th century and the early years of this century than they are now. The game book of the Dashwood Estate, West Wycombe records that 192 Grey Partridges were shot between 14 and 23 Sep 1872. On The Lee Estate, an area of c700 hectares near Great Missenden, 355 Grey Partridges were shot between 1925 and 1933. They were much more numerous than Common Pheasants and were known as 'the poor man's pheasant'. Indeed they were common enough to be the subject of some advanced gastronomy. Partridge Salmi combined goose liver, truffles, chopped lemon, and Madeira, and was served in a silver casserole!

Since the Second World War there has been a considerable decline in numbers. For instance none has been seen at The Lee since the 1970s, although 1970 and 1976 were considered comparatively good years in the south of the county. The map shows a discontinuous distribution with most birds in the south and the Vale of Aylesbury. Grey Partridges are birds of arable fields with hedgerows, although they have occasionally occurred in woods with clearings and rides, such as Little Hampden and Homefield Wood.

Coveys of over 20 are now unusual. The largest since the 1990s are 32 on Lodge Hill on 5 Dec 2003, 25 at Oving in November and December 2008, 56 at Dinton on 5 Aug 2010 and 24 at Kimblewick on 17 Nov 2011.

The maps show that large areas of the county are now devoid of the species. The mapping and the National Common Birds Census data gave a population in the county of 2000 pairs in 1986. The population in 2011 may be no more than 300 pairs.

The decline has a number of causes. The break up of country estates and lack of keepering has increased the amount of nest predation, while the removal of hedgerows and bramble clearance has reduced the nesting area so that the nests are closer together and thus easier for predators to find. These factors account for about half the post-1940 decrease. The other half is due to the use of herbicides and insecticides which has had a catastrophic effect on the population of insects upon which the chicks feed in June. The disappearance of winter stubbles and old stack yards which were frequented in hard weather must also be a factor. Modern farming practice, whereby silage replaces hay, is another cause. Silage has a dense, lush grass and is frequently cut, and is thus a difficult feeding ground (O'Connor and Shrubb 1986). More recent studies have identified two other possible causes for the decline: infection with caecal nematodes from farm-reared Pheasants (Tompkins, *et al* 2002) and releases of Red-legged Partridges which may result in Grey Partridges being shot by mistake (Watson, *et al* 2007). Releases of Pheasants and Red-legged Partridges are widespread in the county.

The large area of set-aside in the county since the late 1980s is not thought to be useful for breeding gamebirds. The vegetation structure is such that young chicks become readily soaked and these open areas allow easy viewing for aerial predators. Partridge parents are more likely to take their chicks into a cereal crop, even if the insect supply there is lower. (Game Conservancy Trust, pers comm). The Trust considers that the Conservation Headland scheme, whereby edges of arable fields have restricted spraying of pesticides is of much greater benefit to the birds.

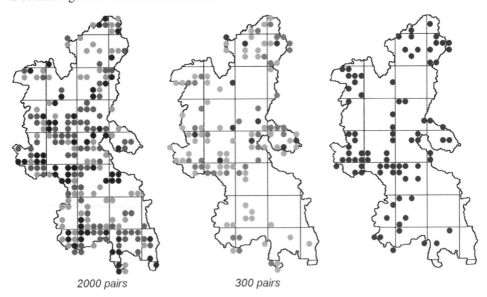

2000 pairs   300 pairs

SC & DMF

Quail
Coturnix coturnix

Rare summer visitor which occasionally breeds.

There appears to have been a decline in the Quail's fortunes towards the end of the 19th century. Clark Kennedy wrote 'a visitor in spring and autumn...the majority are shot in either May or September... a few are killed near Drayton Beauchamp almost every September.' The mention of this village refers to the presence there of Clark Kennedy's correspondent, the Rev. Harpur Crewe, and not for any particular liking of the birds for this locality. The impression given is that Quails were regular passage migrants through the county in small numbers.

In 1920 H & J stated 'now very rare summer resident', a comment that still holds true. A few are heard almost every year and occasionally larger numbers are recorded. In 1970 about 20 were heard calling in fields around Wolverton, while a few other birds were scattered around the county. The next large invasion took place in 1989 when about 34 birds were recorded at 20 sites.

The seasonal graph clearly shows that birds begin to appear in early May, peak in June, and are gone by September, or have stopped calling. There is no evidence of the passage hinted at by Clark Kennedy. Birds can turn up in arable land almost anywhere in the county, particularly in fields of barley, but there may be a preference for certain areas. A bird was recorded at Dorney in five years between 1952 and 1966, while the Pitstone/

Ivinghoe Beacon area has recorded birds since Clark Kennedy's time. The Milton Keynes area has also had a number of records.

There has been one confirmed record of breeding in the county: a nest with 12 eggs, which hatched on 12 August 1947, was found near Newton Blossomville. Breeding was also possible at Coleshill in 1950, Monks Risborough in 1965, and Sherington in 1982. The latest record is of a bird flushed by a dog at Rowsham on 3 Nov 2011. A covey at Monks Risborough on 23 Oct 1965 is also noteworthy.

Almost all of the records refer to calling birds. Quails are very secretive and are rarely seen. It is possible that most are single males and not breeding birds. They are known to travel considerable distances and may therefore cause duplication of records.

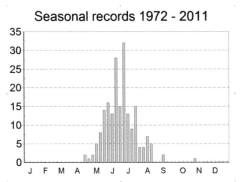

Seasonal records 1972 - 2011

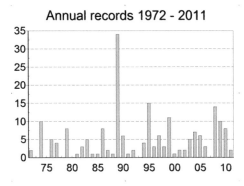

Annual records 1972 - 2011

DMF

Common Pheasant
Phasianus colchicus

Common introduced resident.

The sub-species *P.c.colchicus* from the Caucasus was probably introduced to Britain in the late 11th century as a cagebird, although introduction may have been as late as the 14th century. By the 16th century it had become fairly well established. In the 18th century *P.c.torquatus*, which has a white neck-ring, was introduced from China. The

Prestwood, 12 Apr 2011   *Richard Billyard*

Dowager Duchess of Portland brought some to Bulstrode Park, near Gerrards Cross, at this time, and in 1900 Lord Rothschild introduced birds into the county. H & J mention other sub-species being introduced and also *P. versicolor*, the Japanese Pheasant. It can be safely assumed that all these variations are now hybridised.

Artificial rearing of Pheasants is widely practised in Buckinghamshire. Pheasant pens and feeders are a common sight in the Chilterns and in the woods in the Vale of Aylesbury, and these undoubtedly keep the population at an artificially high level. Many Pheasants are reared on country estates and farms holding syndicated shoots, where keepers remove the eggs and hatch them in incubators. In addition, poults are bought from game farms and reared in pens, and fed with corn when they are released, mainly to keep them from straying onto neighbours' land. In the early years of this century, pheasant farming was a rural industry. Those who tended them lived in shepherd's huts in the rearing field which had wire netting enclosures for the birds known as keep pens. This artificial rearing was carried out at The Lee and Prestwood among other places.

The first survey map shows gaps in the Chilterns and in the north of the county, but these are certainly due to under-recording while the obvious hole in the north of the county in the second survey maps outlines the city of Milton Keynes. It is likely that almost every wood in the county holds the species. In areas where artificial rearing is practised the population density can be up to eight times that of areas where there is no artificial rearing. This makes estimating populations particularly difficult. Mapping and the National Common Birds Census data gives a population of around 6000 pairs.

Food consists of a wide variety of fruits and berries, and it is said that they are the only birds to eat Deadly Nightshade, though Dr David Snow reports that despite hours of watching in the hills above Kimble, he did not see any berries taken (Snow & Snow, 1988).

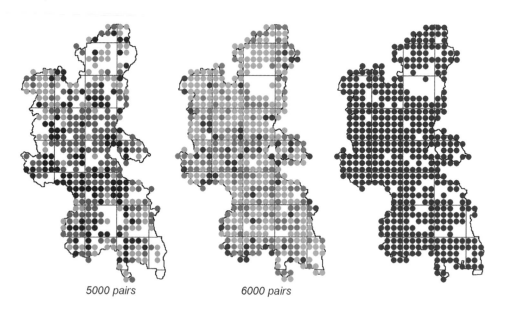

5000 pairs   6000 pairs

SC

Golden Pheasant
Chrysolophus pictus

Introduced or escaped in very small numbers.

The spectacular colouration of the male makes the Golden Pheasant a popular bird in collections. Single birds have been recorded in Brickhill Woods and in the southeast of the county in 10 years between 1976 and 1998 and are presumably escapes from collections. Up to three birds have been recorded in the Dropmore area. Anecdotal evidence suggests that birds have been present in the Dropmore Estate since at least 1947. They were last recorded there on 13 Dec 1998, but it is quite probable they are still in the area. Birds were released at Taplow Court around 1987 and they may now be breeding ferally at this locality. Smaller numbers of birds were also released at Winchbottom in late 1990 or early 1991. Most of the records are in spring which may be due to the fact that these secretive birds are more obvious at this time of the year.

DMF

Lady Amherst's Pheasant
Chrysolophus amherstiae

Formerly a very local introduced resident now extinct.

Although Lady Amherst's Pheasants were brought to England from China in 1828 it was not until around 1900 that they were released at Woburn. The birds gradually spread from the estate until the western edge of their range became the Brickhill Woods. Birds were released at Mentmore in 1930 and maintained a small population until the late 1960s. In the 1930s birds were released at Whipsnade and these spread to the nearby Ashridge Estate. One was heard here on 15 May 1994, the first record at this site since 1985. The last record from the feral population was on 10 July 2005 at Back Wood when a male was heard. A bird at Hambleden on 24 Apr 2008 was an obvious escape.

Lady Amherst's Pheasants are exceptionally wary and are usually located by the call of the male, which is heard in the morning and evening. When disturbed, they prefer to run and hide rather than fly. Their value as sporting birds is nil. Very little is known of their breeding biology; indeed there is no record of a nest ever having being found in Buckinghamshire. Proof of breeding is confined to sightings of broods of young birds.

The population was always very small. The largest number recorded was 20 calling males on 2 May 1976 which probably reflected the maximum number of breeding pairs.

The decline in Buckinghamshire is parallelled by a similar decline in neighbouring Bedfordshire, which held the main population. The birds inhabited conifer woods with a dense undergrowth of brambles and with rhododendron thickets. One reason for the extinction may be the destruction of undergrowth by Muntjacs. Habitat change was probably the most significant factor leading to their extinction (Nightingale, 2005).

DMF

Red-throated Diver
Gavia stellata

Rare vagrant. All records are given.

There is an undated record from Burnham in Clark Kennedy.

A few years before 1910: shot near Aylesbury Station and presented to the County Museum.
1952: adult on 27 Oct to 7 Nov, Little Marlow.
1970: 1 from 11 to 31 Mar, on R.Thames at Hurley.
1976: 1 from 13 to 16 Feb and 22 Feb, Calvert.
1978: 1 from 5 to 12 Mar, Wotton Lakes.
1979: 1 on 14 Mar, Willen.
1980: 1 from 7 to 10 Oct, Willen.

1986: 1 on 7 Feb, Willen.

1987: slightly oiled adult 8 to 10 Dec, Weston Turville Res, was taken into care where it died.

1989: 14 on 2 Apr, Willen. Six were present just after dawn on 3rd and two remained until 09:00.

1990: juvenile from 16 Dec to 12 Jan 1991, Little Marlow.

1994: 1 on 20 Jan, Stowe.

1994: 1 on 2 Feb, Stoke Mandeville Hospital was taken into care.

1996: adult female on 14 Mar, Weston Turville Reservoir was taken into care but it died.

1997: 1 on 11 Nov, Taplow Lake.

1997: 1 on 22 Dec, Startopsend Reservoir.

2005: 1 on 27 Nov, Little Marlow.

2010: 1 on 10 Nov, over Steps Hill

The extraordinary 1989 record may have been prompted by sudden snowfalls on the east coast.

Black-throated Diver
Gavia arctica

Rare vagrant. All records are given.

Taplow Lake, 26 Dec 2002   *Rob Andrews*

1954: 1 on 25 Dec, Hartigan's GP, Broughton.

1955: 1 on 9 Jan, Little Marlow.

1972: 1 early Mar, Willen where it was picked up dead after an overnight storm.

1976: 1 at Tring reservoirs from 12 to 13 Mar, flew W into Bucks on 13th.

1979: 1 on 18 Feb, Little Marlow.

1983: 1 on 13 Nov, was found in a field near Waddesdon and taken into care where it later died of aspergillosis.

1985: 1 first-winter from 31 Oct to 17 Nov, Caldecotte.

1994: 1 on 2 Jan, Haddenham.

1996: First-winter from 18 to 22 Dec, Bradwell Lake.

1998: First-winter on 6 Nov, Calvert. It was found dead the following day.

2002: First-winter from 27 Nov to 5 Jan 2003, Taplow Lake.

2008: 1 on 19 May, Calvert.

It is surprising that there should be almost as many Black-throateds as Red-throateds recorded in the county, because on the east coast (the most obvious source of our divers) Red-throateds outnumber Black-throateds by 100:1. It is possible that the present species is more likely to visit inland sites, either deliberately for food or because some birds regularly migrate over land. The pattern is also shown in neighbouring counties.

Great Northern Diver
Gavia immer

Rare vagrant. All records are given.

1774: 1 on 3 Dec, Ford area.
1850: a 'young bird' on 9 May, was captured alive in a ditch at Chequers Court.
1859: 1 Nov or Dec, Chesham.
1865: 1 killed Nov or Dec on R.Thames at Marlow.
1865: 1 killed at Temple Island near Henley.

Caldecotte, 24 Dec 2011   *Keith O'Hagen*

1944: 1 immature shot on 11 Nov, Calvert.
1964: 1 found on 4 Nov in field by Foxcote Reservoir. It was released later on the reservoir but was found dead two days later.
1965: 1 on 17 Jan, Iver GPs.
1971: 1 in Feb found dead in Willen Village.
1972: 1 on 12 Nov, Linford GPs.
1986: 1 from 12 Dec to11 Jan 1987, Taplow Lake.
1994: 1 from 16 to 17 Dec, Willen.
1997: adult from 27 to 28 Nov, Calvert.
1997: first-winter from 23 Dec to 6 Jan 1998, Caldecotte Lake.
2002: 1 on 28 Nov, Calvert.
2009: 1 from 14 to 15 Nov, Calvert.
2011: first-winter from 17 Nov to 3 Jan 2012, Caldecotte Lake.

Diver species
Gavia spp.

1971: 1 from 25 Feb to 8 Mar, Stanton Low GP was considered to be a Red-throated.
1978: 1 on 19 Feb, River Thames below Hurley was considered to be a Red-throated.
1980: 1 on 12 Nov and 6 to 25 Dec, Little Marlow.
1988: 1 on 17 Nov, Calvert was considered to be a Red-throated.

Little Grebe
Tachybaptus ruficollis

Fairly common resident and winter visitor.

Though widespread in Buckinghamshire, the Little Grebe is often overlooked because of its shy nature; in fact it is more often heard than seen. Clark Kennedy classed it as 'common on our ponds, streams and lakes, and on the river Thames'. H & J reported that it 'breeds in considerable numbers on the reservoirs ... and on the Thames from Boveney to Hambleden'. However, Fraser and later F & Y commented that it was 'Not uncommon on the Thames and other waters but numbers appear to be decreasing', a point echoed in the 1981 BBC report where it was suggested that numbers were declining owing to loss of habitat.

Shardeloes, 2 Dec 2009   David Ferguson

As a breeding bird in the county, the Little Grebe is found on lakes, large ponds, rivers and canals wherever there is sufficient marginal vegetation and little disturbance. The two breeding maps show a considerable change in distribution. The Ouse, formerly a stronghold of the species, appears to have been largely deserted, as have the canals and waters in Milton Keynes. This has been compensated by an increase in the south-east where the Jubilee River and new ponds at Dorney Lake have provided suitable habitat.

In the autumn there is some dispersal, with Latimer Park, Fulmer, Shardeloes and the Jubilee River often holding over 20 birds. Wycombe Rye and Abbey Lakes which used to hold up to 30 birds has decreased in importance while the new Jubilee River has recorded up to 42 birds (on 22 Nov 2010).

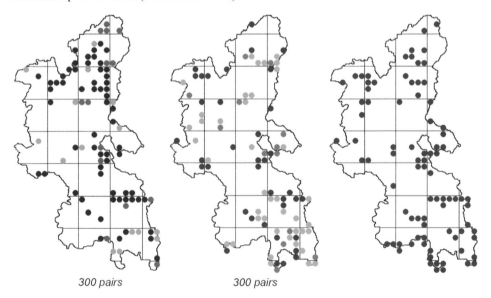

300 pairs   *300 pairs*

NHFS

100

Great Crested Grebe
Podiceps cristatus

Local resident and winter visitor.

The earliest record of a Great Crested
Grebe in Buckinghamshire is that of a bird
shot at Dinton Hall in 1744, but otherwise
it is unrecorded in the county before 1901,
when a pair bred at Stowe. H & R stated
that 'the bird is occasionally obtained in the
county and breeds in some numbers at
Weston Turville Reservoir'. Throughout
this century, however, the increasing

Little Marlow, 3 Aug 2007   *Julia Eyles*

availability of suitable breeding waters, mainly as a result of mineral extraction, has
produced a steady and continuing increase in the population. The Great Crested Grebe has
a preference for waters at least 2 ha in area, with a depth of 0.5-5m. For breeding, a
shallow, shelving shore with a flat or sloping edge is essential, together with some
fringing or emergent vegetation. Fish must be present, for the bird feeds only in its
breeding waters. The main breeding season in southern England is March to June and it
is preceded by a period of display from January to March although there have been several
reports of very early breeding. For instance, the first of three eggs hatched at Weston
Turville Res on 7 Feb 1975 implying a laying date of about 10 Jan (BB 70:9, 398).
Another pair with two young were seen at Tongwell on 20 Feb 1994. The distribution of
breeding records largely follows the deposits of river gravels in the valleys of the Thames
and Ouse; some ornamental lakes and reservoirs, such as those at Stowe, Wotton
Underwood, Weston Turville, and Willen, are also used.

The Great Crested Grebe is still increasing as a breeding species in Buckinghamshire,
not only as further gravel extraction takes place, but also along the Rivers Thame, Colne,
and Ouse (F & Y). The increase in the number of breeding sites as recorded by the BTO
surveys demonstrates the scale of the colonisation: in 1931 Great Crested Grebes were
recorded at just six sites; by 1965, three of those sites (Black Pit at Lillingstone Dayrell,
Latimer House, and Shardeloes) had disappeared or become unsuitable, and a fourth held
no birds, but the number of breeding sites had increased to 17, including 11 that had not
existed in 1931. In the 1975 breeding survey there were 32 sites. The first pair breeding
on the Ouse in Buckinghamshire was found in 1970; the first record of breeding on the
Thames in the county dates from 1971 (Youngman 1977). In recent years non-breeding
birds have summered on some waters; at Willen during the breeding season up to 37 adult
birds have been recorded (2 Jun 1984), though the breeding population is thought to
beonly two pairs.

Autumn sees gatherings of resident birds and winter visitors from northern Britain and
Europe, including Denmark. There has been no study of marked birds in the county and
it is not known what proportion of the Buckinghamshire breeding population winters here.
BWP states that 'it is unlikely that any western palaearctic population is truly sedentary,
though some individuals may be'. The number of birds wintering in the county between
October and February has remained fairly constant since 1970, usually with 110-130 birds
recorded on all waters. The maximum count was of 164 in December 1983, the minimum
was 11 in January 1982. In extreme weather few of the Buckinghamshire waters remains

free of ice, and Great Crested Grebes then move out to larger, deeper lakes in adjoining counties (Grafham Water and Stewartby Lake to the north and east, Wraysbury and the London reservoirs to the south) and also possibly to the coast.

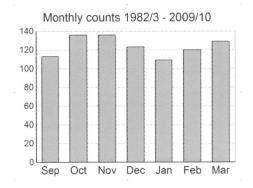

Monthly counts 1982/3 - 2009/10

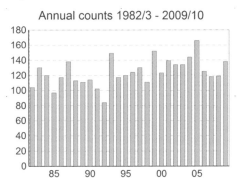

Annual counts 1982/3 - 2009/10

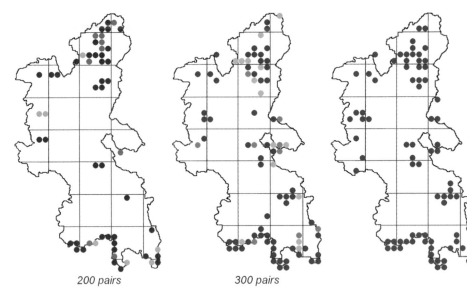

200 pairs   300 pairs

JK

Red-necked Grebe
Podiceps grisegena

Scarce migrant and winter visitor.

Prior to 1979 there are two records:

1848: 1 shot 10 Oct, Saunderton.
1974: 1 from 9 to 26 Nov, Weston Turville Res.

Since 1979 there have been 39 records of 41 birds. 25 were in the north of the

Willen, 15 Mar 2006   *Mike Wallen*

county, seven in the middle, and nine in the south. They are shown on the graphs.

There is an interesting contrast with Slavonian Grebe in the seasonal distribution. Red-neckeds tend be recorded in January and February, while Slavonians are found in November and December.

In February 1979 there was a major influx of Red-necked Grebes throughout inland England, the harbingers being two birds at Willen on the 14th. A total of 481 birds were recorded, of which four were in the county (Chandler 1981). A number of other species were involved, in particular Red-breasted Merganser. The reason for the influx appears to have been severe conditions on the Baltic and Continental North Sea coasts.

Another influx of Red-necked Grebes took place in January 1989 when five birds were found in the county.

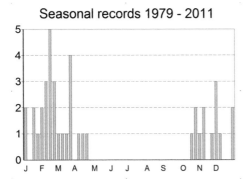

Seasonal records 1979 - 2011

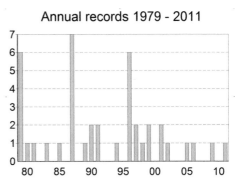

Annual records 1979 - 2011

Slavonian Grebe
Podiceps auritus

Scarce migrant and winter visitor.

Prior to 1973 there are eight records:

1860s: 1 shot at Great Marlow.
Between 1874 and 1880: 2 shot Weston Turville Res.
1924: 1 from 29 Jan to 10 Feb, Weston Turville Res.
1937: 1 from 6 Feb to 6 Mar, Weston Turville Res.
1937: 1 on 14 Feb on pond at Bletchley Station.
1964: 1 on 29 Nov, Foxcote.
1969: 1 from 31 Aug to 1 Sep, Foxcote.
1972: adult summer from 18 to 21 May, Weston Turville Res.

Little Marlow, 6 Nov 2011   David Ferguson

Since 1973 there have been 54 records of 60 birds. 46 were in the north of the county, six in the middle and eight in the south. They are shown on the graphs. Most were single birds, but four birds were seen on 13 Nov 1984 at Caldecotte. Exceptionally, a bird stayed at Caldecotte Lake from 15 Dec 1988 to 3 Mar 1989, and a bird was there again from 29 Nov 1989 to 29 Mar 1990. It is likely that one individual was involved in both these records.

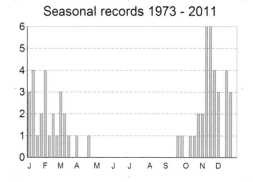

Seasonal records 1973 - 2011

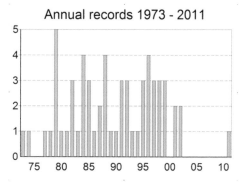

Annual records 1973 - 2011

Black-necked Grebe
Podiceps nigricollis

Scarce migrant.

Prior to 1973 there are six records:

1776: 1 shot 20 Nov, Dinton Hall.
1925: 2 on 9 May, 1 on 16 May, Weston Turville Res.
1953: 1 on 7 Sep then for several days, Marlow.
1957: 4 from 9 to 10 Jun, Foxcote Res.
1961: 1 on 21 Oct, Foxcote Res.
1968: 1 from 26 May to 7 Jun, Shardeloes.

Willen, 3 May 2009   *Mike Wallen*

Since 1973 there have been 74 records of 109 birds. 73 were in the north of the county, 21 in the middle and 15 in the south. They are shown on the graphs. The records are scattered between February and November with distinct peaks in early April and late August.

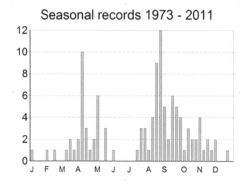

Seasonal records 1973 - 2011

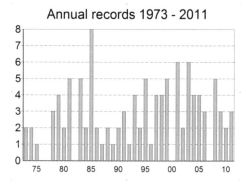

Annual records 1973 - 2011

Fulmar
Fulmarus glacialis

Very rare vagrant. All records are given.

1989: 1 on 4 Sep, Cliveden.
1989: 1 on 11 Sep, Caldecotte. What was presumed to be the same bird was found dead on 16 Sep.
1989: 1 on 10 Nov, Marlow.
1990: 1 on 30 Mar, Willen. Most of the country was cloaked in dense fog that day.
1993: 1 from 1 to 2 Mar, Willen.
2000: 1 on 6 Apr, Great Brickhill when it was taken into care.
2001: 1 on 2 Mar, Willen.
2004: 1 on 29 Feb, Calvert.
2006: 1 on 25 Feb, Calvert.

Great Shearwater
Puffinus gravis

Very rare vagrant. All records are given.

There is one confirmed record:

1999: 1 on 27 Dec, Willen (Ploszajski, 2000).

This extraordinary record of a bird that should have been in the South Atlantic but which lingered briefly at Willen makes the following record slightly more plausible.

1911: 1 killed by striking telegraph wire, Olney.

H & J recorded the following:
    'Mr Archibald Allen, writing in *The Field* (October 28, 1911, p.968), records a Greater Shearwater *Puffinus major* as having been killed by striking telegraph wires 'a few weeks since' near Olney. No investigation appears to have been made as to whether the specimen in question was correctly identified, and the date suggests the probability of confusion with the Manx Shearwater, which frequently occurs inland during September, though, curiously enough, there appears to be no record of this species from Bucks.'
    The Countryman also carried an article about this bird on 29 Oct 1911.

Manx Shearwater
Puffinus puffinus

Rare vagrant. All records are given.

1927: 1 caught 17 Sep, Bradenham House.
1967: 1 found dead 9 Sep, Marlow Common.
1970: 1 found Sep, Chesham. It was released at Beachy Head.
1970: 1 found Sep, High Wycombe. It was released at Beachy Head.
1972: 1 found 6 Sep, Mentmore Towers.
1980: 1 recently dead 17 Sep, Lillingstone Dayrell.
1982: 1 found 7 Sep, Pitstone. It was released off the Devon coast.

1983: 1 on 7 Jun, Tilehouse North GP.
1983: 1 found alive 7 Sep, Quainton, released at the coast.
1983: 1 on 16 Sep, Calvert.
1984: 1 found 1 Sep, Aylesbury.
1984: 1 found 3 Sep, Calvert.
1984: 1 found 21 Sep, Buckingham.
1988: 1 found 8 Sep, Weston Turville Res.
1988: 1 found 14 Sep, Penn Street.
1994 1 on 28 Aug, High Wycombe.
1994 1 on 9 Sep, College Lake.
1996 1 found dead on 8 Oct, two miles north of junction 13 of the M1.
2010: 1 found 23 Sep, Aylesbury.

All five 1984 and 1988 records were of birds found alive and taken to Aylesbury Wildlife Hospital.

The small number of records in the county is in contrast to Oxfordshire where there is an average of two records per year (Brucker et al. 1992). The counties to the east have a similar number of records to Buckinghamshire, which suggests that the birds are originating from their western breeding sites.

Gannet
Morus bassanus

Rare vagrant. All records are given.

1847: 1 caught Nov, Sherington near Newport Pagnell.
1886: 1 killed on canal near Wendover. The specimen is in Tring Museum.
1910: 1 found alive 9 Dec, Hambleden.
1978: 1 found dead 9 Oct, Heavens Lea, near Skirmett.
1981: 1 from 27 to 28 Apr, Willen, was plunge diving.
1981: 1 on 27 Apr, Walton, Milton Keynes.
1981: 1 picked up exhausted 27 Apr, Woughton, Milton Keynes.
1990: 1 adult picked up partially oiled 25 Jan, Chalfont St Peter. It was later released.
1990: 1 adult 28 Oct flew SW into Bucks from Wilstone Res.
1994: 1 on 19 Aug, Little Marlow.
2002: 2nd-year on 9 Sep, Willen.
2009: 1 imm on 5 Oct, Jubilee River.
2010: 1 adult and 1 other flew N on 25 Sep, Calvert.
2010: 1 on 25 Sep, Gallows Bridge Farm.
2010: 7 imm flew N on 25 Sep, Lakes Lane, Newport Pagnell.
2010: 4 imm flew W on 25 Sep, Steeple Claydon.

The remarkable events of 25 Sep 2010 were part of a large inland passage through south-eastern counties. Most of the other records followed storms.

Storm Petrel
Hydrobates pelagicus

Rare vagrant. All records are given.

There is one undated record from Buckingham in H & J.

Other records are:

1859: 1 found dead Oct, Burnham Priory.
1865: 1 shot near Burnham.
1868: 1 on 21 Jan, near Wycombe.
1880: 1 picked up Nov, near Wendover.
1928: 1 found dead 28 Nov, Whaddon.
1929: 1 found alive 8 Dec, Grendon Underwood. It later died.

Leach's Petrel
Oceanodroma leucorhoa

Rare vagrant. All records are given.

There is one undated record at Woughton in H & J.

Other records are:

1859: 1 found 1 Nov, Latimer Park.
1881: 1 on 14 Oct, Bierton.
1910: 1 in Nov, Westcott.
1929: 1 found dead 14 Dec, Lenborough.

Startopsend Res, 6 Dec 2006   *Mike Wallen*

1948: 1 found dead 24 Dec, Chalfont Park
      Lake.
1952: 1 found dead 26 Oct, Great Brickhill, presumably this species.
1952: 1 found dead on 31 Oct, Penn.
1952: 1 found dead 7 Nov, Penn.
1976: 1 found injured 24 to 26 Nov, Drayton Parslow. Died 28 Nov.
1983: 1 on 3 Sep, Willen.
1987: 1 on 16 Sep, Willen.
1989: 1 found 21 Sep, Fishermead, Milton Keynes. It was taken into care where it died.
1989: 1 on 29 Oct, Little Marlow.
2001: 1 on 10 Sep, Calvert.
2006: 1 on 6 Dec, Little Marlow.
2006: 1 on 6 Dec, Startopsend Res flew briefly into the Bucks section.

The two in 1952 were part of a huge wreck involving 6700 birds that took place between 21 Oct and 4 Nov (BB 47:5, 137-163). The 2006 records were also part of large wreck which hit the west coast and blew many birds inland. The frequency of records compared to the more widespread Storm Petrel is interesting though puzzling. Neighbouring counties show a similar pattern.

Petrel species

1877: 1 mid-Oct, High Wycombe was thought to be a Storm Petrel.

Cormorant
Phalacrocorax carbo

Langley Park, 21 Jul 2007   *David Ferguson*

Common passage migrant and winter visitor; recently established breeder in small numbers, mainly at one major colony.

Until the mid-1970s, Cormorants were a very unusual sight in the county. Clark Kennedy referred to one shot near Marlow Railway Bridge about 1857 as an 'extremely rare visitor so far inland'. He also mentions one shot near Weston Turville in 1858. H & J give no certain records for the county, but Price (1947) wrote that it had been recorded six times since 1920: three times in August, once each in October and November, and one irregularly present from February to August near Bourne End in 1943. The predominantly autumn passage nature of this small sample accords well with the pattern of a larger number of contemporaneous records from the Tring reservoirs.

Double-figure counts were not noted until the 1980s. Medmenham recorded c30 in February 1985 and 50-60 in February 1986, while in the same year Marlow recorded a flock of 11. In 1987 up to 15 were seen at Linford GPs and 10 at Willen Lake. A rapid step change saw 43 roosting at Newport Pagnell and 103 at Marlow in 1991. Marlow has remained the most important roost in the county ever since, with successive new highs of 120 in November 1993, 141 in November 1997, 161 in November 1999, 170 in December 1999 and 209 in November 2003. While five monthly counts in three figures in 2004 and 131 roosting there in 2007 confirm its importance, there have been no three-figure counts since then. Elsewhere, the Newport Pagnell roost had rapidly declined in importance by the mid-1990s as the favoured roosting trees collapsed into the water. Conversely some other, and still extant, roosts became established at the same time. Caldecotte became an important roost at that time and while its peak count of 143 in January 2006 is not a regular feature, it retains a significant current roost. The Calvert roost was noted from 1994 onwards and regularly holds 30 or 40 birds. A roost became established at Dovecote Lake in the Linford GPs complex, also by 1995, which is still occasionally used, but some birds have taken to roosting in the heronry in the same complex. Foxcote had established a small roost by 2001, which has slowly grown subsequently, peaking at over 50 birds. The birds choose to roost in trees overhanging the water, preferably on islands. In very strong winds birds may be forced to roost on the ground, but again islands are preferred.

While roosts have provided all the largest counts, birds range widely in large numbers, so that 50+ flocks have been regularly noted at non-roost sites such as Dorney Lake and Willen, and all the larger waters see double figures. 111 over Denham heading towards Broadwater GP in November 1996 is the highest non-roost flock recorded.

Numbers build up rapidly from September, with a normal mid-winter peak from November to January, but high numbers remain well into March, declining markedly in April. Birds can be found in every month at a number of locations, particularly those which have provided recent breeding opportunities.

Once the summering of a few birds became established, some indications of breeding behaviour inevitably followed. Stick carrying was regular in the 1980s and display was noted from 1990 onwards, particularly at Marlow. It was not until 2002 that a nest with three eggs constituted the first proved breeding attempt at that site, even if it was ultimately unsuccessful. Four chicks hatched at Marlow the following year were first noted on Apr 21, with two still surviving on May 23. Six pairs nested the following year and at least one was successful. Thereafter the colony rapidly increased with 14 pairs in 2005, 17 in 2006, 22 in 2007 and 27 (the most yet) in 2008. It remains to be seen whether the decrease to 26 in 2009 and 22 in 2010 is of significance. There is good evidence that breeding also took place at Calvert in 2003 and 2005, Foxcote in 2007 and Linford in 2008, but there is no real sign of a second major colony for the county - yet.

The very considerable increase in the number of birds wintering and indeed breeding is part of a general, but not uniform, trend in the British Isles. The composition of the birds which spend their time in Buckinghamshire is more complex. Definite local information comes almost entirely from birds being colour ringed as nestlings, but of course that is a much more popular activity within the UK than elsewhere. The results are that since 1987, three birds certainly of the subspecies *P. c. carbo* originated from St Margaret's Island, near Tenby, Dyfed. One of these returned for six successive winters. One ringed at Grune Point, on the Solway is unlikely to be of a different subspecies. Two were ringed in northern coastal France, and are quite likely to also have been *carbo*. Two from the Netherlands and two from Denmark will have originated from populations of definite *P. c. sinensis*. More intriguing are three ringed at Besthorpe, Nottinghamshire, one at Little Paxton GPs, Cambridgeshire and seven at Abberton Res., Essex. The assumption that these are of the British form *carbo* no longer holds sway. Indeed while there may be some mixture, the majority of birds are likely to be *sinensis*. This is the result of an extraordinary expansion of this subspecies in northern Europe since 1980, which has been charted by Kohl (2010), drawing on a multitude of sources across the continent. A five-fold increase in the *sinensis* population to 280,000 pairs in the whole of northern Europe (excluding Russia, Belarus, Moldova and Ukraine) from the 1980s to the present day, has been even more marked in the populations of the Netherlands, Denmark, Sweden and the Baltic coasts of Germany and Poland. That is thought to be the main source of the Abberton Res., Essex, breeding colony, which has grown to about 500 pairs since 1981, and the tree nesting populations in the rest of eastern England. Compared to this, the increase in the population of *carbo* has been insignificant.

Individuals which show the characteristics of *P.c.sinensis* have been positively identified in the county. However little attention has been given to detailed observation or photographing birds (they are often rather distant) which allows the key feature of *sinensis*, the shape of the gular patch, to be accurately assessed. This might reveal that not only are our wintering birds more likely to be *sinensis*, but most of the breeding ones are also likely to be so. Intriguingly all the birds recorded in the county outside the passage or wintering periods are known to have originated from populations which are thought to be entirely or mainly made up of *sinensis* birds.

109

While most of this account has concentrated on expansion of the population in the county, shooting, both legal and illegal, will have provided something of a check. Overall numbers wintering in the county are hard to judge because of the mobility of birds, but they do not seem to have risen in the last decade; they may even be declining slightly.

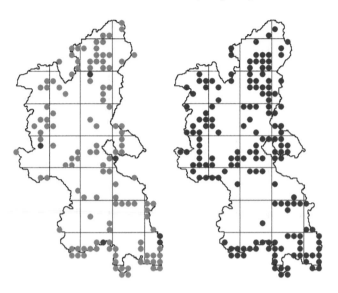

AVH

Shag
Phalacrocorax aristotelis

Scarce migrant and winter visitor.

Prior to 1974 there were 10 records of 11 birds:

Willen, 29 Nov 2005   Mike Wallen

1909: 1 at Oving.
1954: 1 found 6 Feb, High Wycombe was ringed as a pullus 10 Jul 1953 on the Isle of May.
1956: 1 found 23 Sep in a wood near Marlow was released at Staines where it was later found dead.
1958: 1 probable on 26 Jan, Weedon.
1958: 1 picked up 27 Jan on road at Wendover. It was released the next day.
1958: 1 on 27 Jan, flying over Aylesbury.
1958: 2 on 1 Feb on canal, Marsworth. 1 was still present a few days later.
1962: 1 immature mid Mar-late Apr, River Wye, High Wycombe. It was hand tame and fed daily until it was captured and released at Cookham Weir.
1970: 1 from 11 Apr to 31 Dec, Marlow Weir.
1971: 1 undated on Thames at Bisham.

Since 1974 there have been 53 records of 58 birds. They are shown on the histograms. 24 were found in the north, 19 in the middle and 15 in the south. Remarkably, a bird remained at Caldecotte Lake from 19 Jan 1990 to 5 May 1991.

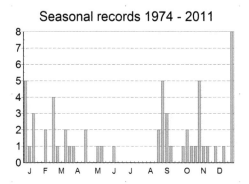

Seasonal records 1974 - 2011

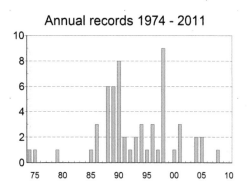

Annual records 1974 - 2011

Bittern
Botaurus stellaris

Regular winter visitor in very small numbers.

Clark Kennedy records that a bird was shot at Medmenham in 1851, another at Fawley Court in Jan 1864, and several near Chesham. The next to be recorded (and shot) was on 12 Dec 1892 at Cholesbury Common. Between 1920 and 1947, eight birds were recorded, the longest staying being one at Weston Turville Reservoir from Dec 1927 to early May 1928. From mid-March it was heard booming.

Calvert, 2 Mar 2010   *John Sheppard*

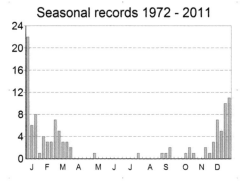

Seasonal records 1972 - 2011

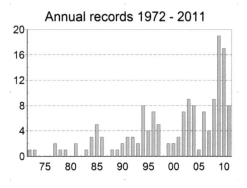

Annual records 1972 - 2011

Between 1947 and 1971 there were 17 records of 19 birds, including a bird booming at Wotton Lakes on 12 Mar 1961. Since 1972, 108 birds have been recorded. There has been a considerable increase since 2000. Factors causing this include increased observer coverage and the success of a conservation program designed to increase the British breeding population. Almost all have appeared in winter but there was an intriguing record of one at Linford on 18 Jul and 15 Aug 1994.

Favoured sites are Calvert, Weston Turville, Tongwell, Wotton Lakes and Linford GPs, but individuals can appear at almost any lake, river, or canal, particularly when they are forced to move by freezing conditions.

Little Bittern
Ixobrychus minutus

Rare vagrant. All records are given.

There is an undated record from Uxbridge in H & R.

The dated records are:

1827: 1 noted in Bucks.
1866: 1 in High Wycombe.
1911: male shot in summer, near Olney.
1921/22: 1 shot during winter, Shardeloes.

Night Heron
Nycticorax nycticorax

Very rare vagrant. All records are given.

1797: 1 immature shot, Cliveden.
1899: 1 in Aug, Taplow; may have been an escape.
1967: immature on 3 Aug, Newport Pagnell GP.
1987: immature on 26 Oct, Willen.
2005: 1 on 13 May, Grand Union Canal, Old Wolverton.

Cattle Egret
Bubulcus ibis

Very rare vagrant. All records are given.

2002: 1 from early Jan to end of Feb, Higher Denham. Presumed same on 16 Jan, Hughenden Valley.
2008: 1 from 30 Nov to 9 Dec, Haversham and then Linford. It was probably present several days before it was found.

Haversham, 1 Dec 2008   *Mike Wallen*

Eight seen near Maple Cross, just outside the county, in May 1992 may have been seen within Bucks airspace near Leighton Buzzard. The 2008 record was part of a national influx.

Little Egret
Egretta garzetta

Very local resident and regular visitor.

Following a couple of probables, the first certain record was in 1989 when 2 on 20 Sep flew from Wilstone Res into Bucks. At the time the species was still classified as a British rarity. Given that status, a few subsequent sightings for which clinching descriptions were not received, but were in all probability of this species, did not form part the accepted record. Nonetheless the 1990s can be characterised by a gradual

Caldecotte, 3 Aug 2010   *Keith O'Hagen*

increase in numbers, with birds being noted at six or seven sites per annum in the last few years of the decade. In that decade two specific events are noteworthy.

In February 1995 three fully-winged birds escaped from a damaged cage in a wild bird collection in Weston Underwood. This information did not come to light until considerably later when the owner reported one bird as returning regularly to the aviary, but the other two as not having been seen again. In several years subsequent to this occurrence it was assumed that this was the source of virtually all sightings in the north of the county. Current analysis of records suggests that this was not the case. For instance, while birds at nine geographically unrelated sites in the county during 2000 may not ensure complete lack of duplication, and similarly 12 sites providing records in 2001 including three together at Calvert, Latimer and Marlow, proves nothing conclusively, the pattern in these two years would suggest having far more to do with the inland infiltration of a rapidly increasing coastal UK population than a couple of escapees. This hypothesis has further relevance since, in 2003, a pair raised four young at the Linford GP heronry. This may well have been the first inland breeding in the UK, though one must consider the possibility that such occurrences in other inland counties were not publicised. The suggestion that this pair were the original escapees has been widely vaunted, but the idea that the pair, if indeed that is what they were, survived in the area for eight years, a scenario not borne out by the number of birds seen in that area in the every year, got back together for an eventual successful pairing, seems most unlikely. On a more positive note, breeding has been successful there in every subsequent year with a probable maximum of three pairs, and breeding has been successful every year since 2007 at nearby Willen Lake in the heronry there.

Harking back to the '90s, the other trend which started then was the wintering of Little Egrets in the Latimer/Chenies area. There were three in 1999, but by 2002, 10 were wintering, and there was a maximum of 13 in January 2005.

To return to the general position, in 2008 600 records were received from 45 different sites. By 2010 records were being received from as many sites as for the much more familiar Grey Heron and the maximum count for one site had reached 23. 2011 saw yet higher levels with several 30+ together counts in the Linford complex followed by a staggering 42 going to roost at Linford GP late in the year.

The dramatic change in the status of this species in the county in just over 20 years, from the very first record to fairly common resident, is part of a colonisation of the UK from southern Europe, a phenomenon almost certainly caused by climate change.

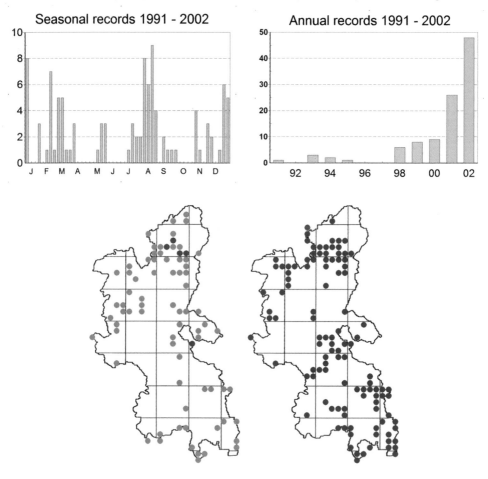

AVH

Great White Egret
Ardea alba

Very rare vagrant. All records are given.

1994: 1 from 22 Feb to 2 Mar, Linford (Hill, 1995).
2003: 1 on 10 Aug flew into Bucks from Wilstone Res, Hertfordshire.
2008: 1 on 11 Apr flew over College Lake having roosted at Tring Res.
2008: 1 on 2 Nov, Grafton Regis.
2009: 1 on 20 Dec flew over Marsworth and Startopsend.

Linford, 3 Sep 2011   *Jason Chalk*

The increase in the number of records may be caused by the increasing breeding population in the Netherlands.

Grey Heron
Ardea cinerea

Local resident and winter visitor.

H & J recorded Grey Herons as breeding in only two or three localities. The oldest was probably one at Harleyford Manor, near Marlow. In 1866 there were 40 nests, but by 1902 this had reduced to only a few nests in tall fir trees. This colony no longer exists. In 1919 a heronry at Fawley Court held 44 nests, but this too has gone. There were also temporary heronries at Dinton and near Gayhurst.

Gallows Bridge Farm, 3 Jul 2010   *Mike Wallen*

By the 1990s the Buckinghamshire population was centred on four heronries where the birds breed every year. The sites - at Hambleden, Taplow Court, Eythrope, and Tyringham - are in the grounds of large houses with nearby water which give the birds comparative seclusion. The coverage of the Buckinghamshire heronries has been patchy so it is rather difficult to establish population trends, but it would seem these colonies have had fluctuating fortunes. Tyringham decreased from a high of 41 occupied nests in 1979 to 17 nests in 1990 only to recover to 33 nests in 1999, while Hambleden decreased from a high of 17 occupied nests in 1978 to two in 1989 and six in 1993. In contrast, the heronry at Taplow Court has fluctuated between 5 and 15 occupied nests between 1973 and 1997, when it was last counted. At Wotton Lakes a heronry was created which reached a high of 21 nests in 2003 only for it to disappear after 2006.

Since the mid 1990s there has been a trend for Grey Herons to nest on islands in gravel pits or balancing lakes. In 1994 a pair nested at Little Marlow. Numbers increased until there were 22 nests in 2003. Since then numbers have decreased slightly, possibly due to competition for nest sites with Cormorants. 12 nests were found at Weston Underwood in 1996 and 14 at Addington in 1998 but there have been no records since. Small but regular colonies have been found at Linford and Willen since 1999 and at Mount Farm since 2005.

Heron populations are subject to decreases in severe winters. The mortality rate of first-winter birds can be very high during prolonged cold weather. After the severe winter of 1985, all five heronries counted that year showed their lowest numbers of the decade.

The second survey maps show that outside the breeding season birds tend to disperse to suitable waters within the county. Occasionally large groups can occur. Double-figure counts are regular at many of the larger waters.

Ringing records show that most birds keep within a 100 km radius. There is some indication that birds from E England winter in the county. There have been recoveries of birds ringed in Kent, Essex, Norfolk, and Lincolnshire, and there has been one continental recovery. A bird ringed at Taplow on 24 Apr 1928 was found at Cuidad Real, Spain on 16 Nov 1933.

NHFS

Purple Heron
Ardea purpurea

Very rare vagrant. All records are given.

1978: immature on 28 May, Newport Pagnell.
1980: 1 adult 13 Apr, Hyde Lane.
2006: 1 first-winter from 13 to 20 November, River Chess at Latimer.
2008: 1 adult on 10 May, College Lake.

The spring records are typical dates for this species but the 2006 record is one of the latest ever for the UK.

White Stork
Ciconia ciconia

Rare vagrant. All records are given.

1846: 1 shot in Sep, a few miles from Buckingham.
1996: 1 flying on 12 May, Great Horwood.
1996: first-summer from 28 to 30 May, Buckland Common.
2003: 1 on 2 Dec, Bledlow.
2003: 1 on 9 and 12 Aug, Tingewick. Presumed same 28 Aug, Wing, 25 to 27 Sep, Leckhampstead and 4 Oct, Foxcote.
2004: 1 on 1 Apr, Dorney.
2004: 1 on 26 Apr, Newport Pagnell.
2004: 1 from 30 Jun to 4 Jul, New Denham. This and the earlier 2004 records probably refer to the same bird.
2006: 1 on 17 Apr, Stowe Park.

116

2006: 1 from 25 to 28 Apr, Bourton near Buckingham.
2008: 2 juvs on 16 Aug, Pitstone.
2009: 1 on 23 Apr, Terrick.

Black Stork
Ciconia nigra

Very rare vagrant. There is one record.

2008: 1 on 9 June, Winchenden and presumably the same bird on 23 June flying over Dancersend (Gearing, 2009).

Glossy Ibis
Plegadis falcinellus

Dorney Lake, 7 May 2011   Jim Rose

Very rare vagrant. There have been two certain records.

1886: 1 shot in Oct, by the canal at Halton.
2011: 1 from 7 to 8 May, Dorney Lake was previously seen in Berkshire.

After review by the BBRC the record of a bird at Willen on 29 May 1987, which was previously accepted, has been rejected on the grounds that the long-staying Puna Ibis *Plegadis ridgwayi* normally to be found at Whitwell, Hertfordshire, was not eliminated from the descriptions and thus could have been the Willen bird.

Spoonbill
Platalea leucorodia

Linford, 17 May 2007   Ben Miller

Very rare vagrant. All records are given.

1947: 1 on 9 May at Wilstone Res flew into Buckinghamshire airspace.
1969: 1 on 11 May, Marlow.
1976: adult on 28 Jun, Willen.
1977: 1 on 27 Apr, Willen.
1995: 1 on 1 Sep, Willen Village.
2000: 2 juv on 20 Aug, Wilstone Res flew into Buckinghamshire airspace.
2003: 1 juv on 27 Nov, Wilstone Res flew into Buckinghamshire airspace.
2007: 3 imm on 16 May, Dorney and 17 May, Linford.
2009: 2 imm from 14 to 15 May, Willen and Linford.

The increase in the population in the near continent undoubtedly accounts for the increase in records.

Honey Buzzard
Pernis apivorus

Scarce migrant. One or two pairs may breed.

All records are given, with the exception of those of late September and early October 2000 and September 2008 which are summarised.

1837: reported by John Gould to have nested in Burnham Beeches.
1842: 1 captured, Chesham/Missenden.
1882: 2 killed about 23 Sep, Shabbington Woods.
1969: 1 on 2 Aug, Newport Pagnell.
1986: 1 on 12 Jun, Rushbeds Wood.
1988: 1 on 29 May, Phillipshill Wood.
1990: 1 on 16 Sep, Cheddington,
1991: 1 on 14 Jul, Windsor Hill NR.
1993: 1 from 29 to 30 Aug, Back Wood.
1993: 1 on 2 Oct, Beaconsfield.
1994: 1 on 15 May, Linford.
1998: 1 on 10 June, Windsor Hill NR.
2000: 1 on 7 May, Rowsham.
2000: 1 on 15 Aug, Wolverton.
2001: 1 on 24 May, Aylesbury.
2001: 1 on 16 Sep, Stowe.
2004: 1 on 5 Jun, Chalfont St Giles.
2005: 1 on 2 May, Black Park.
2005: 1 on 30 Jul, Marlow.
2005: 1 on 8 Sep, Whaddon.
2008: 1 on 1 Jun, Rowsham.
2009: 1 on 19 Sep, Marlow Bottom.
2010: 1 on 22 Sep, Steps Hill.

An unprecedented passage took place over southeast England in late September and early October 2000. Birds were seen arriving over the east coast and leaving the south coast a few days later in large numbers. The Buckinghamshire records are summarised.

The passage began with 11 past Pitstone Hill on 22 Sep. Some of these dropped into nearby Ashridge to roost. On 23rd seven passed Pitstone Hill, and three the following day dropped into trees in Ashridge where they were seen rising the following morning. A further four were seen this day. On 25th one was seen at Whaddon and one or two at Marlow. On 27th five flew past Pitstone Hill and a juvenile was seen at Denham Green. Singles were seen at Little Kingshill, Stony Stratford and Cheddington. The next bird was seen over Thorney on 30th, the following day saw two over Pitstone Hill, one at Marlow, one over Dorney and one that flew into the county from Hertfordshire at West Hyde. The last were three over Bledlow Ridge on 2 Oct.

Another passage occurred during eight days in September 2008. It began with two adults and two juveniles on 9th at Ivinghoe Beacon followed on 14th by one over Shenley Wood and a juvenile over Steps Hill. The next day juveniles were seen at Ivinghoe Beacon and Princes Risborough. The passage ended with juveniles over Ivinghoe Beacon on 21st and Langley Park on 22nd.

There were signs that a pair bred at a site in the south of the county in 1995, 2000, 2001 and at two sites in 2005. The secretive nature of this species makes confirmation of breeding very difficult.

DMF

Black Kite
Milvus migrans

Very rare vagrant. There are two records.

2003: 1 on 8 May, Little Marlow (Stevens, McQuaid & Bullock, 2004).
2003: 1 on 10 May, Pitstone and Steps Hill (Wallen, 2004).
2011: 1 on 30 Aug, World's End, Wendover.
2011: 1 on 31 Aug, Whaddon. This, of course, may be the same as the bird seen above.

It is likely that two birds were involved in 2003 as the Marlow bird was in moult, a feature not noted by the observer of the second bird.

Red Kite
Milvus milvus

Formerly a scarce vagrant, but following a JNCC/RSPB reintroduction programme now a common resident in the south of the county.

It is likely that Red Kites formerly bred in most of the larger woods of the county, but by the mid 19th century it had become 'very rare' (CK). H & J give undated reports of nesting near Quainton. Since the middle of the 19th Century there were only three records prior to 1967: in the 1880s,

Hedgerley, 26 Nov 2009   *David Ferguson*

in 1913, and in 1914. These records were followed by a long gap until one was seen in 1967. Two more were recorded in the 1960s and two in the 1970s.

The 1980s saw a marked increase, which may be explained by the improvement in the species' fortunes in Wales. Seven birds were seen between 1981 and 1988. Two birds were seen in each of January, March, and August, four were seen in April, and one in December. All were seen in the southern half of the county with six over or near the Chiltern escarpment. All were briefly seen except for one bird which remained at Littleworth Common from 28-30 Apr 1988.

An experimental reintroduction programme between 1989 and 1994, involving the release of 93 kites, mainly from Spain, has resulted in the establishment of a large breeding population, mainly in the south of the county. Young birds were released in the Chilterns, close to the Oxfordshire border and, although the first cohort of four birds from Sweden and one from Wales did not produce any local breeding pairs, it was not long before birds started to breed in the Chilterns. The first four successful pairs raised nine young in 1992 and these included birds that were only a year old. This was the first time that successful breeding at one-year of age by Red Kites had been recorded anywhere (Evans et al 1998). Pairs continued to be very productive in subsequent years, producing around 45% more young per successful nest than pairs in Wales as well as breeding a younger age. Between 1992 and 2006 the average brood size was 2.07 chicks compared to 1.43 in Wales at around the same time (1991 to 1999) (Cross & Davies 2005). The Chiltern broods included eight broods of four chicks, something that had not been recorded in Wales before 2011, when a single brood of four was found (Welsh Kite Trust 2011). This high productivity resulted in a rapidly expanding population with the number of pairs increasing by approximately 26% each year up until at least 2004. So successful was the release programme that by 1997 there were enough breeding pairs (over 50) to allow some chicks to be taken from nests for other release projects. Between 1997 and 2009 a total of 291 young kites were taken from nests in the Chilterns for release in Northamptonshire, Yorkshire, Dumfries and Galloway, Northumberland and Aberdeenshire. Despite this, numbers continued to increase and the breeding range expanded into all of the counties surrounding the Chilterns, including Berkshire, Hampshire, Wiltshire and Hertfordshire. In 2004 there were an estimated 201 breeding pairs in the Chilterns and surrounding areas (Carter & Whitlow 2005). Nest monitoring by the Southern England Kite Group (SEKG) has largely been confined to a relatively small core area centred near the Oxfordshire county boundary in the south west corner of Buckinghamshire. There were at least 92 pairs in this area of the county in 2011. It has not been possible to provide an accurate population estimate for the whole of the county for 2011 because nest densities vary so much and very little fieldwork was carried out by the SEKG in the outlying areas, away from the core area. However, it appears that the population is still increasing and spreading to new areas.

Given the rate of population growth, it is perhaps surprising that kites are still scarce in the north of the county. There were very few winter records north of Milton Keynes and breeding was only confirmed in three tetrads north of Whitchurch. However, this is almost certainly due to Red Kites tendency to breed close to their natal area. Like the kites in Wales, Chiltern kites normally return to breed close to their natal area. For the most part, they have expanded their breeding range on a "rolling front", rather than striking out into distant unoccupied areas (Newton et. al 1994). This has resulted in the development of a core area with an increasing density of breeding pairs close to where the birds were released. The confirmed breeding records on the summer map clearly shows this core area in the south-west corner of Buckinghamshire where artificial feeding is probably helping to maintain a high density of breeding pairs. Kites are now a common sight in towns and villages in this area of the county where they have become regular visitors to gardens, as many people now provide them with food. Although most pairs nest in the mature beech woods that are widespread in the south of the county, some pairs were recorded nesting in gardens and in isolated clumps of trees close to main roads, probably because food was being provided nearby. Red Kites build a large stick nest often adapting the disused nest of Carrion Crows, Common Buzzards and squirrel dreys. Around 85 % of the nests monitored by the SEKG were in beech trees. The highest nest density recorded during the atlas period was close to the original release site where 14 pairs nested in a single tetrad. Three of these were in beech trees within 90 metres of each other. Brood sizes in the densely populated areas have generally been smaller, probably because of competition for food. In 2011 a sample of 53 nests within 7 Km of the release site had an average brood of 1.42 chicks per nest while a sample of 24 nests more than 7 Km from the release site, where densities are lower, had an average brood size of 2.107.

Red Kites are gregarious birds. They are often seen feeding in groups where food is plentiful and gather at dusk to form communal roosts. Communal roosts have been recorded in all seasons in the Chilterns but the largest gatherings are found in the autumn and winter when over 200 birds have been recorded roosting together. These can be a spectacular sight with large numbers of birds wheeling above a favoured wood at dusk making a shrill mewing call. To add to the spectacle they are sometimes joined by other raptors and ravens. Counts at roosts in the Chilterns appear to have peaked between 2004 and 2005 when there were two main roosts within 6 km of the release site and a higher proportion of first year birds in the core area. The number of roosts has increased since then but the number in each has generally decreased, with most of the larger roosts being found away from the core area. Between November 2008 and February 2009 a sample of 18 roosts counted by the SEKG had an average of 31 birds. The largest of these was recorded near Marlow where 79 birds were counted on 21 Jan 2009. Availability of food probably influences the size of these communal roosts as some of the largest were recorded close to where birds were being provided with food.

Gatherings at feeding sites can also be large and have included: over 60 following a plough near Turville, over 40 at an unofficial feeding station near Stokenchurch and many counts of over 30 at landfill sites near Beaconsfield and Calvert but it seems likely that EU regulations limiting the dumping of waste to landfill will reduce numbers at these sites in the future. Numbers are already down at Springfield Quarry where the dumping of waste was suspended in the summer of 2011.

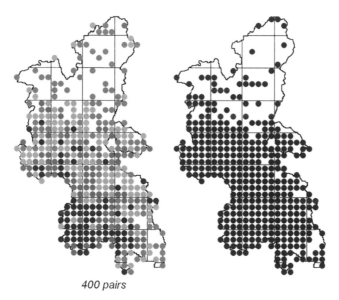

400 pairs

Once they have established a breeding territory, Red Kites in Buckinghamshire are largely sedentary, spending the winter on or near their summer ranges, though a few shift to places with more reliable food supplies. Most movement occurs during the first year, generally during late summer/autumn or the following spring/early summer after the birds have wintered in their natal area. Although most of these movements are within 40 Km from their natal areas, first year birds have been recorded visiting Wales, Yorkshire, East Midlands, West Sussex and Wiltshire. A nestling tagged near Fawley on 5 Jun 2009 was recorded visiting the Argaty feeding station in Perth and Kinross on 15 Aug 2010. Kites visiting Buckinghamshire from outside the area have included birds from Dumfries and Galloway, Yorkshire, Northumberland, Wales, East Midlands, West Sussex, Wiltshire and Hampshire. One of the young kites taken for release in Yorkshire in 2002 returned to Buckinghamshire twice during its first year and, on both occasions, it made the journey south in a single day.

PJS

White-tailed Eagle
Haliaeetus albicilla

Very rare vagrant and winter visitor. All records are given.

1846: 1 trapped Chequers Court.
1857: 1 shot Hambleden.
1894/5: 1 Fawley.
1983: 1 3rd/4th year, from 22 Nov to 18 Feb 1984, in the area of Longwick, Brill, Chilton, and Oakley.

The last record, of arguably the most spectacular bird ever seen in the county, was of an unringed bird, and was thus not a bird from the release scheme in the Hebrides. It probably originated from East Europe or the Baltic whose birds are increasing as winter visitors on the British east coast and in northern France. During its time in the county it was seen to feed on rabbits and, once, a muntjac.

Marsh Harrier
Circus aeruginosus

Scarce migrant.

Clark Kennedy made the remarkable statement: 'resident throughout year, nowhere numerous. Distributed sparingly.' He gave Chesham and Risborough as sites. H & J showed some scepticism towards these remarks and only gave one record: of a male shot at Spade Oak Ferry on 19 Jan 1881. Between this date and 1975 there was only one record, a single at Shardeloes on 28 Aug 1955.

   The graphs show that records were scarce until 1993 when there was a sudden increase which was a reflection of the increasing UK population. There is a double passage, stronger in the spring, and birds occasionally are found in winter. Almost all are briefly seen migrants which probably reflects the lack of suitable habitat in the county.

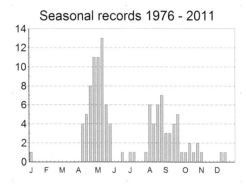

Seasonal records 1976 - 2011

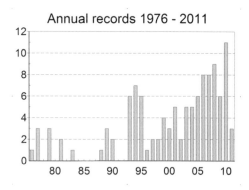

Annual records 1976 - 2011

Hen Harrier
Circus cyaneus

Rare migrant.

There are undated records for Chesham and Langley Park in Clark Kennedy.

There were five records to 1961:

1921: 1 shot in Dec, Olney.
1924: ringtail on 9 Mar, Pitstone Hill.
1939: 1 shot Jan, St Leonard's.
1951: male 24 Mar, Iver.
1952: ringtail on 9 Nov, Halton golf course.

Gallows Bridge Farm, 30 Nov 2011   *Jason Chalk*

During the 1960s there were four records, in the 1970s there were 12, in the 1980s there were four, in the 1990s there were 10, and from 2000 to 2011 there were 21. There is a tiny spring passage, somewhat more in the autumn and a few birds in winter. All records have been of singletons except for up to three present at Gallows Bridge Farm in Dec 2011. There are no summer records. Birds have been found throughout the county although the Vale of Aylesbury and the Upper Ray Valley tend to be favoured. There has been a welcome increase in records since the blank years of the 1980s.

Montagu's Harrier
Circus pygargus

Very rare vagrant. All records are given.

1929: 1 late Apr or early May, trapped by gamekeeper, Black Park.
1968: adult female 24 Jun, Frieth.
1977: female 26 May, Marsworth.
2005: male on 7 May, south Bucks.
2008: ringtail on 15 Aug, Pitstone Hill.

Harrier species
Circus sp.

1950s: 2 records of ringtails.
1960s: 1 record.
1970s: 2 records of ringtails.
1980s: 5 records of ringtails.
1990s: 7 records. Two were thought to be Montagu's Harriers and one a Hen Harrier.
2000s: 9 records. Five were thought to be Marsh Harriers, two Hen Harriers and one a Montagu's Harrier.
2010s: 2 records of ringtails.

Goshawk
Accipiter gentilis

Very rare resident.

The history of the Goshawk in Britain is well summarised in the Breeding Atlas. It appears to have ceased nesting in England well over a century ago and to have become re-established in recent decades, probably due to the release of birds by falconers or by escapes. Two sixteenth-century breeding records are quoted by F & Y. First, in a wood near Amersham 'there hath bene this twentie or thirtie yeres an Ayerye of goosse hawks contynually there bredyng'; and second, Thomas Hawtrey was summoned to appear before the Court of the Star Chamber for taking the young from a nest near Ellesborough. A male shot on 10 Sep 1789 near Dinton Hall by the Rev. W. Goodall figured in the Dinton Hall MS. The first twentieth-century sighting was one near Denham Green in March 1955 (F & Y). More recently, the 1984 BBC report commented that sightings in three separate areas may all have indicated the presence of breeding pairs.

Extensive woodland is the Goshawk's chief requirement for nesting, and widespread planting of conifers in post-war years provided this to some extent. However, beech is much favoured on the Continent and the Chiltern woodlands of Buckinghamshire must include many suitable localities. No large wood can be discounted as long as it is reasonably undisturbed. Prey supplies are unlikely to be a problem. An experimental study with released birds in Oxfordshire found the chief prey to be Woodpigeon, rabbit and Moorhen (Kenward 1979).

Identification of Goshawks is non-trivial and many sightings fail to make it past the county rarities committee. Coupling this with the difficulty of locating birds, which have the stealthy ways of Sparrowhawks and actually spend more time in woodland, the task of determining the status of Goshawks in the county has proved uniquely problematic. It is likely that a pair bred in the north of the county between 1992 and 1999 and that up to two pairs have bred in the south since 1995 and up to two pairs have bred in the middle of the county since 2000. However, no breeding has been proved.

Breeding sites several kilometres apart may be used in alternate years, adding further to the difficulties. Soaring display flights in spring offer the best chance of discovering a breeding pair. The nest itself may be hard to find, situated as it is in a high tree fork. This is to the bird's advantage, for although it receives special protection under the Wildlife and Countryside Act, it is still subjected to the depredations of egg-collectors and falconers.

PJKB

Sparrowhawk
Accipiter nisus

Radnage, 19 Aug 2005   *Gerry Whitlow*

Fairly common resident.

The history of the Sparrowhawk in Buckinghamshire has been one of fluctuating fortunes. Earlier this century, it was regularly persecuted by keepers (H & R, H & J), though common enough where unmolested. Recent decades have seen a change in attitudes, and while direct persecution does still occur, it is a much smaller problem than formerly. A more serious threat, due to the effects of organochlorine pesticide residues on breeding success, became evident during the 1960s, and the population dropped severely, both in the county and nationwide. Stricter controls on the use of certain pesticides since then have permitted a gradual recovery, as noted in MTNHS reports since the early 1970s, and confirmed by the 50% increase in the number of occupied tetrads between the two atlas surveys. The species is now arguably at least as abundant in Buckinghamshire as at any time this century.

The Sparrowhawk is primarily a woodland bird, especially during the breeding season, and the distribution shown on the map closely matches the extent of tree cover. Highest densities in the county are reached in well wooded areas of the Chilterns, where Fuller et al (1985) record a mean nearest-neighbour distance of 0.94 km, with a range from 0.5 to 1.5 km. North of the Chilterns, the more scattered woodlands of the Vale of Aylesbury, Woburn Sands and near the Northamptonshire border provide the main breeding habitat. However, a few pairs nest in small spinneys or hedgerows in otherwise open farmland. Parkland around stately homes, with mature trees such as cedars, is also used despite the higher levels of human disturbance. In the Chilterns study area conifer plantations were found to be a favoured habitat; 73% of the nests recorded were in larch, 22% in other conifers, and only 5% in broad-leaved trees. Elsewhere in the Chilterns, especially where there are extensive pure beechwoods, broad-leaved trees are presumably used more frequently. In the Vale of Aylesbury, nests in hedgerow hawthorns and willows have been recorded.

Sparrowhawks commence breeding from mid to late May, and most young fledge in late July or early August. A period of two to three weeks is then spent in the vicinity of the nest, with the young attended by the parents. The birds may be conspicuously noisy at this time. From early autumn onwards, young birds disperse away from the breeding areas, and mortality at this time is high. Of 44 recoveries of Chiltern Sparrowhawks analysed by Burton (1986), 11 occurred within 100 days of the ringing date, with a peak in September. On the national scale, this dispersal appears random in direction (Newton 1986), but the Chiltern-ringed birds showed a strong bias towards moving along the scarp, especially north-east or southwards. Only eight had moved out into the Vale of Aylesbury, and seven of these were females, confirming the trend noted by Newton (1986) for females to venture more readily into open country. Most birds do not move very far, over half of all recoveries being under 10 km. The longest recorded is one of 122 km, from Essex to Berryfields. More usual is the next longest, one of 63 km, from a site near Hastoe to

Basingstoke, Hampshire. This is fairly typical of Sparrowhawks in S England, although those from the north and Scotland often travel considerably farther. Sparrowhawks breeding in the Vale of Aylesbury have been less intensively ringed than those in the Chilterns, and the few birds recovered have stayed within the low ground to the north and west of the Chilterns. To what extent Vale-bred birds may move into the Chilterns remains unknown.

150 pairs   400 pairs

During the winter, a proportion of Sparrowhawks move out of woodland to hunt in open country, or even in suburban gardens, where concentrations of small birds at feeders and bird tables can prove an attraction. Winter roosts of thrushes or Starlings may also have their attendant Sparrowhawks. At the Calvert roost, for example, up to five have been seen in the air together on an evening when Redwings were abundant. These birds are usually females, as are the majority of Sparrowhawks recovered around human dwellings. Such recoveries commonly occur through collisions with windows or greenhouses while in pursuit of prey.

From late winter onwards, Sparrowhawks may be seen soaring in display flights near the breeding areas, and nest building often commences many weeks before egg laying. A new nest is usually built each year, and other half-completed structures may also be seen in nearby trees. Whether egg laying will follow, and how successful it will be, depends on conditions in early spring. Harsh winters and late springs may reduce breeding success considerably among early-nesting passerines, whose fledglings form an important food source later, when Sparrowhawks have their own young to feed. Consequently, hard weather early in the year is often followed by a poor year for Sparrowhawks, as happened in 1979, 1982 and, less severely, in 1986. Poor productivity is caused both by the failure of nesting attempts, and by failure to breed at all. In the latter case, birds may remain in regular attendance at a nest, without ever laying in it.

PJKB

Common Buzzard
Buteo buteo

Common resident.

Changes in the distribution of Buzzards in England are well documented. Persecution of Buzzards by man is said to have started as early as the beginning of the 17th century (BWP) although at the beginning of the 19th century the range of breeding Buzzards still extended right across England and Wales (the Breeding Atlas).

Radnage, 4 Jun 2011   *Gerry Whitlow*

By 1865 the main breeding range had significantly contracted with the low point being around 1915 when they were virtually confined to Cornwall, Devon, Wales, the Lake District and West Scotland. It seems very unlikely that any Buzzards would have been seen in Buckinghamshire at this time, even as vagrants, as they do not normally wander far from their breeding site (Brown 1976). By 1954 the breeding range had extended eastward to as far as Buckinghamshire (the Breeding Atlas) although there is evidence that Buzzards were regularly summering in the west of the county for some years before that. The introduction of myxomatosis in 1955-56, along with organo-chlorine poisoning, caused some retraction in the range in central and southern England (BWP) and may explain the lack of Buzzard breeding records from Buckinghamshire for the period between 1954 and 1967. The Breeding Atlas only has Buzzards recorded in three 10-km squares (two confirmed and one possible breeding), these being from tetrads which are partly shared with other counties. The BTO Buzzard survey (Taylor, *et al* 1986) concluded that 'the population has not extended significantly since 1972'.

The graph shows the increase in the number of records up to 1994 when the species had become so regular that it was impossible to calculate accurate numbers. Possible breeding activity was noted in most years since the late 1970s. However confirmation was rarely obtained. There was usually just one territory involved but in some years records for up to three territories were received.

By 1995 four pairs were breeding in the southern Chilterns and by 1999 it was regarded as 'genuinely common in the real south-west' and was regular in the middle of the county. The range continued to expand at an astonishing rate so that by the time of the second survey birds were widespread throughout the county.

There is no convincing explanation for the rapid range expansion which has taken Buzzards from the West Country and Wales right across England to the east coast, but possible factors are decreased persecution, an increasing rabbit population, and a reduction in the use of organochlorine pesticides (Clements, 2002). Ravens have also spread across England in a similar manner, though in fewer numbers. It is likely that the reasons for their increase is due to the same factors.

While Buzzards are widespread throughout the county it is probable that the population is at its densest in the well-wooded Chilterns. The breeding map probably exaggerates the actual breeding distribution as the birds have large territories and are often seen over farmland that is unsuitable for nesting. Common Buzzards are often seen at landfill sites although in the south of the county they are outnumbered by Red Kites, a sight that, a few decades earlier, would have been unthinkable.

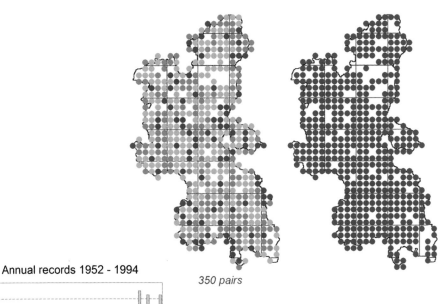

Annual records 1952 - 1994

350 pairs

JER & DMF

Rough-legged Buzzard
Buteo lagopus

Very rare vagrant. All records are given.

1839: pair shot Nov, Bledlow Woods.
1880: 1 trapped 6 Dec, near Wycombe.
1890 or 1891: 3 trapped in late autumn, Halton. Two of these birds are now in the Tring Museum.
1912: 1 Aston Clinton.
1966: 1 from mid Dec to 28 Jan 1967, Chiltern escarpment.
1971: 1 on 17 Apr, Dorney Common.
1995: 1 on 1 Jan, Middle Claydon.

There is some evidence that the bird is under-recorded in the county as there are more records in neighbouring counties, including Oxfordshire, where one would expect this Fenno-Scandinavian vagrant to be rarer (Brucker et al. 1992).

Osprey
Pandion haliaetus

Scarce migrant.

Prior to 1968 there were 10 records of 11 birds.

1845: 1 killed Chequers.
1854: 1 shot in Feb, canal at Halton.
1858: 1 seen in winter, Fawley Woods.
1862: 1 killed on 9 Sep, Ditton Park.
1863: 1 shot on 26 Sep, Ditton Park.
1864: 2 in Sep, Weston Turville Res
     & Wendover Canal. The female was shot on 30th.
1901: 1 shot 11 Oct, Aston Hall, Halton.
1938: 1 on 14 Sep, on Bucks bank of Thames 3 km west of Maidenhead.
1952: 1 injured Latimer. The bird was released after treatment.
1958: 1 on 6 or 16 Sep, Shardeloes.

Latimer, 28 Mar 2009   *Mike Wallen*

Since 1968 there have been 199 records of single birds. The increase in the number of records is a reflection of the increase in the Scottish breeding population.

The birds have all been found at the well-watched lakes, or flying over. Their visits are normally of brief duration, but one bird was present in the Willen-Linford area from 7 Sep to 13 Oct 1991. Another in the same area from 1 to 17 Jun 2000 was ringed as a nestling in Scotland in 1998.

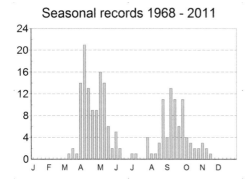

Seasonal records 1968 - 2011

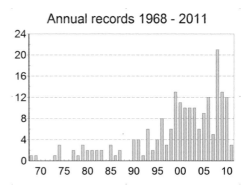

Annual records 1968 - 2011

Kestrel
Falco tinnunculus

West Wycombe, 9 Jan 2004 — *Gerry Whitlow*

Common resident and partial migrant.

In the early part of the century the Kestrel suffered persecution by keepers, but shooting and nest robbing no longer pose a major threat. In fact, the bird is popular with farmers and landowners, and many now actively encourage it. Kestrels were affected by the pesticide problems of the 1960s, but much less severely than the Sparrowhawk, presumably because their more varied diet did not concentrate the organochlorine residues so intensely.

The dramatic increase shown by the maps, which implies a doubling of the Buckinghamshire population since the first atlas, is not reflected by the population in England which has been oscillating within 10% of the mean since the mid-1980s.

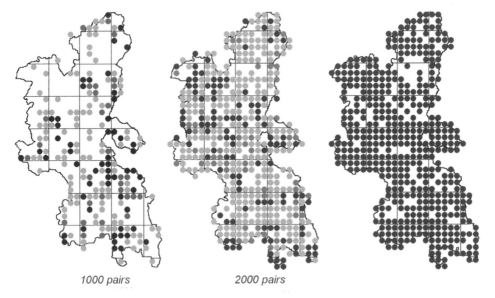

1000 pairs   *2000 pairs*

The Kestrel is essentially a raptor of open ground, which in Buckinghamshire means mainly farmland. Valuable habitat is also provided by road verges, gravel pit surrounds, marginal areas of rough grass, and woodland edges adjoining farmland such as abound in the Chilterns.

Most prey is taken from the ground. Rodent numbers have a significant effect on breeding success, though much less so here than, for example, in the Scottish borders. Moderating the effect of rodent fluctuations is the more dependable food source provided by newly fledged Starlings and House Sparrows. Pellets and kill-remains at nests show these to be the principal food source for Kestrel nestlings at most sites in the county.

Another vital habitat feature is the availability of nest sites. Like all falcons, Kestrels make no nest but use various natural sites, tree cavities being the predominant choice in Buckinghamshire. Old crows' nests, bale ricks and farm buildings are also used, but less frequently than in some parts of England. Where elms were dominant, extensive felling following Dutch elm disease has probably reduced breeding density. In one such area in the county a network of Kestrel nest boxes has proved highly successful, providing sites for the majority of breeding pairs over some 200 sq km. Fieldwork in the Vale of Aylesbury from 1981 to 1986 indicated a density of 9-10 breeding pairs per 100 sq km, perhaps 11-12 in a good year. Figures for the Chilterns are harder to establish, due to the difficulty of locating all pairs in this habitat, but data so far suggest perhaps 12-15 per 100 sq km in an average year. Both figures are far below the densities suggested in the Breeding Atlas, which appear to be a considerable overestimate for most parts of Britain (Village 1990).

The start of breeding is spread over 5-6 weeks, with extreme first-egg dates ranging from 12 April (1985, near Amersham) to 2 June (1986, near Winslow). Early clutches are larger on average than late ones. Intensive monitoring since 1981 has shown that Kestrels breeding in the Chilterns consistently start earlier and produce larger average clutches and broods than those in the Vale. In most years the former generally start before the end of April and Vale birds from early May onwards. This presumably reflects a difference in habitat quality, perhaps related to the greater extent of woodland edge in the Chilterns. Fledging is correspondingly spread out, from early June to the end of July. In two years, 1984 and 1985, cold wet weather in late May and early June severely reduced breeding success. Newly fledged young generally spend some time in the nesting locality, attended by their parents, but a few long distance recoveries occur within 4-5 weeks of fledging. Possibly these are birds which become separated too early from the family group and keep on moving in deteriorating condition.

Mortality in the first autumn appears even higher than in the Sparrowhawk; of 77 recoveries of local Kestrels since 1978, 37 have occurred within 100 days of ringing. Preliminary analysis of recoveries of Kestrels ringed in the county reveals an interesting pattern. There are many recoveries under 50 km and over 100 km, but surprisingly few between 50 and 100 km. Intriguingly, those under 50 km show a north-east bias, while those over 100 km show a south-west bias. Possibly land immediately to the north-east provides better winter habitat than that in other directions. Certainly, E England is an important wintering area, as shown by the Winter Atlas. Recovery distances in other directions can be considerable. Recoveries over 200 km away include 12 in Spain (Bilbao and Zaragoza), six in France, several in Wales, and five in N England.

By winter, many locally-bred young Kestrels have moved out of the county, while others have moved in. Older birds mostly remain near their breeding places, and some nest sites serve as roosts throughout the year. Precise hunting areas alter in line with the changing pattern of farm work through the winter (Shrubb 1980). Recoveries in autumn and winter are mainly of birds found dead in poor condition, with relatively fewer accidental deaths than in the Sparrowhawk. Accidents that do occur commonly involve drowning in farm water troughs, and collisions with cars or trains. One unfortunate Buckinghamshire Kestrel ended up on the track in Euston station, presumably having been carried there by the train which killed it.

Diving and grappling courtship displays can be observed as early as January, reaching a peak in March and early April. For some established pairs with a well situated traditional site, nest selection is a foregone conclusion; one such site in the Vale has been used successfully for at least eight consecutive years. Others find their site, if at all, only just before breeding (Village 1990). The number of these marginal pairs (often first-year birds) varies from year to year, as does the average starting date, which may differ between seasons by as much as ten days. In most years, a few pairs occupy sites without actually nesting in them. More detailed discussion of the factors involved is to be found in Cave (1968), Snow (1968), and Village (1990).

PJKB

Red-footed Falcon
Falco vespertinus

Very rare vagrant. All records are given.

1983: male on 27 Jul, Woughton, Milton Keynes.
2008: female on 31 May, Richings Park, Iver.
2010: male which spent most of its time at Wilstone Res, Herts, was seen at Drayton Beauchamp on 26 May and in Bucks airspace on 2 June.

Wilstone Res, Herts   Mike Wallen

A record of one shot in Jan in 1858 at Steeple Claydon has a remarkable date which must cast considerable doubt on its authenticity. The more recent records have a more typical date for this East European species.

Merlin
Falco columbarius

Uncommon winter visitor and passage migrant.

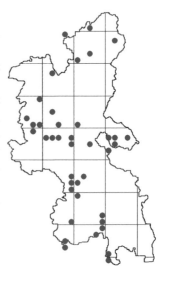

Clark Kennedy noted in 1856 that the Merlin 'was not a common hawk', a laconic statement that is still true. Up to 1992 no more than five had been recorded in a year but since then there has never been less than seven and in 2008 21 were recorded. All were of single birds and most sightings are of birds travelling at speed across open country. There is a small double passage, but most birds have been seen in winter. The map, which shows the records for four successive winters, exaggerates the annual distribution but indicates they have a preference for the Vale of Aylesbury and the Chiltern escarpment around Ivinghoe and Lodge Hill.

Seasonal records 1972 - 2011

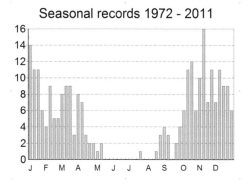

Annual records 1972 - 2011

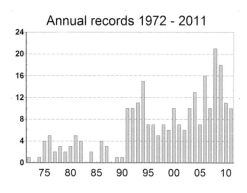

Hobby
Falco subbuteo

Uncommon breeding summer visitor.

Historical records indicate that the Hobby has long been a breeding bird in Buckinghamshire and adjacent counties, and also that it was often persecuted in the past. Clark Kennedy notes that a pair nested in a wood near Datchet in 1861 and that the young birds were shot almost as soon as they had learnt to fly, and H & R

Rowsham, 14 Jul 2004   *Mike Wallen*

state that an adult pair was shot in August 1894 near Long Marston, close to the Buckinghamshire border. F & Y describe the species as a very scarce breeder, though this was just before any thorough fieldwork had been done.

Breeding was confirmed in 19 tetrads for this atlas. The map shows an uneven distribution of breeding records but this is probably an indication of where the targeted

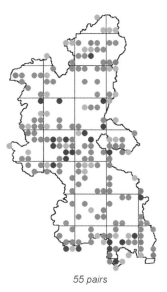

55 pairs

fieldwork was done rather than showing the preferred breeding habitat. Fieldwork for the first atlas revealed that breeding Hobbies were widely distributed within the county with no particular concentrations. Pairs were found breeding both on farmland and in woodland. Many pairs were found in 10 km squares where they were not found during the survey for the first BTO Breeding Atlas, but this was thought to be an indication of better coverage rather than an actual increase in numbers. Hobbies can be extremely elusive during the breeding season and birds may be seen only rarely, even in areas where they are known to be breeding. They appear to spend the day perched unobtrusively in trees or hunting at high altitude. It is likely that many breeding pairs remained undetected, even in tetrads which received a comparatively thorough coverage. Because nest sites are traditional, and Hobbies are known to have suffered from the activities of egg collectors locally in the past, some observers may have been reluctant to submit breeding records. Breeding was confirmed in 3.4% of Buckinghamshire's tetrads with probable or possible in a further 9.9%. The results are similar to the first atlas figures when breeding was confirmed in 4% with a further 10% probable or possible. The lower proportion of confirmed breeding records may be due to less targeted monitoring or under reporting rather than a decrease in numbers. Fuller et al.(1985) found 3-4 pairs per 100 sq km in the S. Midlands but proposed 'a conservative average of two pairs per occupied 100 sq km' nationally. Hobbies appear to have increased in the UK since the first atlas (88-91 BTO Breeding Atlas and BBS 1998-2008) so, all in all, the estimate of 2.5 pairs per 100 sq km given in the last atlas seems conservative. Using this would give a county population of around 55 pairs.

The first spring migrants are normally recorded in April when they are often seen hunting over gravel pits, rivers and other wetlands in small numbers. The earliest arrivals in recent years have mainly been seen in the second half of April but in 2008 single birds were recorded at three sites in early April. Larger gatherings, involving up to 15 birds, are sometimes recorded in May when they can be seen exploiting the mass emergence of mayflies at some wetlands. Groups of four or more birds were recorded at the Jubilee River, College Lake, Little Marlow GP, Linford, Tyringham , Willen and over the Thames. The largest number seen during the atlas period was at Amerden Scrapes on 9th May 2011 when between 9 and 14 were seen hunting mayflies. Groups of birds seen in May probably comprise migrants and non-breeding birds as well as locally breeding birds. Pairs are usually on breeding territories by the second week of May and at this time that they are fairly vocal and perform spectacular aerial displays. After a short period of display, pairs are generally difficult to locate, possibly because they leave nest sites until eggs are laid around the middle of June. The Hobby lays its eggs in the disused nests of other species, especially those of the Carrion Crow. In Buckinghamshire it does not appear to have any preference for particular tree species, with the proportion of crow nests used in each of them being directly proportional to the availability of nests in that species (Fuller et al 1985). Artificial sites may also be used and have included nesting baskets specifically provided for Hobbies (Andrew Freeman pers comm).

Pairs were recorded at several of sites where they were also recorded for the first atlas and one of these was occupied for at least three consecutive years. Fuller et al (1985) refer to a breeding pair which used the same site in 1982 as was used by Hobbies in the late nineteenth century. Young Hobbies usually fledge about mid August. Fledged young are often very noisy, particularly when following an adult with food. The BBC monthly reports show a peak in the number of sites where Hobbies were reported in August and it seems likely that the majority of these relate to recently fledged young. Family groups are sometimes active after sunset but it can be very difficult to observe what prey, if any, is being pursued. They have been recorded taking bats (MTNHS 1965), and young birds have been observed to spend long periods on the ground attempting to catch insects (P. J. Stevens and G. Marsh). Feathers collected from plucking points at four nest sites in the south of the county during the first atlas period indicated that Swifts were the main prey species there.

In September, young birds may be seen hunting with adults away from the nest, often over water where they are able catch migrating dragonflies and butterflies. During the atlas period, groups of Hobbies were reported hunting over Marlow GP, Jubilee River, Shardeloes and the Thames. In the past, birds were frequently seen at Swallow roosts bordering the county. Tring Reservoirs and Slough SF, for example, used to be regular haunts, with several occasionally recorded on the same evening. Family groups do not generally begin to disperse until mid September and most birds have departed by the end of the month, although birds are occasionally reported near nest sites in early October. There was one very late record of a bird near Old Slade NR on 10 Nov 1979 and one ringing recovery from overseas. A nestling ringed at Mentmore on 31 July 1984 was trapped in Kreiss Beeskow, Germany on 6 Aug 1985. This is the most easterly record for a British-bred Hobby.

PJS

Peregrine
Falco peregrinus

Very rare resident and scarce winter visitor.

Aylesbury, 7 Mar 2008   Mike Wallen

Until the late 1990s Peregrines were scarce migrants to Buckinghamshire. Between 1848 and 1919 there were 10 records, then at least 13 until 1957. The late 1950s and early 1960s was the period when Peregrines were subjected to maximum exposure to DDT and only five birds were recorded in Buckinghamshire between 1958 and 1972. One or two birds were then recorded in some years up to 1991 when four birds were noted. Up to this time birds were mainly recorded in the winter with the Vale of Aylesbury as a favoured area. The ban on poisonous pesticides, mainly DDT, and reduced human persecution led to a boom in the UK population. Between 1991 and 2006 there were 279 records, with a significant increase from 1998, the numbers increasing year on year but still mainly confined to the winter period. Many of the county records are attributed to younger birds; the adults tend to stay on the breeding territory or winter at a favoured site nearby.

On 27 June 2007 a first summer male, carrying prey, was seen to alight on the County Council Office building in Aylesbury; this was to be the beginning of summer residency of Peregrines in Buckinghamshire and exciting events in Aylesbury town centre. This location subsequently attracted other Peregrines of both sexes and in common with other towns and cities across Britain residency was established. This led to the erection of a purpose built nesting platform on the building in February 2008.

Over the next few years regular monitoring in Aylesbury gave us an insight into their urban diet, and demonstrated that the birds were adept at hunting at night, using the lights of the town from below to light up the prey flying above. Prey species were varied, but waders were very common, particularly in winter months or at the times of those species migrations, with Golden Plover and especially Woodcock taken. Other interesting prey species were Great Spotted Woodpecker, Black-headed Gull, Swift, Common Snipe and Ruff. This monitoring demonstrated that the Peregrines were caching food when available.

The platform remained unused but modifications were made both on and around it and the building was still favoured by a number of birds. For example in autumn 2010, five different birds were seen to use the building and three birds were seen roosting together; communal roosting by Peregrines is known to occur.

In the winter of 2010 a young pair were constantly present and they remained into April 2011 when they settled on the platform. This subsequently led to a very late breeding attempt where one egg was laid which was incubated but never hatched.

Elsewhere in the county, in the spring of the same year, another pair of birds were discovered visiting a nest site. This breeding attempt was monitored and two young were subsequently seen. In July 2011 they fledged, and in doing so became the first recorded Peregrines to fledge in Buckinghamshire. This record is not shown on the map.

With the continued rise in the Peregrine population, provision of further platforms would no doubt be met with success. Their ability to adapt to man-made structures provides us with the opportunity to see not only the fastest animal on the planet, but also this most magnificent of birds in the towns and cities as well as the countryside of the county.

The probable breeding in the far southeast of the county took place in Uxbridge which, though in a Buckinghamshire tetrad, is in fact in Middlesex.

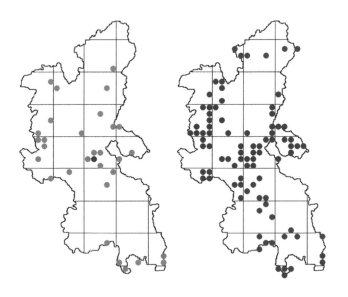

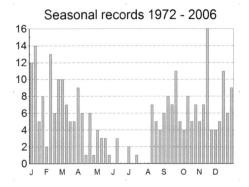

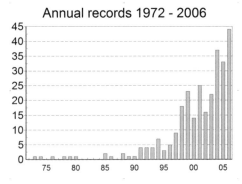

MSW

Water Rail
Rallus aquaticus

Rare resident and local winter visitor.

The specialised habitat requirements of Water Rails have meant that the species has probably always been a very local breeder in Buckinghamshire. Clark Kennedy described Water Rails as 'not very plentiful, but specimens have been killed at all times of the year'. He mentioned Chesham, Drayton Beauchamp, and Aylesbury as sites. H & J commented 'not uncommon winter visitor; resident in very small numbers.' No nests had been found in Buckinghamshire, though two nests had been discovered near Wraysbury (then in the county) in 1896.

Calvert, 16 Feb 2009   *John Sheppard*

The only locality where the species is known to breed regularly is Weston Turville Reservoir where the extensive reed beds provide an ideal habitat. There are usually two or three pairs present, although in 1965 six to 10 pairs were thought to have bred. The only other sites where breeding has been proven since 1947 is Old Slade (now in Berkshire) where breeding took place in 1970, Mursley where a nest with nine eggs was found on 10 May 1995, Wotton where a juvenile was ringed on 4 Jul 2004 and Little Marlow where a juvenile was seen in Jul 2004. The species is not difficult to locate in the spring when its loud nocturnal calls reveal its presence, but breeding may be difficult to prove. The most productive method is to watch at dusk when the adults may be seen with young birds at the water's edge.

The survey for the first county breeding atlas revealed only one tetrad where breeding was proven, although there were another nine tetrads where birds were present. During

137

the second atlas survey fledglings were seen at two sites: Wotton Lakes and the Lea Valley. The records shown on the map in the Tring area were in Hertfordshire.

During the winter, birds are more widespread. Overgrown canals, ditches, and even gardens may be utilised as well as larger wetland sites such as Shardeloes, Calvert, and Caldecotte. One was even found on a window ledge in central high Wycombe. The largest number recorded at one site during the winter is 11 at Shardeloes in February, 1969, while Waterside, Chesham and Calvert have held up to 10 birds. National ringing data suggests that many of these birds originate from continental Europe, although there have been no ringing recoveries involving county birds.

DMF

Spotted Crake
Porzana porzana

Very rare vagrant. All records are given.

There is an undated record from High Wycombe in Clark Kennedy, and both he and H & R note several records by the R. Thames. They are however with no date or localities and are probably in Berkshire.

Dorney Common, 14 Oct 2000   David Ferguson

1897: 1 Olney.
1925: 1 on 7 Feb, Westhorpe, Little Marlow.
1995: adult from 19 to 23 Aug, Willen.
1995: juvenile from 5 to 19 Sep, Willen.
2000: juvenile from 9 to 19 Oct, Dorney Common.
2003: 1 from 26 to 30 Mar, Little Marlow.

The 1995 records were part of a national influx of about 60 birds.

Corncrake
Crex crex

Very rare migrant. Formerly a breeding summer visitor.

The decline of the Corncrake in Buckinghamshire began in the second half of the 19th century. Clark Kennedy described its status as 'very numerous', but H & J wrote 'not now common. Only a few pairs in the Thames Valley.' By 1947 Price was writing 'summer visitor in decreasing numbers.' Since then the records are:

1948: 1 calling all summer, Hambleden.
1949: 1 calling all summer, Fulmer.
1952: 1 on 29 Aug, Ivinghoe.
1957: 1 calling 26 Jun, near Ickford.
1959: 1 from 25 to 27 Aug, Hyde Heath/Great Pednor.
1960: 1 on 17 Apr, Newport Pagnell GPs.

1960: 1 on 4 Jun, Great Linford GPs.
1960: 1 on 2 Aug, Haversham.
1961: 1 in Jul and Aug, Great Pednor.
1961: 1 from 15 May to 10 Jun, Haversham. 2 were present on the last date.
1974: 2 heard 14 Sep, Newton Longville.
1985: 1 calling from 25 to 30 Jun, Shipton Lee.

The decline of Corncrakes in the county parallels its decline in the country as a whole. The process began in the SE of England in the second half of the 19th century and continued until 1993 when conservation management began in its strongholds in the Hebrides. In 2010 this initiative resulted in the number of calling males increasing to 1200, compared to just 480 in 1993. This increase has not been reflected in any increase in the number of Buckinghamshire records although there have been several quite convincing claims of birds in the county having been heard calling for a few days in the spring, but none have been confirmed.

The cause of the decline from being a widespread and well known species to one almost restricted to remote islands has been well studied. The primary habitat of Corncrakes is hay fields which need to remain uncut until the young are fledged. Mechanisation of hay cutting has had two effects: first, the machines do not allow the birds to escape so easily as hand-cutting did, and second, mechanisation, together with increased fertiliser output, enables cutting to take place earlier in the year. This means nests have a greater chance of being destroyed. Improved grasslands, which have largely replaced traditional hay fields, have a limited insect population, and are thus unattractive to Corncrakes, while it has recently become clear that the birds require tall, rank vegetation when they first arrive, a habitat that has all but disappeared with modern agricultural practices. (Cadbury 1980).

DMF

Moorhen
Gallinula chloropus

Common resident and winter visitor.

The Moorhen is found everywhere near water as long as some cover is available. Their status appears not to have changed much, if at all, since the 1850s.

In Buckinghamshire even the smallest water may harbour a few Moorhens. It is conceivable that when the Ouse valley was mainly swampland they were more a bird of reeds, but they do seem to be able to

Dunsmore, 2 Jun 2011   David Ferguson

adapt to changing circumstances and readily associate with man. To a certain extent they complement the Coot: Moorhens prefer smaller waters while Coots are mainly found at the larger lakes.

The main concentrations of breeding birds are along streams, rivers and canals, but there are also many breeding records from wet ditches and small farm ponds. The introduction of piped water for livestock has meant that many farm ponds are no longer used and have been filled in, which may have led to a reduction in the Moorhen population. However, the species is still numerous in most parts of the county, though the map suggests that there are fewer in the Chilterns than elsewhere, presumably due to the lack of ponds and ditches on the chalky soil.

The Moorhen is remarkably adaptable when breeding. Nests can be found at the waterside at ground level as well as quite high in bushes. Second and third broods often occur, particularly if the first one is destroyed, and it is common for females to dump eggs in the nests of other Moorhens.

Birds do move around a little but never go very far. The most distant recovery involving Buckinghamshire is of 81 km (from Surrey), although it is known that some birds bred on the Continent occur in Britain.

In winter, Moorhens can form small feeding flocks in winter. Since 1997 these have been reported in the BBC bulletin beginning with 60+ at Lake End Road, Taplow on 5 Mar 1997. Flocks of over 50 have been found at Chalfont Park, Little Missenden, Broughton, College Lake, Wycombe Abbey, Shardeloes and the Jubilee River. The largest flock reported was 94 at Shardeloes in Jan 2004. The species may suffer quite heavily in hard winters and it is a fairly regular road casualty. A leucistic bird was seen on a pond at Gayhurst House on 18 Jul 1988.

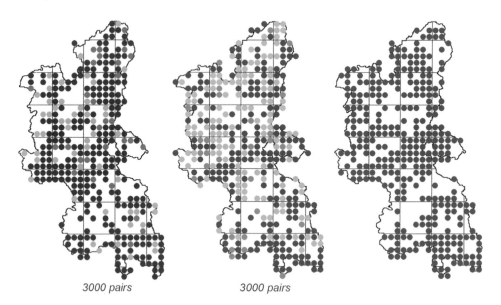

3000 pairs   3000 pairs

NHFS

Coot
Fulica atra

Common resident and winter visitor.

Weston Turville Res, 24 Apr 2010   *Mike Wallen*

The status of the Coot does not seem to have changed much since the 1850s. Earlier authors all considered it a fairly numerous breeding bird on ponds and lakes in Buckinghamshire, with numbers augmented considerably in winter.

It is clear from the breeding distribution map that the Coot is widespread in the county but much more restricted than the Moorhen to larger waters. The old gravel pits and other lakes in the north of the county, together with all the main rivers - Ouse, Thame, Chess and Thames - form the main breeding areas. Deeper water with a plentiful supply of submerged plants is a necessity, and many of the older gravel pits and other mineral workings are favoured. The Coot's breeding requirements are more conservative than those of the Moorhen, with nests nearly always over water.

In winter large numbers of birds arrive from the Continent, the intensity and timing of influxes apparently being linked to climatic conditions there. Waters such as the Linford/Haversham complex, Caldecotte and Willen regularly hold 300-400 birds throughout the winter, and over 800 were recorded at Willen in November 1982 and December 1987. The south of the county usually holds rather fewer birds.

Coots which breed in Britain are mostly sedentary although local movements do occur. The farthest recorded by ringing recoveries affecting Buckinghamshire is of a bird moving to Kent and one ringed at Abberton Res, Essex on 18 Oct 1982 recovered at Weston Turville on 27 Jan 1995.

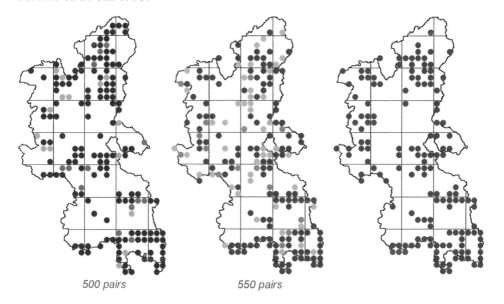

500 pairs   550 pairs

NHFS

Common Crane
Grus grus

Scarce vagrant. All records are given.

1987: adult or first-winter on 11 Jan, flying W over Withybridge (Slough) and two hours
later over Dorney Common.
1993: 1 on 10 Dec, Fenny Stratford.
1995: sub-adult from 25 to 26 May, Little Horwood.
1999: 2 on 28 April flying over Weston Turville. They landed at Broughton, Aylesbury
and were seen the following morning.
2000: 1 on 14 Aug, Padbury.
2003: 9 on 2 Mar flying over Hedgerley.
2004: 1 on 11 Apr flying W over Stoke Common.
2005: 1 on 29 Apr flying over Ford.
2008: 1 on 26 Jan flying N over Little Linford Wood.
2009: 2 on 25 Jun flying E over Ivinghoe Beacon and Edlesborough.
2010: 2 on 3 Mar flying over Linford.
2011: 1 from 4 to 5 Apr, Gallows Bridge Farm.

The 1987 record was originally accepted as two individuals (adult over Withybridge and
first winter over Dorney Common) but there is clearly a strong possibility of only one bird
being involved. The increase in the number of records parallels the increase in the British
and near European populations.

Crane sp
Grus sp

2005: 1 on 26 Apr, flying NW over Milton Keynes.

Oystercatcher
Haematopus ostralegus

Very local breeding summer visitor and
uncommon migrant.

The first record was as recent as 24 Apr
1953 at Little Marlow. There were only
five more records before 1975, but after
this birds became annual and slowly
increased their numbers. The graphs show
the increase up to 2001, the year after the
first successful breeding in the county.

Gallows Bridge Farm, 12 Jun 2010   Mike Wallen

The status of the Oystercatcher, from being a regular migrant in small numbers to
becoming a regular breeder is part of an expansion into the English Midlands possibly
from inland sites to the north. Their cheerful piping calls are now a familiar sound at a
number of wetland sites in the spring and summer.

Through the 1990s visits by migrants were becoming more common and stays more lengthy, culminating with a pair apparently on territory at Linford in 1999 where mating was observed and a bird was seen sitting in May. Only singles were present subsequently and it was presumed that the attempt had failed. What is believed to be the same pair was also present at Gayhurst Quarry at the end of April but there were no further records, although they were clearly looking for a suitable breeding site.

The new millennium marked an exciting new chapter in the fortunes of this species in the county as breeding took place for the first time. Gayhurst Quarry was the favoured choice of this significant event where a pair raised two juveniles and so began what has become a successful colonisation of suitable wetland sites. During the following three years Gayhurst continued to be favoured with single pairs raising a total of six young, while another pair attempted to breed at Stony Stratford NR. In 2005 there was successful breeding at Linford and Stony Stratford where single pairs raised two young each. The spread south continued the following year with a pair at College Lake raising two young, while other pairs bred at Gayhurst (1 juv), Hillesden (3 juvs), Linford (2 juvs) and Stony Stratford (1 juv).

Between 2007 and 2011 breeding success was confirmed at College Lake, which has become the most important site, where a total of 12 juveniles fledged, with totals at the remaining sites during the same period as follows: Caldecotte (1 juv), Gayhurst (4 juvs), Hillesden (6 juvs), Linford (3 juvs) and Stony Stratford (4 juvs).

Returning pairs usually arrive at their breeding sites in February, with numbers fluctuating during March as other birds pass through and pairs search out potential sites to set up territories. They can be remarkably unobtrusive for such a large noisy bird when at the nest and one of the pair may regularly feed at a location away from the breeding site. The juveniles usually remain close to the adult birds until they all leave the county, usually by the end of August. There is a small autumn passage but winter records are unusual.

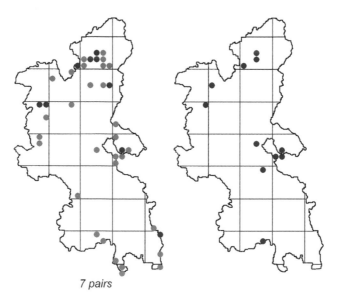

7 pairs

143

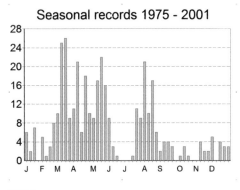

Seasonal records 1975 - 2001

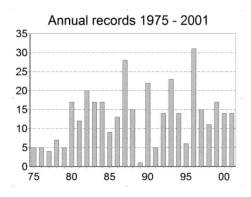

Annual records 1975 - 2001

RDA

Black-winged Stilt
Himantopus himantopus

Very rare vagrant. There has been one record.

1988: a pair of first-summer birds, from 7 to 18 Jun, Willen. Copulation was observed on the 9th.

This is a typical date for this Mediterranean species.

Avocet
Recurvirostra avosetta

Rare vagrant. All records are given.

1975: 6 on 18 May, Linford.
1976: 1 on 21 Nov, Willen.
1979: 1 on 17 Jun, Willen.
1983: 24 on 27 Mar, Willen.
1984: 1 on 13 Mar, Little Marlow.
1984: 1 on 24 Mar, Willen.
1992: 1 on 3 Feb, Willen.
1992: 2 on 23 Apr, Caldecotte.
1992: 2 on 8 Jun, Linford.
1995: 1 on 11 Aug, Willen.
1996: 3 on 23 Mar, Linford and Willen.
1996: 5 on 19 May, Little Marlow.
1998: 1 on 25 Apr, Calvert.
2002: 1 on 24 Mar, Little Marlow.
2004: 1 on 16 Apr, Willen.
2006: 1 on 10 Apr, Calvert.
2007: 4 on 6 Apr, Broughton, Aylesbury.
2008: 3 on 6 May, Dorney Lake.
2008: 1 on 26 May, Dorney Lake.
2008: 5 on 26 May, Willen.

Willen, 18 Mar 2011   Keith O'Hagen

144

2010: 1 on 21 Apr, Dorney Lake.
2010: 1 on 29 May, Dorney Lake
2011: 1 from 17 to 18 Mar, Willen.
2011: 2 on 23 Mar, College Lake.

Although an increase since the mid-1970s is a typical pattern for the rarer waders in the county there is no doubt that the increase in the British breeding population has contributed. The flock in 1983 is an exceptional record for inland Britain.

Stone-curlew
Burhinus oedicnemus

Very rare migrant; formerly a local summer visitor.

Even in Clark Kennedy's time Stone-curlews were in decline. He states that they 'used to be numerous in the vicinity of Ivinghoe and Drayton Beauchamp'. Other sites apparently still used then included Aylesbury, Buckingham and Chesham but by the time of H & J they were in 'greatly reduced numbers, breeding very locally.' They seemed to have suffered a considerable decrease around 1910 as before this date they were numerous in the Skirmett/ Turville Heath area and also bred at Fawley Park and Saunderton. In 1947 Price wrote 'regular summer visitor, breeding locally'. Since then they have been only four breeding records: in 1950 at Fingest, in 1956 at Wormsley, in 1959 again at Fingest, and again there in 1964. Between 1950 and 1967 birds were seen or heard at Saunderton, Fawley, High Wycombe, and Northend. It is unlikely that they bred at these localities.

There then followed a gap until a bird was recorded in late June and early July 1984 at a potential breeding site in the Chilterns, and a bird was seen on 23 May 1985 at Caldecotte.

There were no more records until 1996 since when there were seven. They are:

1996: 2 on 31 Mar, Fawley Bottom. One of the birds was colour-ringed.
1999: 1 on 21 Apr, Drayton Parslow.
2004: 1 from 1 to 2 May, College Lake. This bird was ringed as a chick in Berkshire in 2003.
2005: 1 on 19 Apr, Chalfont St Peter.
2006: 1 on 14 Apr, Rowsham.
2007: 1 on 22 Apr, Quainton Hills. It was ringed in the UK in 2006.
2007: 1 on 8 May, Broughton, Aylesbury.

As a bird on the north-western edge of its range it is likely that temperature is one of the limiting factors of its distribution. It may be significant that the birds disappeared from the Chilterns first in the north around Ivinghoe and lastly in the south around Fingest and Wormsley.

But the major cause of the extinction is loss of habitat. Stone-curlews are birds of dry open spaces. In Buckinghamshire they occurred typically on chalk grassland heavily grazed by sheep or rabbits. Sheep rearing has decreased considerably in the Chilterns and rabbits were decimated by myxomatosis during the 1950s. This has resulted in the grassland becoming covered in scrub and thus unsuitable for Stone-curlews. This, coupled with ploughing, has reduced the amount of unimproved chalk grassland in the county to less than 300 ha. Because of public access very little of this is suitable for Stone-curlews.

Many of British breeding birds now nest on arable land, the chicks hatching in late May before the crop is harvested.

Stone-curlews are summer migrants. They arrive in Britain in March or early April and leave in September and October. There are two remarkable ringing records involving county birds. A nestling ringed at Fingest on 12 Jun 1959 was recovered at Landes, France on 14 Oct 1961, while its sibling, ringed three days later, was shot at Guipuzcoa, Spain on 31 Oct 1959.

DMF

Little Ringed Plover
Charadrius hiaticula

Scarce summer visitor and migrant.

Gallows Bridge Farm, 17 Apr 2011   *Rod Scaife*

Little Ringed Plovers first bred in the UK at Startopsend Reservoir (Hertfordshire) in 1938. In 1948 there was a sighting of this species at Slough STW which was then in Buckinghamshire. Breeding was first recorded in the county at Marlow GPs with a nest and three eggs being found on 9th June 1949. Unfortunately this breeding attempt failed. Breeding occurred elsewhere in the county in 1953 (MTNHS). In 1976 (F & Y) described the species as 'breeding regularly in very small numbers throughout the area'. The numbers are no doubt limited by suitable breeding habitat and so the fact that more has been made available in the intervening period, at such sites as Gallows Bridge Farm, the Jubilee River and Dorney Lake, has helped somewhat and contributed to an increase in the population. With the species being regularly reported from approximately 12 sites in the past ten years, and with some sites not providing suitable conditions in some years, it seems likely that the breeding population is currently between five and ten pairs. The maps, which are a cumulation of four years, show an exaggerated picture of the actual annual distribution.

The distribution map essentially shows much of the suitable breeding habitat in the county at the present time, this typically being flooded gravel workings where exposed areas of gravel provide the preferred nesting conditions. They also breed near more mature lakes where flat stony areas exist, particularly if an island nest site is available. The preference for fresh gravelly areas can lead to pairs setting up territories in areas of active gravel workings which sometimes leading to breeding failure as work progresses. The species is however known to readily replace lost clutches, sometimes up to three times (Parrinder 1964). Breeding success may also be affected by the presence of the more dominant Ringed Plover where these occur.

Birds are usually seen in the county from the end of March (exceptionally from 10th March) with breeding territories being formed shortly after. The last records in autumn are typically the second and third weeks in September but exceptionally into early October. Small flocks can occur on passage, most often in April and May where up to 11 birds have been seen together. On leaving their breeding grounds many Little Ringed Plovers move

south through

France and down the east coast of Spain before crossing to North Africa and eventually reaching their winter quarters south of the Sahara (BWP).

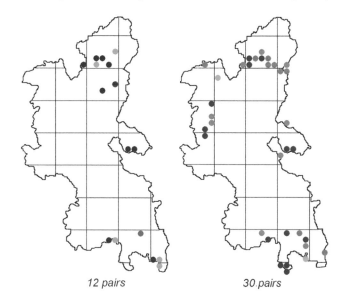

Migration dates	
Earliest:	2 Mar
Ave earliest:	21 Mar
Ave latest:	10 Sep
Latest:	15 Oct

12 pairs   30 pairs

JER

Ringed Plover
Charadrius hiaticula

Scarce breeding summer visitor and migrant.

H & J (1920) stated (using data based upon observations at the Tring Reservoirs) that the Ringed Plover was a 'regular bird of passage' with greater numbers seen in the autumn. However they do add 'used to occur not infrequently along the banks of the Thames'. Ringed Plovers remain a regular passage migrant within the county.

Startopsend Reservoir, 21 Sep 2009   *Mike Wallen*

The first breeding record for the county was in 1975 at Willen Lake. Since that time a regular breeding population has built up at various sites in the north of the county, further south at College Lake and more recently on the relatively new habitat at Dorney Lake where construction started in 1996.

Ringed Plovers breed on areas of gravel or shingle adjacent to lakes or gravel pits and a large proportion of the county population breed on nature reserves or in protected areas such as Linford GP complex, Willen Lake, Stony Stratford NR, College Lake NR and Dorney Lake. In the 1980s up to five pairs bred at College Lake on an 300 sq metres of shingle which was provided specifically for that purpose, while at Willen up to three pairs bred on an island and on exposed gravel bars. Since the turn of the century numbers have been somewhat less, with few sites reporting more than one pair breeding, and in some years there are no records of breeding at all. One other change since the first survey is that Ringed Plovers now breed in the south of the county at the newly created site at Dorney Lake, although not necessarily annually.

Birds are normally seen passing through the county between early February and late May and between late September and mid November - hence some records on the winter map. Larger flocks are normally seen in the spring with single flocks containing over ten individuals recorded in most years. The largest flock recorded was 48 at Willen Lake on 7th May 1981. Our breeding birds and their young leave their breeding sites shortly after breeding activity is finished. Inland, Ringed Plovers usually are single brooded (The Breeding Atlas) so this movement can be from mid June onwards. These birds move to coastal areas, this being supported by a colour ringing project that took place at College Lake in the summer of 1987. Four breeding Ringed Plovers were caught and colour ringed. One bird ringed on 13 May 1987 was recorded in Swansea Bay, South Wales between 28 July and 3 Oct 1987. Another bird, which was ringed on 30 June 1987, was recorded on the Taff estuary near Cardiff on 13th September 1987. At least two of the four colour ringed birds returned to College Lake in the spring of 1988 and one of the four was again seen on the Taff estuary in September 1988 (Kirby 1988). This example also demonstrates the site fidelity of this species. The only other ringing recovery was a bird ringed as a nestling at Pitstone on 21st July 1982 and controlled at Holme Pierrepoint, Nottinghamshire on 29th May 1984.

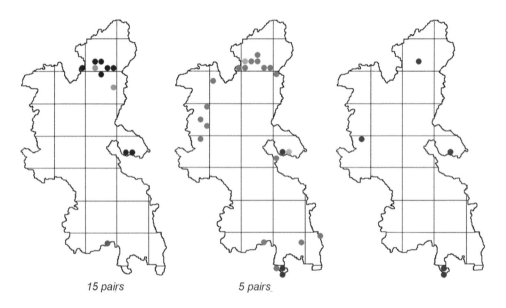

15 pairs   5 pairs

JER

Kentish Plover
Charadrius alexandrinus

Very rare vagrant. There has been one record.

1981: 1 on 13 Apr, Willen.

Dotterel
Charadrius morinellus

Very rare migrant. All records are given.

There are undated 19th century records for Aylesbury, Drayton Beauchamp, Boveney, and Beaconsfield.

The dated records are:

1857: a few shot in the spring, Burnham.
1862: adult male killed on 14 Aug, Ivinghoe.
1967: 4 on 3 May, near High Wycombe
1985: juv on 23 Sep, Newton Longville.
1993: juv on 6 Sep, Drayton Parslow.
1995: 25 on 15 May, circled low over Mursley.
1996: 1 from 10 to 11 May, Drayton Parslow.

The paucity of the records is in contrast to the situation in Hertfordshire, where it is a regular passage migrant. The last four records were found by the same acute observer.

American Golden Plover
Pluvialis dominica

Very rare vagrant. There has been one record.

1991: juvenile from 12 to 17 Nov, 21 Nov, 25 Nov, Broughton (MK).

The bird spent its time between a field of winter cereals near Broughton and Cranfield Airfield in Bedfordshire where it remained into December. It was probably the same individual that was present at various Midlands localities prior to 12th November. This is one of the few records of this North American species for an inland county (Ward 1991).

Golden Plover
Pluvialis apricaria

Locally common visitor in autumn, winter and spring.

At the turn of the century Golden Plovers were thought to be much rarer than formerly (H & R). However, they were certainly widely overlooked until the mid 1970s when Fuller & Youngman (1979) started to study the species in the Vale of Aylesbury.

The winter map shows birds range over mid and north Buckinghamshire, the Thames Valley and to the north of

Little Marlow, 25 Nov 2011   *David Ferguson*

Chalfont Common. The main concentration is in the Vale of Aylesbury where flocks of over 1,000 birds occur in most years though flocks have become more localised since the 1980s . South of the Chilterns, flocks are irregular in occurrence and are much smaller. A flock of 800 birds at Dorney Lake in Jan 2006 is exceptional.

The regular wintering grounds are on the open farmland north of the Chiltern escarpment. A survey during the 1980s showed that six tracts of farmland in the Vale of Aylesbury regularly held substantial flocks: Shabbington/Worminghall; Berryfields/ Quainton; Bishopstone/Ford; Haddenham; Marsh Gibbon; and Hulcott/Long Marston. At that time these `flock ranges' each essentially supported one flock of Golden Plovers, although sometimes the birds were distributed within the range in smaller `sub-flocks'. Recent records show that birds still occur in these areas, though in recent years RJF has been unable to find such large flocks as in earlier years and these ranges are substantially unchanged except for Berryfields which has now been partly urbanised and appears to be no longer used. Mentioned in the First Edition are regular sites near North Crawley, Hillesden/Padbury, North Marston/ Hoggeston and Edlesborough/Slapton, a statement which still holds true.

There is some evidence that since the mid 1980s global warming has resulted in Golden Plovers wintering further east with a consequent decrease in flock sizes in southern England (Gillings et al. 2006). It is difficult to estimate the Buckinghamshire winter population, but the statement in the First Edition that total numbers in the county have probably exceeded 3000 in most years probably is no longer true.

Within flock ranges certain fields are strongly favoured for winter feeding, although the exact distribution of the birds can vary considerably from year to year (Fuller 1990). The types of fields used by Golden Plovers in Buckinghamshire vary with the time of year and according to the activity of the birds. In the 1980s in autumn and spring the birds did much feeding on cultivated land but in the colder winter months they feed almost exclusively on grasslands, especially permanent pasture. All the 1980s flock ranges in the Vale of Aylesbury supported substantial tracts of permanent grassland but it is unclear whether the bird remain so strongly dependent on these. Interestingly, in the mid 1980s the Bishopstone/Ford site was largely deserted by both Golden Plovers and Lapwings, possibly because most of the favoured grass fields were converted to cereals (Fuller 1990).

Golden Plovers share their feeding fields with Lapwings and Black-headed Gulls, the latter pirating worms from both species of wader. At all times of the winter Golden Plovers roost and rest mainly on cultivated land, both on plough and short winter cereal crops.

Small flocks, perhaps passage migrants, are reported as early as August but substantial flocks do not arrive until October. However, in the 1980s some flock ranges supported very few birds until midwinter when the major influx occurred, usually in December. Numbers remained high throughout the winter unless there was hard weather. Golden Plovers are deprived of their food in prolonged periods of severe frost and/or snow cover. The birds disappear very quickly at the onset of heavy snowfall but frost has to be continuous for several days before the birds move away. Such cold weather movements may be followed by a return, often to exactly the same fields, once a thaw has set in.

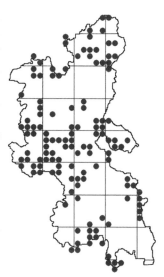

Flocks can be found as late as mid April. Many birds in spring are in full breeding plumage and these are certainly of foreign breeding origin, possibly Scandinavian, because British birds are on their breeding grounds by then. Whether these birds are the same individuals that are present in mid winter is unknown.

RJF & DF

Grey Plover
Pluvialis squatarola

Scarce migrant and very rare winter visitor.

Prior to 1974 there was only one record.

1819: 1 obtained 25 Nov, Dinton Hall.

Since 1974 there have been 110 records of 179 birds. There were 129 in the north, 28 in the middle and 22 in the south. Most were of singles but there was a flock of nine birds on 7 May 1981 at Willen. Most of the birds appear at the usual wetland sites but several have been in the company of flocks of Lapwings and Golden Plovers on farmland.

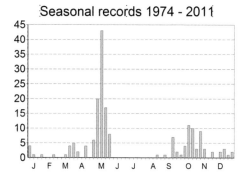

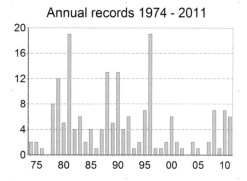

Lapwing
Vanellus vanellus

Common but decreasing resident breeder and winter visitor.

Numbers of breeding Lapwings have almost certainly decreased in Buckinghamshire during the 20th century. Unfortunately there is no detailed historical information, although H & R state that Lapwings once nested on Coombe Hill, near Wendover, a site long since deserted.

Gallows Bridge Farm, 16 Jun 2010   Mike Wallen

The maps show that breeding Lapwings have, along with many other farmland species, disappeared from the area now occupied by Milton Keynes and the far south-east of the county. On the other hand, again along with several other species, they seem to have increased in the area north of Tring.

The species is a semi-colonial breeder and several pairs will nest in one field where the habitat is favourable. Although they will nest on grass or tilled land, much of the grassland in the county is now devoid of breeding Lapwings and most probably nest on cereal fields. Autumn-sown cereal fields with well-grown crops in the early spring are, however, scarcely used by nesting Lapwings. The dense vegetation may reduce visibility for adults when incubating and is probably an unsuitable feeding habitat for the chicks. Lapwings usually select fields where the crop is low or sparse, sometimes as a result of winter flooding. By the 1980s spring-sown cereals were rare in the county but such fields presumably once provided an important nesting habitat for the species. The Lapwing is an opportunist, nesting wherever it can find suitable conditions. Consequently birds do not necessarily use the same fields each year. This is illustrated by observations of Lapwings breeding on fields near Wotton Underwood over a three year period ®. J. Fuller). In each year Lapwings nested in several of these fields; there was always a marked concentration in one, but not in the same field every year. In 1983 some 10 pairs nested in a patchy cereal crop which had much bare ground due to winter flooding. In 1984 this field supported a far better crop but few Lapwings were seen there and no nests were found. The majority were nesting in a short cereal crop nearby. In 1985 most birds moved once more, this time to a field which had recently been ploughed, where some 10 pairs nested. Not only will Lapwings use different fields in different years but they will even move their chicks away from the nest site to new fields more suitable for them to feed in (Redfern 1982). Lapwings nesting on cereals will sometimes move their chicks on to adjacent grassland soon after hatching ®. J. Fuller, H. Galbraith pers comm).

The statement in the First Edition that in most winters since the mid 1970s the Vale of Aylesbury has probably held some 20,000 Lapwings in midwinter is no longer true. There have been only three flocks of 5000+ since 1993, all at Bletchley Brick Pits. The four flocks over 3000 during the same period have also been away from their traditional agricultural areas: at Aylesbury STW, Little Marlow GP, Calvert and Woodham. Midwinter surveys undertaken between 1998 and 2007 in the Vale of Aylesbury confirmed that most of the areas occupied by large numbers in the 1970s and 80s were now nearly deserted. An exception, however, is the upper Ray headwaters near Marsh

Gibbon where substantial flocks still occur (R.J Fuller). This decline in numbers is probably part of an eastward shift in the national distribution of wintering Lapwings (Gillings *et al.* 2006) It is possible that many flocks on agricultural land escape detection due to the cessation of regular surveys.

In the 1980s the birds returned each winter to use traditional wintering grounds, often the same areas used by Golden Plovers. However, they were more widely distributed than Golden Plovers and greatly outnumbered them. Winter habitat use was very similar to that of Golden Plovers. Arable fields were frequently used for autumn feeding but in midwinter the birds depended heavily on grassland, especially permanent pasture. Roosting was mainly on plough or cereal fields with short vegetation. which have only a short crop. Lapwings do much feeding at night, even in midwinter, provided the weather is mild. At such times in the 1980s the birds spent much of the day loafing or roosting, with birds from a large area often gathering in one huge flock. Milsom (1984) has suggested that night-time feeding is most frequent around full moon periods but in Buckinghamshire large flocks of day-roosting Lapwings have been found during most stages of the lunar cycle ®. J. Fuller).

Flocks of Lapwings start to build up in June. These may include local breeders but the majority are probably immigrants from continental Europe (Imboden 1974). There are several records of birds ringed as chicks in Buckinghamshire being recovered to the south in the autumn and winter. One was found in Cornwall, six in France, two in Spain and one in Morocco, suggesting that locally bred birds often move away for the winter. Numbers in the county in winter appear to increase only gradually until the main midwinter immigrations. The timing of these influxes varies from winter to winter, presumably according to weather on the Continent and elsewhere in Britain. In two winters in the mid 1970s Fuller & Youngman (1979) reported major influxes in late December and January. In the 1980s, however, most midwinter influxes were in November or December, with the main arrival usually in early December. In mild winters numbers could remain high until birds suddenly departed in mid March. Prolonged periods of freezing weather or snow cause the birds to leave the feeding grounds. The birds appear to leave as soon as heavy

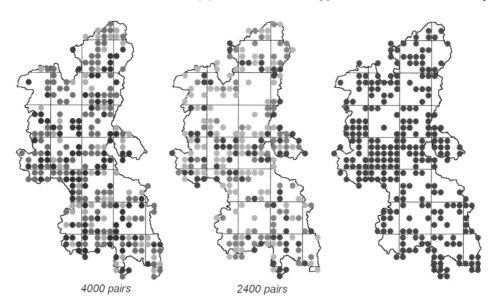

4000 pairs   2400 pairs

snow falls, usually moving off to the south or south-west. Remarkably, they often return to exactly the same fields a week or so after the thaw has set in.

Seasonal trends in numbers of Lapwings in the county differ from those of Golden Plovers in several respects. Lapwings show a marked influx in midsummer rather than in autumn, and few, if any, flocks of Lapwings stay into the spring. Where the Lapwings return to is not known for certain but recoveries of birds ringed elsewhere would suggest that N Europe and Scandinavia are likely destinations.

RJF & DMF

Knot
Calidris canutus

Scarce migrant.

Prior to 1977 there were only three records.

1911: 1 on 28 Jan, Halton (specimen now in County Museum).
1937: 3 on 1 Feb, near Olney.
1960: 1 on 18 Sep, Emberton GP.

Since 1977 there have been 64 records of 155 birds. They are shown on the graphs. 96 birds were recorded in the north of the county, 32 in the middle, and 27 in the south. Most were of singles but a flock of 29 flew from Wilstone into the county on 14 Aug 2008, and there was 20 on 21 May 1992 at Willen. There is no obvious pattern to the occurrences but there are few winter records.

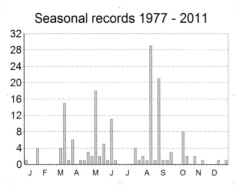

Seasonal records 1977 - 2011

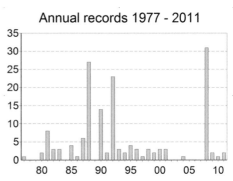

Annual records 1977 - 2011

Pectoral Sandpiper
Calidris melanotos

Very rare vagrant. All records are given.

1988: 1 intermittently between 28 Sep and 9 Oct at Dorney Common. The bird spent much of its stay at Slough Sewage Treatment Works in Berks.
1989: 1 on 1 Sep, Linford.
1995: 1 on 13 Sep, Linford.
1998: juv from 18 to 23 Oct, Little Marlow.

These are typical dates for this North American/Siberian vagrant.

Sanderling
Calidris alba

Scarce migrant.

Prior to 1978 there were only two records.

1956: 1 on 4 Feb, Bourne End
1959: 2 on 22 May, Foxcote.

Since 1978 there have been 123 records of 232 birds. They are shown on the graphs. 188 birds were recorded in the north of the

Calvert, 26 Jul 2009   *Tim Watts*

county, 12 in the middle, and 32 in the south. The majority of the records occurred in May with a distinct peak in the second week. This is similar to the situations in neighbouring counties.

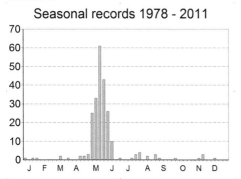

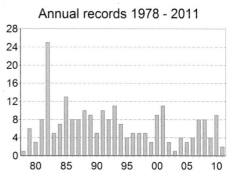

Least Sandpiper
Calidris minutilla

Very rare vagrant. There is one record.

2003: 1 on 5 and 6 Aug, Startopsend Res flew in Bucks airspace during its stay in Hertfordshire.

Little Stint
Calidris minuta

Scarce migrant.

The first record in the present county was not until 1964.

1964: 1 on 27 Dec, Foxcote.

There were no more records until 1975, but since then there have been 96 records of 244 birds. They are shown on the graphs. 187 birds were recorded in the north of the county, 29 in the middle, and 28 in the south. There is small passage in the last week of April and May, and a larger autumn passage peaking in early September. Birds have normally gone by mid-October, but one which appeared at Willen on 31 Oct 1990 remained until 16 Dec. The earliest was one at Pitstone on 18 Mar 1995. The large numbers recorded in Sep 1996 were part of a huge influx of juveniles into the UK. The largest flocks recorded were during that month: 16 birds at Willen from 25th to 27th and another of 16 at Startopsend which spent most of its time in Herts but wandered into Bucks on 23th. The decline in numbers since 1999, when only 23 birds have been seen in 13 years, is probably due to the decreased attraction of Willen for waders. Only one bird was seen at this site during this time.

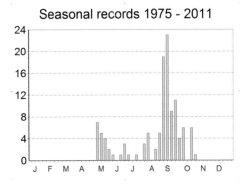

Seasonal records 1975 - 2011

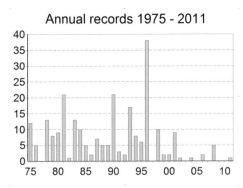

Annual records 1975 - 2011

Temminck's Stint
Calidris temminckii

Rare migrant.

The first record was not until 1980. All but one of the records have been of single birds.

1980: 1, from 12 to13 May and from 18 to 19 May, Willen. Two birds may have been involved.

Foxcote, 1 Sep 2006   *Phil Tizzard*

The first 10 records were all in late spring and all from Willen. It is possible that only one or two birds were involved. There have been a further 16 records, three at Willen, six at Linford, three at Little Marlow, two together at Dorney Lake, and singles at Hillesden and Foxcote. The demise of Willen as a stopover site for small waders is apparent.

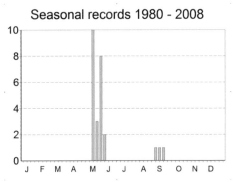

Seasonal records 1980 - 2008

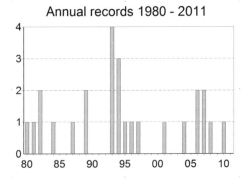

Annual records 1980 - 2011

Curlew Sandpiper
Calidris ferruginea

Scarce migrant.

There are only two records prior to 1975.

1949: 2 on 2 Mar, Iver SF.
1959: 1 from 30 Aug to1 Sep, Hartigan's Pit, near Broughton (MK).

There were no more records until 1975, but since then there have been records of 119 birds. They are shown on the histograms. 96 birds were recorded in the north of the county, 11 in the middle and 12 in the south. Very few are seen in the spring, but there is a larger autumn passage with a distinct peak in mid-September. The largest flocks recorded are one of eight birds on 28 Aug 1978, and one of seven birds on 9 Sep 1985, both at Willen. There has only been one bird recorded since 2000, a summer adult at Linford on 30 Apr 2004. As with Little Stint, this decline is largely due to the demise of Willen as an attraction for small waders.

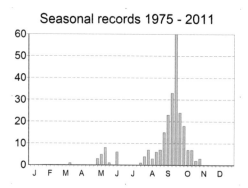
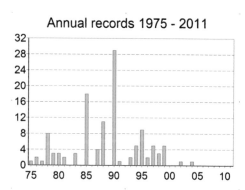

Purple Sandpiper
Calidris maritima

Very rare vagrant. All records are given.

1976: 1 on 27 Oct, Hambleden.
1977: 1 from 11 to 22 Nov, Willen, with 2 on 14 Nov.
1997: first-winter on 18 Oct, Thorney.

Dunlin
Calidris alpina

Regular passage migrant.

College Lake, 17 May 2011   *Rod Scaife*

In 1920 H & J stated that Dunlin were a 'not uncommon passage migrant and occasional winter visitor' with the largest flock reported as 14. This situation did not change too much with F & Y in 1976 describing Dunlin as 'Recorded on passage in small numbers in most years. Has regularly been recorded during the winter in recent years'.

Despite this it is clear that during the early part of the 20th century Dunlins were much more infrequently recorded in the county than at the present time. Even in the 1960s and early 1970s the total number recorded in any one year was often no greater than 10 birds. Since the mid 1970s records of single flocks of this size, plus many other records, are received in most years.

Dunlin are seen throughout the county, primarily at lakes and gravel pits which have suitable muddy or sandy scrapes, but are also reported from flooded farmland particularly in the winter months and are often with other wading birds such as Golden Plover and Lapwing.

Timing of migration through the county is confused somewhat by movements of wintering and non-breeding summering birds. Spring migration begins in March continuing until early June with one to three birds usually reported from a number of sites. Flocks in excess of 10 are not uncommon during spring passage. Autumn migration starts during July continuing until October, but with birds more widely reported during July and August. Larger flocks are however most likely to be seen between October and December, these probably being winter movements within the UK rather than migrant birds. The largest flock ever recorded in the county was at Quarrendon in November 1991 when approximately 70 were reported in a large mixed flock of wading birds in a waterlogged field. A flock of over 60 at Calvert in December 2004 runs this fairly close.

The extended periods of migration through the county are probably due to a combination of Dunlins from different races and countries being involved as well as winter movements. These are likely to be from the races *arctica*, which breeds in NE Greenland and is believed to winter in NW Africa, and *schinzii*, which breeds in SE Greenland, Iceland, S Scandinavia and Great Britain, many of which spend the winter in NW Africa. To make matters even more complicated, *schinzii* birds from different breeding areas pass through Great Britain at different times, as do adults and juveniles. Icelandic birds are the most numerous in the spring (BWP). British birds are usually the first to pass through the county in the spring, this being from mid March. Other birds of the *schinzii* race are seen two to three weeks later and birds of the race *arctica* follow in late May. In the autumn failed breeding birds are likely to be seen first with birds from Great Britain and Finland appearing any time after mid June. Birds from Greenland (both races) are usually seen between July and September, while juveniles from the Finnish populations may still be passing through in October (BWP).

Winter movements do apparently follow a pattern with birds moving westwards, away from the east coast in October and November (after moulting) with the return journey being made in February and April, before migration to the breeding grounds begins (The Winter Atlas). This type of movement could well explain the regular winter records of relatively large flocks. It is likely that some or all of the winter records involve individuals of the northern form of the race *alpina* as birds of this race regularly winter in Britain. Three ringed birds of this race were recorded in the West Midlands in February 1976.

There are no ringing recovery data for this species in the county nor is there any information on the race or origins of birds seen in the county. Without more effort in identifying races this situation will not change. We will therefore have to continue to speculate as to the origins and destinations of these long distance travelers.

JER

Ruff
Philomachus pugnax

Scarce migrant and rare winter visitor.

The first record was:

1774: 1 shot 8 Aug, Dinton Hall.

Clark Kennedy records one killed near Chesham in the 1860s, but H & J give no records at all for Buckinghamshire. In fact there was only one more record within the present county boundary (a pair at Weston

Hillesden, 18 Apr 2010   Tim Watts

Turville Res on 16 Sep 1935) until 1957 when four were seen at Hartigan's Pit near Broughton. MK on 29 Apr. Between 1958 and 1974 there were 32 records of 63 birds. In common with many of the Buckinghamshire migrant waders, Ruffs became much more frequent between the mid-1970s, when the south basin of Willen Lake was filled in 1975 and of the north basin in 1978. In 1975 22 birds were recorded, but the following year saw a maximum of 18 birds at Willen on 18 Sep in addition to 13 birds at other sites. 1981 saw the largest flock: 43 birds at Willen on 16 Sep, but two years later the autumn maximum was down to just six birds. This halcyon period lasted until 1999 when the area became urbanised and the water level was kept high. Since then, along with many other migrant waders, numbers at this site have dropped dramatically. The graphs show the records since

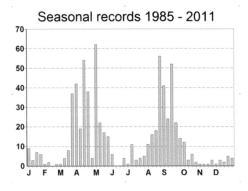

Seasonal records 1985 - 2011

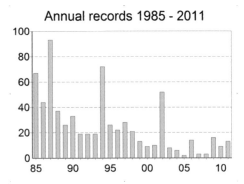

Annual records 1985 - 2011

1984 when 665 birds were recorded in the county. 549 were recorded in the north, 66 in the middle and 50 in the south. The graphs show distinct peaks in spring and autumn. The occasional winter records are a relatively recent phenomenon. The first winter record was of a bird seen at Bletchley SF on 24 Dec 1964, but the next was not until 31 Jan 1976 when a bird was recorded at Wendover SF.

Jack Snipe
Lymnocryptes minimus

Uncommon winter visitor.

The first record within the present county boundary is:

1936: 2 shot on 5 Feb, Olney.

In the 1950s eight birds were recorded, in the 1960s 89 birds, in the 1970s c160 birds, and from 1980 145 birds.

Broughton Trout Pools, 10 Feb 2008   *Mike Wallen*

The maximum annual total since 1980 is 19 birds in 1989, and the minimum only one bird in 1984. Jack Snipes are unobtrusive birds and are certainly under-recorded, although their wetland habitat is often well-watched. The increase during the first three decades since 1950 may be accounted for by increased observer activity, but since 1980 there appears to have been a genuine decrease. This is parallelled by a similar decrease which has been noted in neighbouring Oxfordshire (Brucker et al. 1992).

Typical sites have been Weston Turville Res, Broughton (Aylesbury), Chesham cress beds, Bletchley SF, Aylesbury SF, and Stoke Common as well as the normal wader sites. Most records have been of single birds, but occasionally up to six birds have been recorded. There is one exceptional record of 20 birds at Bletchley SF on 12 Feb 1975. Jack Snipes normally arrive in October and leave in March. The earliest arrival date is 5 Sep 1982 at Willen and the latest 21 Apr 1996 at Fulmer.

Common Snipe
Gallinago gallinago

Common migrant and winter visitor;
irregular breeder.

The Snipe was considered by H & R to be `common in suitable places' and H & J said that it had `undoubtedly increased considerably in numbers in the Thames Valley'. The number of breeding birds has declined considerably in recent years, most probably because of loss of habitat. As Mead & Smith (1982) observed for Hertfordshire, the Snipe is now a bird which observers expect to see in winter but not in summer.

Birds are usually found in water meadows and along the marshy edges of streams and rivers. Suitable breeding habitat in Buckinghamshire has been reduced significantly due to field drainage over the last 30-40 years. In winter birds can be found in flooded fields, and muddy gateways seem to be especially favoured.

During the fieldwork for the first county breeding survey, breeding was proved in only one tetrad although suspected in several others. The majority of these were adjacent to the River Thames, with none in the valley of the River Thame where they used to breed. In the period between the two atlas surveys the only signs of breeding were birds displaying at Weston Turville on 20 Mar 1993, Fulmer on 4 Apr

Calvert, 7 Feb 2009   Mike Wallen

1995, Shardeloes on 10 Apr 1997 and Woodham on 24 Apr 2004. During the second atlas there was a pair at Calvert.

Spring passage appears to be most pronounced in March and April with very few records in early May, although birds in March could still be overwintering birds. There were 200 at Olney on 20 Mar 1982 and 450 at Marsh Gibbon on 16 Mar 1975.

There are very few records from May to early July. The main autumn passage starts in late July and August with concentrations on flooded meadows and reservoirs, for example 42 on Aylesbury SF on 31 Aug 1980 and 60 at Willen on 7 Sept 1980. Numbers build up in the early part of the winter period and fluctuate according to weather conditions. Snipe tend to be found in the same sites as winter flocks of Lapwings and Golden Plovers at Marsh Gibbon, Bishopstone, Shabbington and Berryfields. Also in common with those species, Snipe move off the meadows during prolonged periods of cold weather when the ground is frozen. Maxima of 100 have been reported from several localities with over 700 at Marsh Gibbon on 24 Nov 1974, over 200 at Aylesbury SF on 25 Jan 1981, 150 at Berryfields on 20 Feb 1982, 100 at Willen on 26 Jan 1984, 100 at Caldecotte Lake on 10 Nov 1984, 200 at Aylesbury STW on 9 Jan 1999, 100 at College Lake in Jan 2003, and

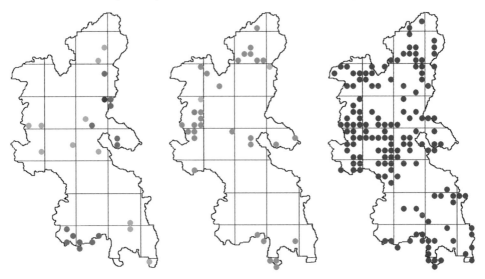

102 at Gallows Bridge on 18 Feb 2009. Some of these birds are certainly immigrants from farther afield, as there are reports of birds ringed in Buckinghamshire being recovered in the Netherlands, France and near Moscow.

CEY

Great Snipe
Gallinago media

Very rare vagrant. There is one record.

1962: 1 from 23 Dec to 17 Feb 1963, Alderbourne and Rush Green watercress beds, Iver.

This bird made the longest recorded stay of any Great Snipe in Britain. A record at Marlow in 1871 is reported rather tentatively by H & J, and should probably be disregarded.

Woodcock
Scolopax rusticola

Very local resident and local winter visitor.

It is evident from the early accounts that Woodcock did not breed in the county until after the First World War. Clark Kennedy described its status as 'regular winter visitor, does not often remain to breed' while H & J did not give any breeding records at all, and wrote that it was 'nowhere very common' in winter. Price stated 'resident in small numbers, a few pairs breeding'. This equates with the national trend which suggests an increase during the late 19th and early 20th centuries until it was breeding in almost all English counties by 1930. The first recorded nest in the county was one found at Whaddon on 6 April 1926.

The first atlas map, based on data obtained in the early 1980s, shows a concentration of

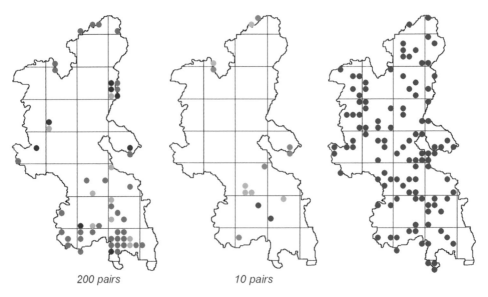

200 pairs   10 pairs

breeding records in the south Chilterns, the Brickhills, and along the northern boundary. Based on admittedly very sketchy CBC data, a population of about 200 territories was arrived at. The second atlas breeding map shows only 11 occupied tetrads, six with probable breeding but none with confirmed breeding. There is, as yet, no convincing explanation for this decline, but it may be significant that several of the former breeding sites, Ashridge, Black Park, Burnham Beeches and Stoke Common have become increasingly popular with dog walkers, so that there is a greater risk of disturbance to nesting birds.

The optimum habitat for the birds is dry deciduous woodland with damp areas for feeding. It is possible that climate change has led to a drying out of this habitat with a detrimental effect to Woodcock populations. It must be noted that, although Woodcock are not difficult to locate when they are roding, they are rarely seen at other times and are no doubt under-recorded.

Woodcock are more widely scattered in winter, and are found in small numbers at places where they do not breed. In hard weather they may even be found in large gardens. The birds arrive in October and leave in March and may well include birds from N Europe. They tend to be found at sites that are well watched such as Newport Pagnell GPs, Willen, and Weston Turville. The Chiltern woods are rather avoided by birdwatchers during the winter and it is likely that many wintering Woodcock are undetected. During a shoot at The Lee on 1 Jan 1979, 20 birds were seen, which may give an indication of its true numbers in some Chiltern woods in winter. 30+ leaving Little Linford Wood for nearby fields at dusk 18 Jan 1996 and 47 seen on a pheasant shoot in N Bucks during Jan 2008 also give an idea of the true status of this elusive bird. A flock of 18 flying NW near Drayton Parslow on 21 Nov 1985 is also noteworthy. Remarkably, this species is a regular prey item of the wintering Peregrines in Aylesbury.

DMF

Black-tailed Godwit
Limosa limosa

Scarce migrant.

Prior to 1974 there were five records.

1941: 2 from 28 to 29 Aug, near Olney.
1955: 1 on 26 Apr, Little Marlow.
1957: 1 on 23 Apr, Hartigan's Pit, Broughton (MK).
1961: 1 on 28 Oct, Bletchley SF.
1962: 1 on 11 and 18 Mar, Newport Pagnell GP.

Calvert, 21 Jul 2005   *Tim Watts*

Since 1974 there have been 232 records of 642 birds. 331 birds were recorded in the north of the county, 187 in the middle, and 124 in the south. Birds have been recorded in all months but there is a small spring passage and a much larger passage in late summer.

Unlike most migrant waders on the county list, the number of sightings of Black-tailed Godwits has increased. The appearance of 29 at Linford on 25 May 1992, then a record flock, was the vanguard of more regular sightings which peaked with 49 at College Lake on 4 Jul 2004. They were all of the Iceland race *L.l.islandica* which perhaps hints at the origin of most of our birds.

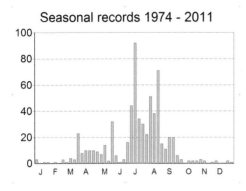

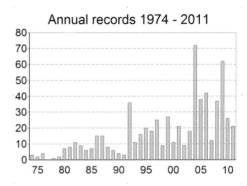

Bar-tailed Godwit
Limosa lapponica

Scarce migrant.

Prior to 1974 there were five records.

1846: 2 early May, Slapton.
1895: 1 shot in winter, Ivinghoe.
1947: 1 on 3 May, Fulmer.
1960: 1 on 4 May, Newport Pagnell GP.
1969: 1 on 12 Jan, Calvert.

College Lake, 5 May 2007   *Mike Wallen*

Since 1974 there have been 93 records of 688 birds. 378 birds were recorded in the north of the county, 225 in the middle, and 85 in the south. Compared to Black-tailed Godwit, Bar-tailed Godwit records are fewer but contain a higher proportion of large flocks. Flock size reached a maximum on 29 Apr 2007 when 80 flew over Linford. Exactly three years later, on 29 Apr 2010, 69 birds were counted passing over College Lake, 28 over Calvert and 4 over Little Marlow. On the following day, 27 were recorded at Calvert and a further 15 over Lee Common. These unprecedented numbers were part of a huge passage over E England which saw flocks of over 1000 arriving on the south coast. Prior to this, the largest flocks were 25 on 30 Apr 1978 flying over Willen, 23 flying NE over Stoke Common on 21 Apr 2003 and 14 on 16 Apr 1988 flying over Marlow GPs.

The bizarre record of a bird landing on a front lawn in Gerrards Cross on 3 Dec 2010 could perhaps be explained by the bad weather at the time.

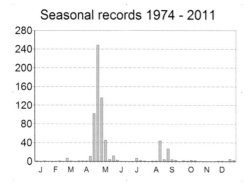

Seasonal records 1974 - 2011

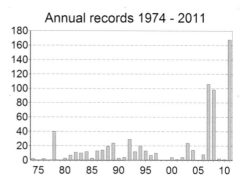

Annual records 1974 - 2011

Whimbrel
Numenius phaeopus

Scarce migrant.

Prior to 1975 there were four records.

1894: 2 shot mid-May, Ouse Valley, NE Buckinghamshire.
1941: 8 on 10 Aug flew over the county near Thame.
1960: 2 on 12 Aug, Newport Pagnell GP.
1961: 1 on 5 Sep, Marlow.

Since 1975 there have been records of about 958 birds. 400 birds were recorded

Rowsham, 24 Apr 2009   *Mike Wallen*

in the north of the county, 307 in the middle, and 251 in the south. Most of the records were of birds flying over. The largest flocks recorded are 77 flying over Little Marlow on 1 May 2000, 28 over Broughton, Aylesbury on 28 May 2004, and 22 over Marlow and Marlow Bottom on 5 Aug 2009. Apart from 2000, annual numbers have oscillated consistently around an average of 24 birds.

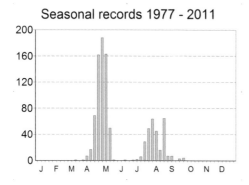

Seasonal records 1977 - 2011

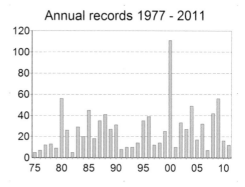

Annual records 1977 - 2011

Curlew
Numenius arquata

Local summer visitor and uncommon migrant.

Gallows Bridge Farm, 11 Apr 2011　　*John Sheppard*

The Curlew appears not to have bred in the county in the early part of this century, for H & R regarded the bird solely as a passage migrant. The first documented breeding was in 1946 at Kingsey. A survey of the main river valleys in 1982 found 26 pairs (Smith & Stone 1984) but this certainly overlooked some birds breeding away from the larger streams and rivers. The present population is probably less than 50 pairs.

The fortunes of the Curlew, like the Lapwing and Redshank, are closely linked to the fortunes of farming. The species undoubtedly benefits from traditional methods of managing grass. It may be no coincidence that the expansion of the species into lowland habitats during this century, which occurred throughout the country (the Breeding Atlas), was in a period of economic depression when much farmland was run down. Particularly in the 1970s, there was intensification of drainage and grassland management throughout the county. It is unclear what effect this has had on the breeding population but certain sites regularly occupied in the 1960s and 1970s no longer appear to hold birds.

The First Edition stated that most of the county's breeding Curlews were along the Thame valley between Worminghall and Cuddington, and in the watershed region between the Ray and Thame around Dorton and Wotton Underwood. This is no longer true. Although the majority of the county's breeding Curlews are in the middle of the county, numbers appear to have decreased in the east and increased in the west. The recently developed Gallows Bridge Farm reserve and the surrounding area in the upper catchment of the Ray between Ludgershall and Marsh Gibbon holds several pairs.

All the strongholds of the Curlew in Buckinghamshire are areas with substantial areas of permanent grassland. The adult birds feed and nest in grassland, often returning to the same fields year after year. Many of these traditional sites lie in valley bottoms which flood in winter. However, unlike Common Snipe and Redshank, the Curlew does not seem to require very damp conditions for breeding. The preferred fields usually have tussocky or fairly rank vegetation. Most are cut for hay and many show ridge and furrow. Heavily improved grassland, short-cropped grassland and silage crops are generally avoided. There are also no reports of any nesting attempts in cereal crops, although Curlew chicks occasionally move into such fields. Another apparent factor relating to nesting fields is the presence (or lack of) livestock. At Gallows Bridge, the surrounding farmland is quite heavily grazed and this may be preventing them using some fields that might otherwise be viable.

Breeding Curlews are usually located by their bubbling song, performed in a display flight over the territory. Despite this far-carrying song, the Curlew can be surprisingly inconspicuous (Fuller 1981). Many of the possible and probable records on the map may have been nesting birds. When incubating, the bird often leaves the nest when the approaching observer is still some distance away. The chicks are extremely difficult to observe because they are usually hidden in long vegetation.

Most Curlews arrive on their Buckinghamshire breeding grounds in early or mid March but some may appear in late February. The birds have left many of the breeding fields by mid July but are sometimes seen along the River Thame meadows into August. Ringing recoveries suggest that the Curlews winter on the coasts of SW Britain or possibly of France or Iberia (Bainbridge & Minton 1978). The bird is a fairly regular passage migrant and is occasionally recorded in winter, but it is most unlikely that any overwinter in the county.

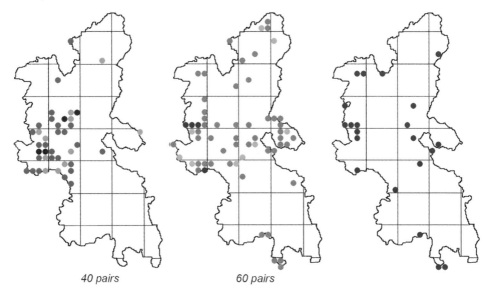

40 pairs   60 pairs

RJF & DMF

Spotted Sandpiper
Actitis macularius

Very rare vagrant. There is one record.

2011: adult on 12 May at Caldecotte.

Caldecotte, 12 May 2011   Keith O'Hagen

Common Sandpiper
Actitis hypoleucos

Common migrant and rare winter visitor. Has bred.

H & J reported nesting near the River Chess at Calne and possibly along the River Thames, and a nest was found along the River Ouzel near Leighton Buzzard in 1929 by A. G. L. Sladen (OOS report). There has been no evidence of breeding in recent years, although birds are occasionally reported during the summer

Willen Lake, 19 Sep 2009   *Keith O'Hagen*

months. Most recently two were seen on the Thames near Medmenham during June 1977 but they might have been late spring or early autumn passage birds.

During the breeding season the Common Sandpiper primarily inhabits upland streams, lakes and other watercourses. On passage it occurs regularly at reservoirs and gravel pits, and also along the banks of rivers and streams. In Buckinghamshire there are regular records along the Thames. The new lakes in the Milton Keynes area at Willen and Caldecotte have attracted small numbers in all recent years, while Linford GPs, Little Marlow, Foxcote , Calvert and Dorney Lakes have a regular passage.

According to H & J the spring passage used to last from mid April to the third week of May, the same as in recent years, with only a few birds earlier or later. There are usually

between two and 10 birds at most sites with maxima reported of 13 at Marlow on 13 May 2000, 14 at Foxcote on 23 May 1977 and 15 there on 17 May 1980.

Only a few birds have been seen in June. The return migration starts in early July with the main passage from late July to early September and peak numbers occurring in August. The autumn passage is usually heavier than that in spring, some sites regularly holding between eight and 10 birds. The largest numbers were 30 at Willen on 9 Aug 1981.

Some birds remain into the winter, and one overwintered at Linford/Haversham in three consecutive years 1981/82 to 1983/84. Other sites that have held wintering birds include Willen, Tilehouse GP, Jubilee River and College Lake.

A bird ringed at Marlow in May 1952 was recovered at Eton in April 1954 suggesting a regular passage of the same birds.

CEY

Green Sandpiper
Tringa ochropus

Fairly common migrant and uncommon winter visitor.

There appears to have been little change in numbers of birds on passage since H & J's time, but there has probably been an increase in the number of sites where wintering birds occur. H & J list only very few overwintering birds.

Green Sandpipers are found on the edges of quite small ponds, lakes, ditches and streams. They also occur on the banks of gravel pits, reservoirs and especially watercress beds which appear to be an ideal habitat.

Gallows Bridge Farm, 25 Jun 2010   *Mike Wallen*

There are some records in most years for all months, but the main spring migration is in April and continues with a few records in early May. There are virtually none in late May or early June. Numbers at most sites are usually only one or two; three at Stony Stratford on 19 Apr 1982 and five at Caldecotte reservoir on 27 Mar 1983 are exceptions.

The return passage starts in late June and is most evident in July and August, with occasional concentrations in September and October. Maxima recorded are 11 at Willen in Aug 2007, 11 at Bletchley SF on 8 Sep 1974 and nine at Newton Longville on 9 Aug 1980.

Birds have been widely reported over the winter period from several sites and most years there are one or two at Chesham, Foxcote, Pitstone, Willen, Latimer Park, Westcott, Gallows Bridge, Dorney, and Linford GPs. Winter concentrations of four at Latimer Park on 7 Dec 1975, and three at Ilmer on 20 Nov 1984 and at South Iver SF on 6 Dec 1984 were unusual.

CEY

Spotted Redshank
Tringa erythropus

Scarce migrant.

Prior to 1974 there were four records.

1960: 2 on 21 Aug, Emberton GP.
1961: 3 on 29 Aug, Emberton GP.
1973: 3 on 6 Sep, Linford GP.
1973: 5 on 16 Sep, Calvert.

Calvert Landfill, 10 Apr 2011   *Tim Watts*

Since 1974 there have been 67 records of 194 birds. 161 birds were recorded in the north of the county, 24 in the middle, and nine in the south. There is a small spring passage peaking at the end of April and a much larger autumn passage peaking at the end of August. The largest flock recorded is 13 juveniles on 23 Aug 1990 at Willen. As with many of the county's migrant waders, numbers have fallen since the 1990s.

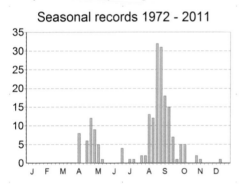

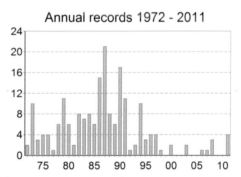

Greenshank
Tringa nebularia

Uncommon migrant and very rare winter visitor.

Clark Kennedy described the status of the Greenshank as 'uncommon', but by 1947 Price was writing 'fairly frequent on migration'. It is now one of the more regularly recorded passage waders in the county.
    It is likely that, in common with other migrant waders, numbers of Greenshanks

Calvert, 27 Apr 2006   *Tim Watts*

have increased since the Second World War with the increase in the area of suitable mud caused by the creation of gravel pits, flood balancing lakes and nature reserves.
    There is an annual but small spring passage and a larger autumn migration which contains a high proportion of birds of the year. Number vary between four and 18 in the spring and between seven and 56 in the autumn. The size of the passage is largely

dependent upon the amount of exposed mud in the county. In the autumn of 2006, for instance, the water level at Foxcote was unusually low and up to 10 Greenshanks were present. The dominance of the lakes in the north of the county for Greenshanks has diminished in recent years while College Lake and Dorney Lake become more important. Nevertheless the largest flock recorded is still 11 at Willen on 6 Aug 1976. Spring migration is between April and June with a peak in May. Autumn migration is from July to October with a peak in mid-August.

From 1974 to 1976 a bird wintered on the River Chess between Latimer and Chenies. There have been other out of season records: one on 24 Nov 2002 at Bletchley Brick Pits and one on 28 Feb 2006 at Broughton, Aylesbury.

DMF

Lesser Yellowlegs
Tringa flavipes

Very rare vagrant. There has been one record.

1977: 1 from 15 Oct to 5 Nov, Denham.

This record is rather late in the year for this North American vagrant.

Wood Sandpiper
Tringa glareola

Scarce migrant.

Calvert Landfill, 25 July 2010   Tim Watts

There were only two records prior to 1974.

1965: 2 on 27 Aug, Shardeloes.
1971: 1 on 12 Sep, Bletchley SF.

Since 1974 there have been 97 records of 130 birds. 91 birds were recorded in the north of the county, 24 in the middle, and 15 in the south. Most of the records were of single birds, but five were seen at Linford on 24 Aug 1996. The bulk of the spring passage takes place during May and the majority of the autumn passage between mid-July and mid-August.

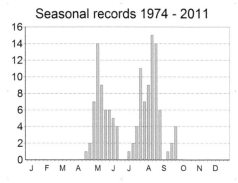

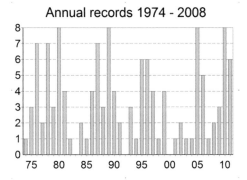

171

Redshank
Tringa totanus

Local summer visitor and uncommon migrant and winter visitor.

Hillesden, 27 Mar 2010   *Tim Watts*

Clark Kennedy described the status of Redshanks as 'uncertain visitants', but H & J wrote 'breeds in small numbers', a remark repeated by Price. This is consistent with the national trend which was of a steady expansion from the east of the country beginning around 1865 until 1940 when the population seems to have stabilised. Price's comment of 1947 still holds although a considerable change in the habitats used by breeding Redshanks has taken place.

Up to the end of the 1960s most of the Buckinghamshire Redshanks bred in damp meadows. Typical localities included Marlow Low Grounds (up to seven pairs), meadows near Newport Pagnell (up to nine pairs), Little Missenden, and Kingsey. During the 1960s drainage became widespread, which resulted in a considerable diminution of the habitat. For instance, the field near Newport Pagnell was drained in 1969 and since then no Redshanks have bred at this locality. A survey of breeding waders in wet meadows was carried out in 1982. A total of 40 sites covering approximately 5500 hectares were surveyed. Three pairs of Redshanks were found, one of which was in a quarry. The other two were probably unsuccessful.

However, there does not seem to have been a reduction in the population. The creation of gravel-pits has provided a suitable substitute for the more natural meadows. Locations such as Willen Lake, Linford GPs and College Lake now hold several pairs each of Redshanks. The total population may be around 20 pairs, which is probably a similar figure to the population in the first half of the century.

Birds arrive at the breeding sites at the end of February or in early March and leave in July. Peak numbers occur at the beginning of the season with the largest recorded number at this time being 35 at Willen on 3 Apr 1987. Outside the breeding season numbers are very small. The autumn passage rarely reaches double figures and occasionally no birds are recorded at all. A flock of c50 flying over Weston Turville Res on 16 Sep 1973 was exceptional. A small number of birds are recorded during most winters although stays of longer than a few days are unusual.

There have been three ringing records of birds moving outside the county. A bird ringed at Newport Pagnell on 15 May 1965 was recovered at Abberton, Essex on 30 Jun 1965; another bird ringed on the same day was recovered at Gironde, France on 29 Aug 1965; and a bird ringed at Weybridge, Surrey on 16 Jul 1934 was recovered at Dorney on 14 Feb 1937.

172

20 pairs   20 pairs

DMF

Turnstone
Arenaria interpres

Scarce migrant.

There was only one record prior to 1974.

1959: 4 on 22 May, Foxcote.

Since 1974 there have been 108 records of 291 birds. 219 birds were recorded in the north of the county, 33 in the middle, and 19 in the south. Unusually for a scarce migrant wader only 60% of the records were of single birds. Small flocks are quite

Pitstone, 2 May 2004   Dave Bilcock

frequent but there is only one double-figure flock, 15 during heavy rain on 27 May 2007 at Dorney Lake.

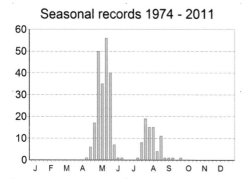

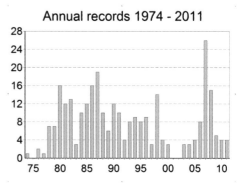

Wilson's Phalarope
Phalaropus tricolor

Very rare vagrant. All records are given.

2006: male from 27 to 30 May, Hillesden (Tunnicliffe, 2008).
2007: adult, probably a female, from 24 to 26 Aug, Willen. This bird was presumed to
    have earlier visited Durham and North Yorks.

The 2006 bird was discovered on a group of scrapes newly created by the landowner
which has subsequently proved to be a great attraction to both migrant and resident
waders.

Red-necked Phalarope
Phalaropus lobatus

Very rare vagrant. All records are given.

1978: female from 8 to 9 Jul, Willen.
1989: female on 1 and 3 Jun, Willen.
1992: juvenile on 19 Sep, Willen.
1995: female on 8 Jun, Willen.
2002: female on 23 May, College Lake.
2005: juvenile from 26 to 27 Oct, Calvert.

Calvert, 27 Oct 2005   Tim Watts

Grey Phalarope
Phalaropus fulicarius

Rare vagrant. All records are given.

1866: 1 on 19 Sep, Halton.
1928: 1 found dead on 27 Oct, Dancers
    End.
1935: 1 on 16 Sep, Weston Turville Res.
1952: 1 found dead on 30 Oct, High
    Wycombe.
1985: juvenile on 8 Sep, Willen.

Weston Turville Res, 4 Sep 2008   David Ferguson

1987: 1 on 16 Oct, Weston Turville Res.
1987: 1 on 16 Oct, then 18th-19th, Willen.
1998: 1 on 7 Jan, Linford.
2008: ad & juv on 3rd Sep with juv remaining on 4th, Weston Turville Res.
2011: 1 on 8 Sep, Calvert.

The 1987 records occurred after the great storm of 15 Oct 1987 when many Grey
Phalaropes were blown inland into southern England from the Bay of Biscay.

Pomarine Skua
Stercorarius pomarinus

Very rare vagrant.

There is one undated record for Crendon in Clark Kennedy. The dated records are:

1859: 1 shot Nov or Dec, Chesham.
1982: immature from 13 to 15 Nov, Willen.
1985: adult on 11 Nov, Caldecotte.
1994: 1 on 5 Nov, Campbell Park, Milton Keynes.

Arctic Skua
Stercorarius parasiticus

Very rare vagrant. There have been two records.

1983: dark-phase adult on 28 Aug, Calvert.
1985: dark-phase adult on 23 Aug, Marsworth.

Long-tailed Skua
Stercorarius longicaudus

Very rare vagrant. There has been one record.

1982: immature from 12 to 17 Oct, Little Chalfont feeding in a freshly-ploughed field.

Great Skua
Stercorarius skua

Very rare vagrant. There have been four records.

1983: 1 on 3 Sep, flew SW into Bucks from Wilstone Res.
1987: 1 on 25 Aug, Willen.
1995: 1 on 1 Jan, Little Marlow.
1998: adult on 27 Sep, Foxcote.

Skua species
Stercorarius spp

1936: 2 on 20 Oct, Olney (a day after gales).
1990: 6 on 17 Aug, flew W into Buckinghamshire from Wilstone Res. They were either Arctic or Long-tailed Skuas.
2000: 1 on 3 Nov, Drayton Parslow. The bird was thought not to be a Great Skua.

Gulls

There are a number of generalisations which can be made about the five commonest species of gull, and these are made here so as to avoid unnecessary repetition in the individual accounts. Least common is the Great Black-backed Gull, followed in ascending order of abundance by Herring, Lesser Black-backed, Common, and Black-headed. All have increased greatly in the UK during the second half of this century, although the trend can be traced back to the 1920s at least. While conditions in Buckinghamshire have little significance for increased breeding success, many more birds pass through the county than formerly, and wintering inland has clearly become a successful strategy for surviving the harsher months for an increasing number. Key elements are the availability of food at rubbish tips and safe roosting sites on the larger stretches of open water. Human refuse disposal has recently become more concentrated on fewer and larger tips or infill sites, the size of which allows birds to feed undisturbed for longer periods. Such sites are commonly based on complexes of disused excavations, with other pits nearby containing open water convenient for bathing and drinking. Gatherings at these locations are often vast, with numbers sometimes reaching five figures. Currently the largest sites in the county are at Hedgerley and between Bletchley and Newton Longville. By their very nature such sites are temporary, but while smaller ones may only be used for a couple of years, the largest may be used for several decades. The level and nature of disposal activity will determine a site's attractiveness to gulls.

Safe roosting sites are of prime importance. Flight lines of at least 25 km are easily identifiable and many birds must travel much further. The preferred roost sites are the largest available sheets of water, several of which are of fairly recent origin. Willen and Calvert are almost always in use from September to April. Caldecotte and Spade Oak are frequently used. Foxcote sometimes has a sizeable roost, but generally holds only a few birds, as does Linford. At the smaller sites there may be substantial gatherings which would appear to be roosts, only for the great majority to leave very late in the day to join a larger roost elsewhere. This behaviour has also been noted occasionally at more established sites and is most obvious in the three larger species. County boundaries are no barrier to any kind of roosting behaviour: birds which feed on the southern fringes of the county can be seen moving off towards the large London reservoirs, whereas Brogborough and Stewartby in the west of Bedfordshire and the Tring reservoirs in Hertfordshire attract birds from the east of the county.

Birds are by no means faithful to one site. Roosts may halve, double or treble from one evening to the next for no obvious reason. Very distinctively-plumaged or colour marked individuals and well described examples of rarer species have been noted at two or even three sites in quick succession. Other apparently suitable sites, such as Weston Turville Reservoir, are hardly used at all, and there is no really satisfactory explanation for this.

While regular watching of roosts has increased considerably in recent years, and some rarer species have been found with greater frequency, much potentially useful information is still not being collected. Gulls are almost totally ignored by most observers, and the published efforts of the rest are themselves meagre. Contempt born of familiarity may be a partial explanation of this situation. Another factor is that identification of the large species in some immature plumages is far from straightforward, especially in the gathering winter gloom. This not only deters some observers, but may also render some records liable to suspicion. The accounts which follow reveal the gaps in our knowledge. A considerable increase in records of all kinds is necessary. In particular, systematic roost counts, by species and by age, are vital if real progress is to be made.

AVH

Kittiwake
Rissa tridactyla

Scarce migrant.

Caldecotte, 24 Apr 2006   *Matt Slaymaker*

H & R document the first record of Kittiwake as one killed at Dinton Hall on 11 Jan 1830. The 20th Century has seen a massive population increase nationally (Coulson 1963), and the recent pattern of records for Buckinghamshire is an interesting one. The dramatic peaks on both the histograms are entirely the product of 1987and 1994. The pre-1987 trends should be examined separately; they are necessarily based on few records and should therefore be treated with some caution. An increase in January records may be due in part to the greater popularity among observers of seeking the scarcer species of gulls in roosts. A more convincing peak in April and May probably represents stragglers from a genuine cross-country passage, some of them late enough to make the three June birds seem less exceptional. The rest of the records are scattered through all months. There is little evidence of birds being storm-driven, as some literature suggests, though it may be adverse weather that causes birds to drop in at the larger lakes and reservoirs on which they are usually seen.

Three records in 1987 and another three in 1994 distort the picture completely. On 18 Mar 1987 an unprecedented 70-80 adults flew north-east from Willen Lake, and two days later 115 adults flew south from the same site. Each flock exceeded the entire pre-1987 county total, while 17 at Little Marlow on 20 Dec exceeded any previous annual total. Seven years later, on 14 Mar 1994, 12 adults were at Linford and the following day, 28, apparently all adults, flew east over Caldecotte. But these astonishing numbers were eclipsed by the events at Weston Turville when, two days later, three flocks of 70-80, 14 and 10 flew west within 30 minutes over the reservoir.

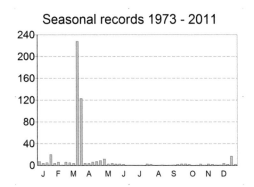

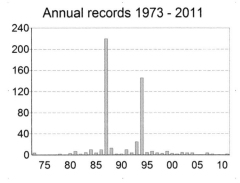

177

Even discounting these records, two-thirds of the birds seen are adults. This bias would seem to be genuine given that immature birds have much more distinctive plumage and are therefore more likely to be detected. In contrast, all but four of the birds seen between mid June and late October have been immatures.

AVH

Black-headed Gull
Chroicocephalus ridibundus

Abundant winter visitor and passage migrant. A few birds summer and it bred for the first time only recently.

H & R and H & J recognised this as the commonest gull in the county, though the largest flock mentioned, of 60 birds, is small by present day standards. In former times it was most likely to be encountered on passage, particularly in spring.

As well as being the most numerous, this is also the most widespread of the gulls, since it is much less demanding in its habitat requirements than the others. Larger lakes and gravel pits, rubbish tips and recently ploughed fields attract the largest flocks, as with the other gulls. However the opportunistic nature of the species means that smaller groups or individuals forage on temporary floods and playing fields, patrol smaller watercourses, venture into urban back gardens early in the morning, or, at the appropriate season, take flying ants on the wing. A small party has even been observed locally forming an aerial queue to pluck rosehips.

A few maturely-plumaged birds are usually among the small number which are present during the summer. So signs of breeding have been constantly sought for the past few decades, since breeding has taken place in neighbouring counties. The first significant evidence was of a pair at an apparent nest at Thorney GP from 10 to 30 May 2001. 2002 saw a pair, one of which was apparently in first-summer plumage, swapping sitting duties in May at Gayhurst Quarry. At the same site an adult was 'sitting' throughout much of June 2003. There was then a gap to 2006, which saw apparent breeding behaviour at Hillesden in June. At last proof came in 2007, when a chick was hatched at Gayhurst Quarry and was seen with its parents on June 26 and July 5. A pair was successful at the same site the following year with again one chick hatched and noted in July. A further attempt there in 2009 failed, and in that year there were also hints of breeding attempts at both Linford GPs and Marlow. There was no proof of breeding in 2010, but that year is illustrative of the gradual increase in the number of summering birds, particularly in the south of the county, though 20 at Dorney and 45 at Marlow in June may largely refer to the same group of birds. So, even more breeding attempts are to be expected in future.

Numbers build up rapidly in July and counts of over 3500 have been recorded before the end of that month. While from August to March roost counts may be significant, all the largest counts are from November to February. At some point in the last 20 years Caldecotte, Calvert and Foxcote roosts have all been estimated at between 5000 and 7500 in those months. Willen has been consistently the largest roost during the last three decades and between 1985 and 1995 there were several counts of 20,000 or more, the largest of which was 40,000 in December 1992. In the last 15 years on only a couple of occasions has the 10,000 barrier been broken, so while still an impressive sight, clearly fewer birds are spending the night in Buckinghamshire.

Through the major passage months as well as mid-winter, rubbish tips and occasionally farmland provide optimal feeding conditions, which may see four-figure flocks away from roosting lakes. Most birds will have disappeared by mid-April. The many birds which move into the county in the early autumn are likely to be of British origin.

The even larger numbers which come later are thought to be largely of continental stock. Our knowledge of this shift in the population is based largely on national data, but local ringing also provides supporting evidence. Birds ringed as pulli in Belgium, Finland, Germany, Holland and Poland have been recovered in the area, and a bird ringed in its first winter at Marlow in January 1968 was recovered in Copenhagen, Denmark, in July 1969.

Several near-albino birds have been reported. One white bird with a grey head and black 'dipped in ink' wingtips seen at Shardeloes on 10 Mar 2002 was rather more unusual.

AVH

Little Gull
Larus minutus

Annual migrant in variable numbers. Rare winter visitor.

Foxcote, 18 Sep 2009   *Phil Tizzard*

The first county record was an adult between 6 and 25 Aug 1958 at Dorney Common. The steady and significant national increase in numbers between 1950 and the early 1970s, as traced by Hutchinson and Neath (1978), was not reflected in county tallies, since the second record was not until 1970. The first record of two birds together and an annual total which exceeded double figures occurred in 1978, since when both annual totals and multiple occurrences have certainly increased.

Old-style sewage farms were occasionally attractive to this species in the early 1970s, but since their modernisation virtually all records have been from the larger lakes, reservoirs and gravel pits.

In the last two decades, the date range of this species has expanded to include mid-winter gull roost records. At the Willen Lake roost birds were noted on 10 and 22 Jan 1997, with these records possibly referring to the same bird, and 4 Jan 2003. There are still only a small number of February and March records, with a few late enough in March to suggest they are early passage birds. One obvious exception roosted at Willen Lake regularly from 16 to 30 Mar 2001. There is a decent number of passage records early in April, but the second week onward to the third week of May is more normal. Only 2002 has experienced a completely blank passage in spring. Around a quarter of the springs in the last two decades have had passage in single figures, around half produced totals in the teens and the remainder 20 or more. Those years which have had the highest totals have almost all relied on one bumper day. As noted at the time, 19 adults at Willen Lake on 25 Apr1983 provided what the observers thought would be a unique sight in Buckinghamshire. However on 1 May of the following year 30 birds in two flocks passed through the same site, while on 2 May 1986 17 adults were present and probably 49 birds passed through in three flocks on 22 Apr 1987, again all at Willen Lake. This hot spot in the records has probably much to do with Willen Lake being an almost constant effort site at that time, so birds in numbers moving rapidly through, as they were known to do in adjacent counties, were recorded. Subsequent similar flocks have been of 16 at College Lake on 21 May 1994, 22 at Weston Turville Res. on 12 Apr 1996 and 15 at Marlow on 23 Apr 2005.

Midsummer records are few, and some later in July probably refer to genuine passage. August and September are the normal months for a weak autumn passage, to which October has contributed only a little. The totals are consistently significantly smaller than in spring, so that four of the last twenty years have been blank, most are in low single figures and only one has crept into double figures. There are only nine November records ever, but the last two decades have seen December roost records in addition to the January ones noted above. These have been at Willen Lake on 6 Dec 1993, 8 Dec 1994 and 4 Dec 1995 with two at Weston Turville Res. on 15 Dec 2008.

A juvenile with largely dark upperwings, seen in company with two normally-plumaged birds at Willen Lake from 8 to 15 Aug 1984 would seem to accord with a rare variant plumage described by Grant (1986).

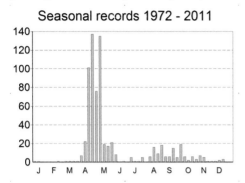

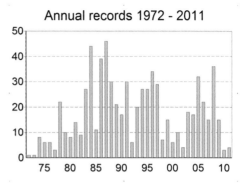

AVH

Sabine's Gull
Larus sabini

Very rare vagrant. All records are given.

1981: adult and immature on 13 Oct, Willen.
1997: juv on 26 Sep, Little Marlow.
1997: juv on 3 Oct, Calvert.
1998: juv on 27 Sep, Foxcote.
2001: juv from 16 to 19 Sep, Foxcote.
2003: adult on 19 Oct, Foxcote.

Adults leave their breeding grounds in the high Arctic for their journey to the south Atlantic before the juveniles, who generally migrate alone. It is thus not surprising that most of our records are of juveniles.

Franklin's Gull
Larus pipixcan

Very rare vagrant. There is one record.

1999: adult from 30 Jun to 1 Jul, Willen (Taylor 1999).

Mediterranean Gull
Larus melanocephalus

Scarce migrant and winter visitor.

The first record was an adult in summer plumage on 19 Mar 1980 at Hedgerley. Between that record and 1991 there were a further 37 records, generally of single birds, with a gradual rise in numbers towards the end of this period. The increase in records is due in part to the establishment of the species in the UK, but also due to increased scrutiny of gulls.

Little Marlow, 11 Mar 2011   *Jim Rose*

In the next 10 years there were 175 records, almost all recorded by the same few observers. It is significant that when one observer left the county in 1997 the number of records for that year was exactly half of the previous year. Between 2001 and 2011 there were 165 records, but considering the consolidation of breeding birds in the UK and the rise in observer numbers it is clear that this species is now under-recorded in the county.

In the early 1990s this bird was generally a winter specialist with adults predominating. First winter birds occasionally appeared in autumn but more were present in the latter part of the winter. We have now seen an increase in birds in juvenile plumage occurring in the summer months and breeding plumaged adults staying well into the spring. While generally seen alone, records of two together have become more frequent and three, possibly even four have been found on more than one occasion.

This species has increased in numbers across Europe, and since gaining a foothold in the UK the population here has continued to build in number and spread in distribution. The flocks of birds to be found in some parts of Sussex and Hampshire at times in early spring are commonly in the tens and can number hundreds. Accordingly the bird has become a frequent sight at the county's water bodies, particularly at Little Marlow and elsewhere in the south of the county.

A ringed juvenile seen at Willen on the 26 and 31 Jul 1994 had been ringed in the Netherlands on 7 June, having last been seen there on 24 June. Another Dutch ringed juvenile was noted at Little Marlow on the 22 Jul 2005. This bird had been ringed on the 9 June. It was then seen near Aberystwyth on the 1 August.

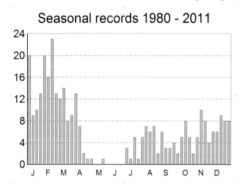

Seasonal records 1980 - 2011

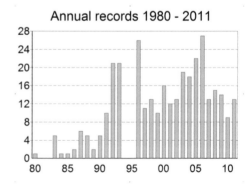

Annual records 1980 - 2011

MSW

Common Gull
Larus canus

Common winter visitor.

In the past the Common Gull was well known but somewhat irregular in occurrence, but in common with many other species in this genus its numbers increased greatly in the latter part of the 20th century and are at least stable at the beginning of the 21st.

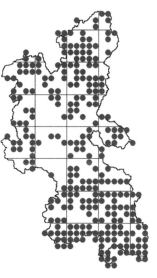

Shardeloes, 12 Dec 2010   *David Ferguson*

A study of the published records from the 1970s indicates that it was only found in large numbers in March and early April. It seems unlikely that there has been a sudden change in its habits and the numbers of birds and the seasonal patterns noted below are thought to be as relevant then as they are 40 years later.

This bird is found in good numbers throughout the county in the winter months, with a marked and compact spring passage and more of a prolonged and less noticeable autumn one. It is generally absent from the county between May and August, when any record is notable, with just the odd bird appearing at sites like Dorney where a few have summered in recent years. This pattern of occurrence accords well with a species breeding very much in the north of the UK and further northwards still.

In mid-winter, counts at regular roost sites, particularly near refuge tips can yield good numbers, with hundreds or even thousands present, for example 2000 at Willen in December and the county's record count of 8000 on 17 January 1995. It is the spring that produces the largest numbers as birds move north, with late February to the end of March as the peak period. Little Marlow, for example, recorded 1500 on 10 Mar 2006 and still 1800 at the same site on 2 Apr 2006. It was in this period that one of the county's largest flocks, 4000 at Turville, in March 1983 was present on farmland. There was also a count of 4000 at Marlow in 2009, also in March, aptly demonstrating not only that the peak period has remained the same, but also the apparent stability in numbers over that quarter of a century. In autumn some birds re-appear in September but October sees a more notable influx as numbers build towards the plateau of wintering birds in the county.

Whilst this species can commonly be found on refuge tips and adjacent water-bodies in winter, its preference for a variety of agricultural land, playing fields, flooded pasture and indeed urban parks is obvious at anytime from autumn right through to spring, often in the company of Black-headed Gulls.

There is only one ringing recovery for the county, a bird ringed on Tylon Isle, Sweden in June 1937 was recovered at Hedgerley in April 1938.

MSW

Ring-billed Gull
Larus delawarensis

Rare vagrant. All records are given.

There have been 11records, the first as recent as 1991. A number of birds have returned to the same site in subsequent winters.

Little Marlow, 17 July 2004   *Michael McKee*

1991: adult on 24 Jan, Fulmer. This bird subsequently took up residence in Uxbridge.
1991: second winter from 7 - 16 Nov, Little Marlow, with probably the same bird seen at Pickeridge Quarry on 23 Nov and again at Little Marlow on 21 Feb.
1994: adult on 9 Feb, Willen.
1994: adult on 16 Feb, Hedgerley.
1994: second winter on a number of dates between 26 Sep and 25 Nov, 12 and 26 Feb 1995, Little Marlow.
1996: adult on a number of dates between 29 Sep and 29 Dec, Little Marlow.
2002: second winter on 29 and 30 Mar, Little Marlow.
2003: second winter on 28 Jan, Foxcote.
2003: adult from 1 to 5 Apr, Little Marlow.
2004: second-summer from 14 Jul to 6th Aug, Little Marlow .
2004: adult winter on 26 Nov, Caldecotte.
2005: adult on a number of dates between 23 Mar and 1 Apr, Little Marlow, was probably seen in the previous few years at the same site in immature plumages.
2008: second-summer on 5 and 21 Mar, Little Marlow.

This is a New World species which has been recorded regularly in the UK since its first discovery. Mixed pairing with Common Gull has occurred.

Little Marlow is responsible for the vast majority of records. This may be due to the relative closeness of birds, which makes picking out this rather subtle species slightly easier. It may be significant that adults and mature sub-adults are the only ages accepted onto the county record to date, almost certainly due to their relative ease of identification compared to younger birds.

MSW

Lesser Black-backed Gull
Larus fuscus

Dorney Lake, 12 Aug 2011   *David Ferguson*

Passage migrant and common winter visitor which has bred in small numbers.

H & R presumed, no doubt correctly, that the Lesser Black-backed Gull was a rare passage migrant in Buckinghamshire on the strength of sightings at the Tring reservoirs. H & J summarised similarly and noted the first certain record for the county, a bird at Bletchley in April 1910.

A huge increase, which is happening at all seasons, began in the latter part of the 20th century and is still continuing. The wintering population is found mainly at the larger rubbish tips and gull roosts, and four-figure counts at the latter are not exceptional. The favoured sites are Hedgerley and Calvert. To demonstrate this rising population some 500 birds at Hedgerley on 6th Jan 1987 was considered significant at the time whereas counts at Calvert in 2011 can be in excess of 3000. This species is more often found in substantial numbers on agricultural land than Great Black-backed and Herring Gulls and during winter floods the birds can stay on soaked farmland until dusk, leaving it very late to move to the lakes to roost, causing frustration to the hardened gull watchers waiting there.

The British breeding subspecies *L f graellsii* winters in the county but its numbers are augmented at this season by the European subspecies *L f intermedius*. There have been a number of claims of the nominate race *L f fuscus*, which effectively have black mantles, but most of these claims are in fact *intermedius*, perhaps towards its northern limit. The true rarity of *fuscus* in the UK is demonstrated by the current thinking that any successful claim of *fuscus* would need to involve a bird wearing a ring placed there on the breeding grounds which are in Finland and Sweden.

The transition from wintering to spring passage birds is difficult to detect but a general increase is obvious from late February to mid April, when flocks of several hundred are common away from the usual winter sites. Birds are reduced to a few in May at which point British birds are firmly on their breeding grounds, and through June birds are difficult to find. By July birds are noted in increasing numbers and in both this month and August they are often to be found feeding on both cut and ploughed agricultural land, but, very rapidly, the favoured roost sites, such as Calvert can contain significant numbers, for example 6000 in October.

As with Herring Gull, the number of birds in these late Spring and Summer months has been on the increase which has led to the species breeding in small numbers at two industrial sites in High Wycombe. At both sites they were associated with Herring Gulls. Breeding was probable in 2002 and confirmed in 2003. They then bred in every year in increasing numbers until 2007 when there were about 15 pairs. The buildings were then demolished and breeding ceased. However there is no doubt that with the right nesting habitat the birds will continue to breed in the county as they can rapidly move into a site. This was shown in Gloucester where, having left their car parked for a few hours, the owner returned to discover not only a nest on the car's roof but that it contained a single egg!

The use of coloured darvic rings with lettering, coupled with the increased quality of optics and certain sites where the gulls legs can be studied, e.g Little Marlow, has led to a significant rise in the information gleaned and our subsequent knowledge of the movements of the different races of this species. For example, a bird seen at Calvert in December 2008 was ringed in Cumbria in 1999, before being seen in Portugal twice during the intervening period. Four different *intermedius* birds seen at Little Marlow in June and July 2003 had been ringed as chicks at Vanse, Norway in 2002. In addition to these four, a concerted effort by a small number of observers at Little Marlow in 2003 produced five birds from the Netherlands, one from Iceland and seven from England, mainly the Bristol area.

An adult found dead at the former breeding site in Cressex, High Wycombe on the 16th August 2007 had been ringed as a nestling at Orfordness in Suffolk in 2000. A bird ringed as a chick on Skokholm Island, Pembrokeshire in July 1960 was found dead at Newport Pagnell on 2 Sep 1976.

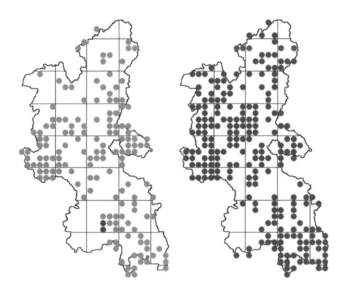

MSW

Herring Gull
Larus argentatus

Locally common migrant and winter visitor, has bred in very small numbers.

Until 1920 Herring Gulls were noted only rarely near Tring Reservoirs and in the Thames Valley (and therefore presumably in Buckinghamshire), usually in association with bad weather. The subsequent considerable increase is presumed to have taken place mainly in the second half of the twentieth century, with numbers continuing to rise in the 21st century.

Shardeloes, 25 Nov 2010   *David Ferguson*

As can be seen from the maps, Herring Gulls are largely winter visitors to the county. The vast majority of these birds are of the Scandinavian nominate race *L.a.argentatus* and not the British *L.a.argenteus*. Three-figure counts cannot be expected before late October or early November, although in some years peak winter numbers have been noted later in that month, e.g 1826 in November 2008, or from early December, for example 900 at Calvert and 500 at Caldecotte. It would appear that a second and more normal peak occurs in January and early February, by which time birds can be very 'white-headed' and cause confusion with Yellow-legged Gull. The largest counts at other sites have been made at this time: 500 at Willen on several occasions, 1680 at Hedgerley, and 800 at Calvert.

Gatherings of reasonable size may be noted up to late March, but thereafter the species is more difficult to locate in any numbers, but certain sites, such as Dorney in recent years hold good numbers throughout the year, for example 200 there in May 2008. There is no significant early autumn passage for this species as there is with the Lesser Black-backed Gull.

The habitats utilised by the species within the county is rather limited. Whilst it is occasionally noted on flooded pasture or ploughed land, all larger flocks are closely associated with rubbish tips and roosting waters, or are noted moving between the two. Most of the dots on the maps are the result of over-flying birds. The apparent intense concentration of birds in the south-east of the county can perhaps be explained by the presence of Hedgerley Tip and fly-lines between this site and the West London reservoirs which hold large roosts.

Whilst we can expect to see similar numbers of the nominate race during the winter months, the British breeding bird, *L.a. argenteus* is in decline, probably due to over-fishing, and is now red-listed as a species of high conservation concern and as such we are likely to see a reduction in records of this sub-species.

Whilst formerly only a wintering bird there was a significant rise in records in the summer months in the early 21st century which led to the species breeding in very small numbers. Breeding was probable in 2002 and confirmed in 2003. These breeding records were alongside Lesser Black- backed Gulls, with industrial buildings utilised. The first of

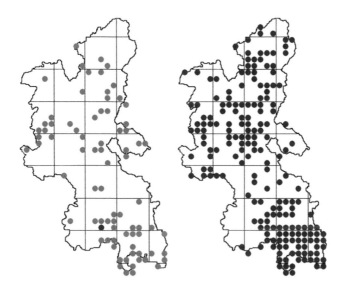

these was in Cressex, High Wycombe which then moved to a disused factory off the Hughenden Road. The colony here became quite well established, with about 20 pairs breeding in 2007, until the buildings were demolished shortly after and the colony wiped out.

The increased use of darvic rings that can be read using optics has led to a huge increase in our knowledge. In June 2008, five different ringed individuals at Dorney were identified, all of which had spent time as orphans at the same RSPCA wildlife hospital in East Sussex.

A first summer sighted at Little Marlow on 12th Apr 2005 was ringed on the 1st Jul 2004 at Bridgend, 196 kms to the west.

MSW

Yellow-legged Gull
Larus michahellis

Passage migrant and winter visitor.

This gull was only elevated to full species level in 2004, having previously been treated as a subspecies of Herring Gull. However, the first records were in 1985:

1985: 1 from 18 to 22 Sep, Pitstone.
1985: 1 on 29 Dec, Denham.

There were 43 records up to 1991, with a dramatic increase in the latter part of this

Dorney Lake, 15 Aug 2009   *Jim Rose*

period. Between 1991 and 2011 numbers rose still further, to astonishing numbers with, for example, 147 recorded in 2005. This dramatic explosion in records is part due to the understanding of the plumage features enabling the identification, but also due to a rise in population and range expansion. The records between 1985 and 1994 are shown on the graphs. After 1994 the records became too numerous to graph accurately.

Calvert is by far the most reliable site to find this species, recording 34 in one evening on 2 October 2001, but other good counts have been made at many of the regularly watched waters, particularly at roost, such as Marlow and Willen. Others can be located by day at refuse sites.

It is clear that there is a distinct peak in numbers from August to October which suggests post breeding dispersal. Records at this time of ringed birds at Portland, Dorset as well as the birds detailed at the end of this account support this. Some of this autumnal peak is probably exaggerated somewhat by closer scrutiny of gravel pits and gull roosts by a relatively small number of dedicated observers.

This species is readily identifiable by observers familiar with the other gulls, but a regular pitfall is Herring Gulls in

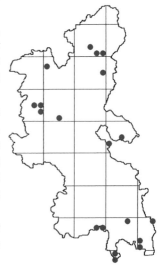

late winter which can be very 'white-headed' and therefore cause confusion. An even bigger headache arises with hybrids between Herring and Lesser Black-backed Gulls but these are fortunately very rare.

In winter smaller numbers of birds are present, often at lakes next to landfill sites. The species is generally absent from the county during the summer months. Most are gone by April and only a few are returning in mid-July.

Yellow- legged Gull has not yet bred in the county, but if a colony of either Herring or Lesser Black-backed Gulls was to become permanently established then there is a possibility of this occurring although perhaps a mixed pairing with one of these species is more likely than finding a mate of its own species.

A bird noted at Little Marlow on 17 September 2003 had been ringed as a nestling at Etang de Salses, South-East France, on the 17 May 2003. Another bird, a first summer, seen at Little Marlow on the 14 June 2004 had been ringed as a nestling on the 26 May 2003 near the Camargue, South-East France.

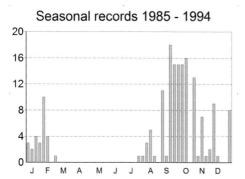

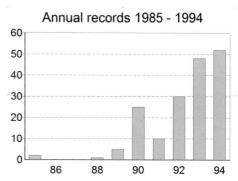

MSW

Caspian Gull
Larus cachinnans

Uncommon winter visitor.

Birds of this species have probably visited the county for at least several decades, but this gull only gained full species status in the UK in 2007; prior to this it was grouped with either Herring Gull or Yellow-legged Gull. Much work has been carried out over several decades across

Calvert, 23 Dec 2010   *Tim Watts*

Europe which has allowed for several of the 'Herring Gull' complex to be split into full species. This work continues and still causes debate.

Caspian Gulls have a diagnostic 'long-call' display, as well as several plumage features, noticeably the wing-tip pattern of the primaries, which allow for separation from similar species if seen well enough.

It is clear that birds were present in the years up to 2007 but as both the interest in gull identification grew, together with better quality optics, both the scrutiny and more accurate recording of its close congener Yellow-legged Gull has allowed us an insight into the status of this gull within the county.

This species is still uncommon in Buckinghamshire with most records coming from a handful of observers committed to the observation of both gull roosts and the challenge of separation from Yellow-legged Gull and Herring Gull. Adults and first winters dominate records at present, probably because they are easier to identify than second and third winters.

This species is very much a winter specialist, with the vast majority of records in mid-winter. There have been very few records in the summer months. They are usually found on rubbish tips or lakes adjacent to these at roost, with the favoured places being Calvert and Hedgerley, in common with the other large gulls.

There were 13 different birds in the county in 2005 when the species was still considered part of a much larger complex of gulls, with 15 in 2007, the first year of it being granted full species status, and a minimum of 20 different birds in 2011. Of the 15 birds in 2005, 12 of these were seen in the months of November – February , with the other three all being 1st years in late September/ October.

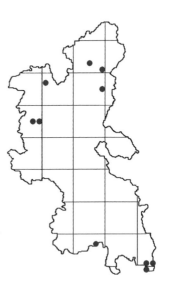

Whilst observers invariably note the age of the birds concerned when submitting records to try and differentiate individuals there is without a doubt duplication with some records. The reason for this is two-fold, firstly that birds can be present at the same site for a matter of weeks but are only seen or identified on a few occasions. Secondly it is apparent that the large gulls in particular wander around both ours and adjoining counties, seeking out food and roosting nearby. For example a gull may be at Willen one week, only to roost at Calvert in the following week. Additional evidence is provided by the movement of colour marked gulls from Hedgerley which were subsequently seen at Calvert.

This gull has spread to the Czech Republic, Hungary, Belarus, Poland and Germany from its core distribution of the Black Sea eastwards to Central Asia, and northwards into Russia. It is likely that the countries at the western edge of the range are the source of the birds found in Buckinghamshire.

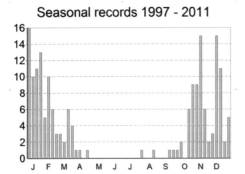

Seasonal records 1997 - 2011

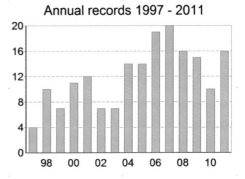

Annual records 1997 - 2011

Although this gull will never be common in the county we can expect the records to remain at current levels, perhaps seeing a slight rise, as both the population consolidates and spreads and the ever increasing number of observers will lead a few more gull scrutineers to those winter gull flocks.

MSW

Iceland Gull
Larus glaucoides

Rare winter visitor.

The first record for the county is :

1969: 1st winter on 1 and 16 Feb at Calvert.

Calvert, 8 Mar 2008   *Tim Watts*

The next record was not until 1981 when a 2nd winter bird was recorded at Hedgerley. Between this record and 1991 there were 11 records. Six were first-winter, four were second winter and one was a third winter.

Between 1991 and 2011 there were 65 records, whilst there will be some duplication in records due to birds moving between sites, there has clearly been a considerable increase in records. Some of this increase can be attributed to high quality optics and the efforts of a few hardy souls prepared to freeze in order to find a 'white-winger'. Of the 65 birds recorded, 24 were first winter, nine were second winter, 3 were third winter while 29 were adults. The first adult was not recorded until as late as 1994. It would seem that adult Iceland Gulls changed their behaviour during the last twenty years.

Most records involve single birds but there have been occasions when two birds were seen together and there were three at Calvert on 11 Mar 2009 where four different birds, all first winters, were noted during that month.

This species is very much a mid to late winter specialist, very much reflecting the movement and records of its larger congener the Glaucous Gull. There are more records of Iceland Gull than Glaucous which is perhaps surprising considering their geographical distribution.

The favoured locations for both of these species are rubbish tips by day and nearby lakes

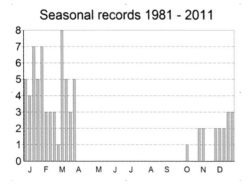

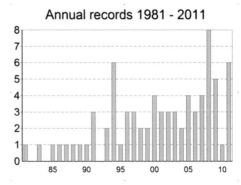

to roost on by night. There have been many records from Hedgerley, Willen and especially Calvert, the last being watched far more regularly than any other site in the county for roosting gulls.

This species breeds only in Greenland, wintering on the coasts there, but with good numbers reaching Iceland and smaller numbers in north-west Europe, the east coast of the USA and north-east Canada.

MSW

Kumlien's Gull
Larus glaucoides kumlieni

Very rare vagrant. There is one record.

2001: adult on 29 Mar, Withybridge (Heard, 2002).

Glaucous Gull
Larus hyperboreus

Calvert, 12 Feb 2005   *Tim Watts*

Scarce winter visitor.

The first record in the present county is:

1972: 1 adult on 2 Dec, Linford.

Between 1972 and 1991 there were 29 records of single birds, all between October and March, but only three of these were outside the period from December to March. Between 1991 and 2011 there was an obvious increase in records, with 46 recorded, but considering the higher quality optics, the rise in observer numbers, and the interest shown in this family of birds it could have been expected to be greater. There is only one multiple record: a first and second winter were present together at Willen on 8 March 1994.

There is an obvious peak in numbers in February and early March. The majority of records involve immature birds, with first winters predominating. Of the 46 birds recorded since 1991, 28 were first winters, seven second/third winters and 11 were adults.

The fact that birds arrive in the county so late in the winter is suggestive of them pushing further and further south during the course of the season, often arriving after the coldest weather of the period.

This species breeds principally within the Arctic Circle with the closest breeding colony in Iceland, where Iceland Gull does not breed. The birds reaching Britain are most likely from the population in Iceland and to a lesser extent Norway whose population is more sedentary; the population in North and West Europe is currently in decline.

It should be noted that not all large gulls seen in the county with white wing tips are either this species or Iceland Gull, as shown by the small number of abnormally plumaged Herring Gulls located at Calvert in recent years. In addition this species and Herring Gull frequently hybridise and these hybrids are not only recorded in the UK and the county but can be a real identification challenge.

192

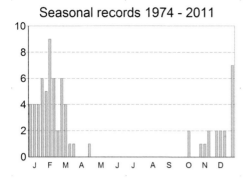

Seasonal records 1974 - 2011

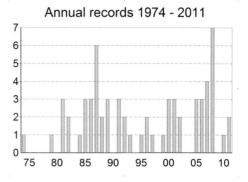

Annual records 1974 - 2011

MSW

Great Black-backed Gull
Larus marinus

Local winter visitor.

Calvert, 4 Feb 2008   *Tim Watts*

Both H & R and H & J presumed the Great Black-backed Gull to be a rare straggler to the county, based on evidence from just outside the county boundary. Its status has somewhat changed since then but still remains the most scarce of the five commonly occurring species of gulls found in the UK.

This is the largest gull breeding in Britain and is more than capable of taking fair sized prey items, whether through scavenging or predation. This ability to deal with almost anything, as well as the sheer size of this bird ensures it is often able to muscle in on an available food source, whether on the breeding grounds or its winter quarters. This factor has significantly contributed to a continued rise in the UK population, as during the breeding season other species of gulls struggle to find enough food for their young. This has resulted in a steady increase in numbers since the 1940s, a process that is still continuing.

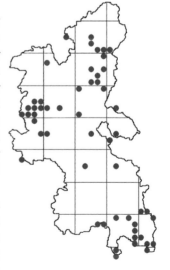

Except for birds flying over, this species is rarely seen away from its preferred habitat on or close to large rubbish tips and the larger gull roosts. In this respect it is much more selective than the other large gulls, therefore the obvious locations for finding this species in any numbers are at Hedgerley and Calvert.

Singles or small parties may be noted from mid March to early May and then again from the first half of August. However, in general few birds are seen outside the period

November to early March and all the three-figure counts are concentrated in December and January. The Willen roost was estimated at over 100 on several occasions in the 1980s, with a maximum of c300 on 20 Jan 1986. The highest single counts have both been of c500 birds, both in January, at Hedgerley and Calvert.

MSW

Little Tern
Sternula albifrons

Scarce migrant.

There are undated records for the Thames and the larger reservoirs given by H & R.

There were four other records prior to 1972.

1850: undated, Slapton.
1946: 1 on 10 May, flying down River Thames at Little Marlow with Black Terns.
1958: 2 on 1 May, Hartigan's GP, near Broughton.
1971: 1 on 6 Jun, Marlow GP.

Since 1972 there were 71 records of 112 birds. They are shown on the graphs. 83 birds have been recorded in the north of the county, 7 in the middle, and 22 in the south. The largest flock recorded was one of six birds on 7 May 1994 at Linford. The majority of the records were in the early spring with a peak in early May.

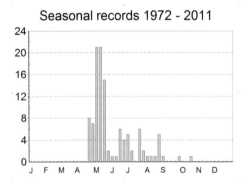

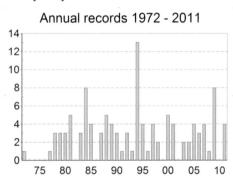

Caspian Tern
Hydroprogne caspia

Very rare vagrant. All records are given.

1992: 1 on 17 Apr, Willen (Tunnicliffe, 1993).
1996: 1 on 13 Apr, Caldecotte,
2001: 1 on 11 May, Linford and Willen.

The first bird was also seen in Bedfordshire and Suffolk.

Willen, 11 May 2001   Steve Blain

Whiskered Tern
Chlidonias hybridus

Very rare vagrant. All records are given.

1994: 2 adults from 16 to 21 May, Willen.
2001: first-winter, from 29 to 31 Oct, Willen.

White-winged Black Tern
Chlidonias leucopterus

Very rare vagrant. There has been one record.

2008: 2 juvs on 31 Aug, flew from Wilstone Res into Buckinghamshire (Evans, 2009).

Black Tern
Chlidonias niger

Local migrant.

Startopsend, 30 Aug 2009   *Mike Wallen*

There has probably been little change in status since records began other than such as are explicable by the creation of more large expanses of water and more observers. 'Not uncommon' was the summary early in the twentieth century by H & J.

The spring passage is often very concentrated. The earliest bird ever recorded in the county is as late as 11 Apr 1979, at Willen Lake. In the last twenty years the first arrival dates of many migrants has become steadily earlier, but this one has not been bettered. This is even stranger since decent passage can be recorded just 10 days later. The peak has also remained around the first week of May. While the passage is usually larger in spring, flock size is generally modest with only Caldecotte in 1993, Calvert in 1997 and Willen in 2010 recording flocks of c25 birds. June birds are rare, as are those in much of July, though a few later in that month presumably are part of autumn return passage.

Numbers in autumn are generally fewer than in spring, and appear to bear no relation to what happened earlier in the year. While autumn records are in many years spread unpredictably across an extended passage period, the very largest flocks have been remarkably consistent in terms of date. 76 were seen at Calvert on 15 Sep 1974, but many more birds passed through on that date. This was a similar picture to 11 Sep 1992 when numbers built up during the day at Willen Lake to 110 and nearly 50 birds were at other Bucks waters. There were 85 at Linford on 15 Sep 1994. Nothing on a similar scale has been noted since. Records after early October remain very unusual. The latest birds were three at Willen Lake on 28 Oct 1984 and an adult with damaged primaries at Weston Turville Res. from 26 to 28 Oct 1987, after the 'Great Storm' of that year.

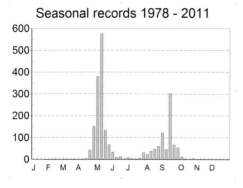

Seasonal records 1978 - 2011

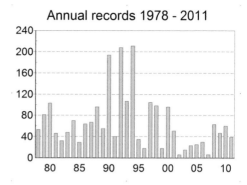

Annual records 1978 - 2011

AVH

Sandwich Tern
Sterna sandvicensis

Scarce migrant.

Prior to 1974 there were seven records.

1895: 8 on 10 Apr, Great Marlow.
1935: 1 on 20 Apr, Shardeloes.
1953: 1 found dead on 7 Jun, Little Marlow.
1956: 1 on 7 May, Hartigan's Pit, Broughton (MK).
1960: 1 on 5 May, Newport Pagnell GP.
1960: 1 on 24 Jun, Newport Pagnell GP.
1961: 2 on 30 Apr, Newport Pagnell GP.

Calvert, 22 Apr 2011   Tim Watts

Since 1974 there have been 93 records of 249 birds. 144 birds were recorded in the north of the county, 69 in the middle, and 36 in the south. The largest flocks recorded are 26 or 27 flying over Wavendon on 20 Apr 1989, and 13 on 22 Aug 1987 at Willen. The earliest record is of two birds at Little Marlow on 17 Mar 1991.

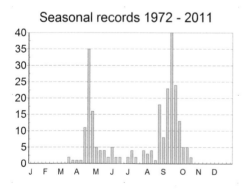

Seasonal records 1972 - 2011

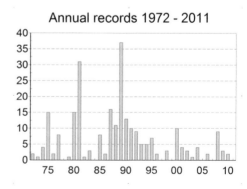

Annual records 1972 - 2011

Common Tern
Sterna hirundo

Local summer visitor and migrant.

In former times Common Terns were regarded as familiar passage birds, but less frequent in autumn than in spring (H & J).

Breeding was first proved in the county in 1968 and has increased markedly since: this is charted in summary below. This first nest was at Old Slade, now in Berkshire, where a pair raised three young. Subsequently from one to four pairs nested at the same site in almost every year until

Little Marlow, 15 Jul 2010   Kevin Holt

1992, after which the rafts on which they bred were removed. A pair bred successfully at Marlow in 1982, and breeding has been regular ever since in increasing numbers: for example there were eight pairs in 2002, 18 young were raised in 2006 and 22 chicks hatched in 2009. The third site to produce young Common Terns was Willen, with a single pair in 1983 and 1985. The large island in the north basin of the lake proved attractive to the species and a thriving colony was rapidly established, albeit one which was difficult to count. 17 young were fledged in 1986 and 1987, and thereafter a minimum of 30 young were raised to the flying stage in every year up to 1999, with a maximum of 60 in 1991. In 2000 there were large numbers of adults but very poor success as birds attempted to breed on the low-lying spit on the island as opposed to the top of the island, where presumably conditions were no longer suitable. Subsequently it has been customary for large numbers of birds to appear in spring, but comparatively few attempt to breed, either on the 'spit' or on rafts which have periodically been supplied. Linford GPs has seen successful breeding occasionally since 1988: rafts have been more productive than the 'bund' where predation rates are extremely high. Several pairs bred at College Lake in 1994, with 28 young raised the following year. The colony has been regularly productive ever since, with numbers rising to around 30 pairs from 2001 to 2010, with just a couple of poor years due to predation. Thorney CP, with three or four pairs was first reported as successful in 1998 and there were 12 pairs there in 2000 and 2001: the rafts there continue to have success. Gayhurst Quarry jumped to prominence in 2002 with 36 young reported. 40 nests were reported there in 2006, but its overall record is much more patchy. 18 chicks were hatched at Langley Park in 2003. Calvert was another successful site where 13 young were raised on rafts in both 2005 and 2006. Caldecotte, Dorney Lake, Foxcote, Hillesden, Jubilee River and Stony Stratford NR, have been the other successful sites, with failed attempts at Bletchley BP and Taplow Lake in recent years. Overall breeding success is highly variable: islands and rafts being more or less essential to reduce predation, which is the major negative factor.

The average first arrival date has shifted earlier by about a week over the last two decades, with the earliest record being on 27 Mar 2006 at Willen. Double figure flocks now appear regularly in the third week of April, but the appearance of the very largest flocks in spring remains variable: any time between the third week of April and the middle of May. Given the numbers which at least attempt to breed across the county, it is difficult to estimate what proportion of these birds are migrants or prospective breeders.

Even subsequent to its demise as a thriving breeding colony, Willen consistently attracts 50+ birds at this time, and in more successful times held around 80 adult birds in May and June. Nonetheless presumably some of 100 birds there in early May 2000 and the 150+ present on 19 May 1994 (the county record flock) were migrants. This might also be the case with 84 which passed through Marlow on 16 May 2005 and 63 adults at College Lake on 3 May 2010. It is also interesting to consider whether the contribution of the Willen ternery is entirely responsible for the counts there of 120+ on 14 Jul 1992 and 135 on 2 Jul 1997.

Adults range widely to feed, or collect food, along all the watercourses in the county, visiting all significant lakes and gravel pits, so that even those sites where no breeding is attempted may record double-figure gatherings throughout the summer.

Because of successful local breeding, autumn passage is even more difficult to detect. Local birds are clearly leaving by end July and most have gone by mid-August. Flock sizes are highly variable, but generally smaller than in spring. 50-60 have been noted at Marlow on 11 Sep 1992, College Lake on 26 and 27 Aug 1994 and Weston Turville Res. on 10 Aug 2004. However Willen has again provided the largest gatherings with 90-110 between 15 and 19 Aug 1986, 50 on 11 Sep 1992, 50 in Aug 2002, 105 on 24 Aug 2005, 81 on 3 Aug 2006, and 77 on 18 Aug 2008.

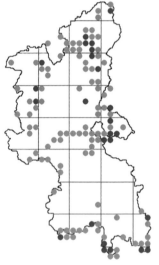

Numbers after mid-September are usually very small, and October reports appear to becoming more of a rarity, with only five records of six birds in the last 20 years, the latest of which (also the latest ever) was at Linford GPs from 27 to 30 Oct 2006.

A nestling ringed at Boston Fen, Lincolnshire on 14 Jun 1980 was found dead at Linford GPs exactly 11 years later. The ringing of young birds at Marlow has established that some do return to that colony as adults. In between they make some spectacular journeys. One ringed as a nestling at Marlow on Jun13 2003, was caught and released by a ringer at Iwik, Banc du Arguin, Mauritania on 26 Sep 2006, a distance of 3777km. A second nestling ringed on the same day made it to Fata, Palmarin, Senegal, where it was also caught and released by a ringer on 6 Dec 2003, 4407km distant, just 176 days later.

AVH

Arctic Tern
Sterna paradisaea

Local migrant.

Historical sources refer only to records close to the county boundary. This lack of an early definite record is not surprising. Even in 1976 F & Y could find only a few certain records and they recognised that the difficulties in separating Arctic and Common Terns in the field, at that time, were obscuring its true status. It was not until 1977 that the first substantial gathering was identified with certainty.

Startopsend Res, 8 Oct 2006   *Mike Wallen*

While the identification process relating to these two species remains non-trivial, the increase in general identification competence is thought to be entirely responsible for the subsequent upsurge in records.

As with many summer migrants the general arrival date has become gradually earlier over the last 20 years. However the earliest recorded arrival for Arctic Tern dates from over 20 years ago - four at Caldecotte, with Common Terns, on 10 Apr 1991, which is extremely early for that era. Subsequently three at Startopsend which flew into Buckinghamshire on 11 Apr 2009 are also noteworthy. Eagle-eyed researchers will find an unattributed report of two at Willen on 9 Apr 1982 in the Buckinghamshire Bird Report of that year, but that lack of attribution has led that report to be now discounted. The size of spring passage is much more variable than is generally perceived and often intensely concentrated, with numerically impressive years often relying on just one day. So the possibility of decent passage occurring, but being 'missed' is a live one. Indeed in some 'poor' springs, decent numbers are noted in adjacent counties. The largest flocks have been of 60 at Willen on 22 Apr 1980, 62 at Startopsend on 1 May 1991, 123 at Linford on 2 May 1998, 54 at Willen on 12 May 2004, 200 through Calvert, with a peak count of 79 present at one time, on 26 Apr 2005, 198 at Willen on 4 May 2005, with 97 at Linford GPs on the same date, and 53 at Calvert on 25 Apr 2009. In contrast, spring passage noted in five of the years in the 1990s saw less than 10 birds, with the same meagre fare in 2000 and 2002. There are a handful of June and July records of adults, and given that separation of Arctic from Common Tern still remains something of a problem, some of those inevitably incur suspicion.

Autumn passage, from mid-August and through September to the earliest days of October, is very much smaller, with six of the last 20 years drawing a complete blank, and some other years with just one or two records. The majority are juvenile birds. 20 such birds at Willen on 17 Aug 2006 and 24 on 5 Sep 2008, again at Willen, are unusual records for the county. The only records after mid-October have been juveniles at Marlow on 18th in 1987 and the latest at Calvert from 17th to 25th in 2001.

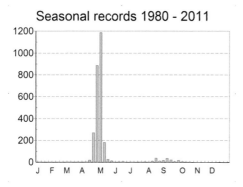
Seasonal records 1980 - 2011

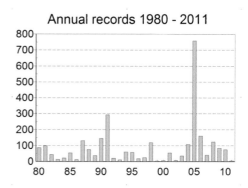
Annual records 1980 - 2011

AVH

Roseate Tern
Sterna dougallii

Very rare vagrant. All records are given.

1944: 1 on 6 Sep, Little Marlow.
1982: 2 on 4 Jun, Willen.
1983: adult on 8 May, Mount Farm, Bletchley.
1994: adult on 7 May, Willen.
2000: 1st summer on 28 May, Little Marlow.

Jubilee River, Berks, 13 May 2011   *David Ferguson*

2011: adult on 13 May, Dorney Wetlands flew briefly along the Jubilee River into Buckinghamshire.

Guillemot
Uria aalge

Very rare vagrant. There has been one record.

1852: 1 caught in R. Ouzel, 13 or 14 Nov, Fenny Stratford.

Razorbill
Alca torda

Very rare vagrant. There has been one record.

1996: 1 on 22 Feb, Caldecotte (Wallen, 1997).

Little Auk
Alle alle

Rare vagrant, usually after storms. All records are given.

1893: 1, Newport Pagnell.
1901 or earlier: 1, Bulstrode Park.
1912: 1, Quainton.
1912: 1, Towersey.
1912: 1, Ivinghoe.
1917: 1, Wendover.
1917: 1, Weston Turville Res.
1919: 1, Skirmett.
1983: 1 on 14 Feb, Aylesbury.
1986: 1 on 2 Feb, found alive at Wingrave, released on Wilstone Res.
1987: 1 on 25 Nov, Akeley.
1988: 1 on 28-31 Oct, Willen.
1988: 1 on 21 Nov, Medmenham.
1995: 1 on 30 Oct, flying over ploughed fields at Bledlow.
1995: 1 on 2 Nov, R Thames at Bourne End.
1999: 1 on 20 Nov, Stokenchurch taken into care.
2008: 1 found in Feb in Milton Keynes. It was taken into care but died.

The 1995 records were part of an influx into inland England.

Puffin
Fratercula arctica

Rare vagrant, usually after storms. All records are given.

1881: 1 on 14 Oct, near Aylesbury caught after gales.
1914: 1 on 19 Nov, Oaken Grove, near Hambleden.
1918: 1 on 23 Nov, at Aston Clinton.
1923: 1 picked up dying on 25 Nov, Kingsey.
1931: 1 found alive on 31 Oct, Nash, was picked up but later died.
1947: 1 picked up on 17 Oct, near Ivinghoe Beacon.
1955: 1 a few days before 25 Oct, near Wycombe, kept for a few days then released.
1958: juvenile from 18 to 20 Oct, Shardeloes.
1974: juvenile, Loudwater, was picked up but later died.
1977: 1 late Jun/early Jul, Quarrendon, Aylesbury, was later released at sea.
1979: 1 on 17 Feb, Amersham, was later released at sea.

Pallas's Sandgrouse
Syrrhaptes paradoxus

Very rare vagrant. All records are given.

1888: flock at Farnham Royal.
1896: 3 on 28 Aug flying overhead, near Halton.
1908: 7-8 on 1 Dec flew up from a turnip field near Buckland.

Although all the records are accepted, the 1896 record has rather less obvious substance than the others since it was not part of an influx into Europe.

Stock Dove
Columba oenas

Common resident.

Marsh, 31 Mar 2011   Richard Billyard

The status of Stock Doves in Buckinghamshire is significantly different from that earlier this century, when H & R (1902) described them as nesting throughout the county 'where old trees afford nesting holes' and H & J described them as 'not rare'. However, there was a sudden decline in the number in the southeast in the 1950s which has been attributed to organchlorine seed dressings (The Breeding Atlas). Recovery from this was recorded in 1969. In 1979 F & Y described Stock Doves as 'fairly common and appears to be increasing'. This trend may have continued as the estimated breeding population for the first atlas was 3000 pairs, rising to 4000 pairs for the latest atlas. However this is not entirely supported by the changes to the breeding distribution maps.

The breeding population in Buckinghamshire is perhaps controlled by the number of suitable breeding sites, this usually being a hole in a tree which may be part of a wood, copse, hedgerow or individual tree. It seems likely that this species could suffer from competition for nesting holes with Ring-necked Parakeets, a species which is still increasing. Stock Doves have been recorded breeding in nest boxes that have been put up for Tawny Owls and Mandarin Ducks.

Breeding commences during March usually with two to three broods of two eggs. Flocks of birds seen during March and April (50 - 200 birds occasionally reported at this time) are probably first year birds and failed breeders. Breeding pairs will usually nest on their own or in a small colony, this being largely dependent upon suitable nest sites. Following the breeding season Stock Doves flock together and groups of up to 200 birds in the summer and autumn are not too uncommon. During the winter months there may be an some influx of continental birds (The Winter Atlas). They are also regularly recorded associating with Woodpigeons. It seems likely that the resident Stock Doves stay in and around the county all year. Murton (1966) states that 74% of ringing recoveries were within eight km of the ringing sites with only 11% more that 40 km from the ringing site.

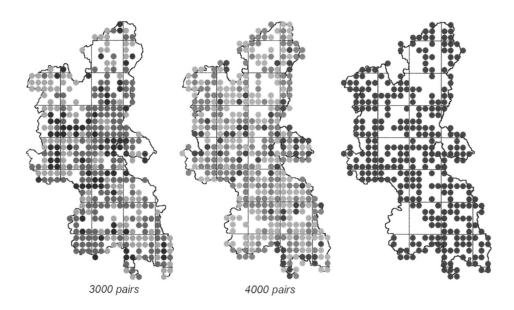

3000 pairs   4000 pairs

JER

Woodpigeon
Columba palumbus

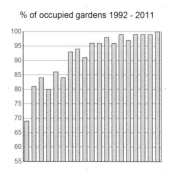

% of occupied gardens 1992 - 2011

Beaconsfield, 29 Oct, 2008   *David Ferguson*

Very common resident.

Many people feel that Woodpigeons have increased since the last Birds of Buckinghamshire was published. This is partly due to the fact that Woodpigeons now commonly breed in gardens and other habitat that was previously rarely occupied. Population estimates for the 1993 Atlas was 50,000 pairs, while the current estimate is 100,000 pairs, which makes it the most numerous breeding bird in the county.

The Woodpigeon breeds very widely and commonly throughout the county. Confirmed breeding is perhaps most readily achieved by locating their easily seen and recognisable platform twig nests. Since food for the fledglings is carried in the crop, confirmation by food carrying is not normally possible. Having fledged, young Woodpigeons may only stay in the immediate vicinity of the nest for a few days (BWP) thus making confirmation of breeding more difficult. It seems likely that many of the probable breeding records (singing and displaying birds) are actually of breeding pairs.

In Buckinghamshire, Woodpigeon use a wide range of habitats including woods, copses, farmland, hedgerows, towns, parks and gardens. Nest sites range from medium sized bushes to large trees.

The breeding season begins in April for some (mainly urban) birds but much later (peak in July to September) for birds breeding in farmland habitat (BWP). At this time their territories are easily located by their gliding and wing clapping display flight, and the familiar song. At the end of the summer, flocks gather and may become very large in the autumn and winter. Flocks of several hundred are not uncommon in the county, with flocks of up to 5,000 recorded in most years. The largest number recorded being an estimated 18,000 in December 2004 which were disturbed by shooting at Stokenchurch. Woodpigeons do not usually travel far from their breeding area and our winter flocks are largely made up of birds from Buckinghamshire and adjacent counties, with a few from further afield. Only a very few birds from the continent are likely to be present in a normal winter. There are however, a few records of birds having bred in and around Buckinghamshire travelling much further afield. A nestling ringed in Cookham (just across the county boundary in Berkshire) was recovered in Finistere, France. Winter flocks begin to break up in early spring when territories start to form.

The Woodpigeon is generally poorly recorded, probably since it is abundant throughout the year. Most county records are of large winter flocks. However the Buckinghamshire Bird Club Garden Bird Survey does record this species and an increase in the number of gardens where this species is recorded has risen from 69% in 1992 to 100% in 2011. Many people now regard this species as somewhat of a pest in gardens due to its ability to eat large quantities of food which are put out for other species. This is just one factor in influencing why the Woodpigeon is likely to thrive in the county for the foreseeable future.

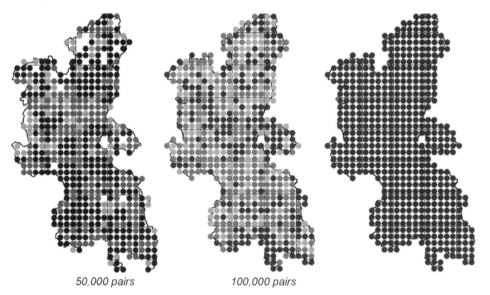

50,000 pairs   100,000 pairs

JER

Feral Pigeon
Columba livia

Common resident.

At the beginning of the century Rock Doves were scarce in the county with H & R (1902) only referring to one colony near Marlow that bred on a high chalk cliff overlooking the Thames. In 1902 the possibility of these birds being infiltrated by Feral Pigeons was considered a real possibility. There is little other historical data and the species is largely left unrecorded. Since then there is little doubt that the increasing number of Feral Pigeons that have colonised towns, villages and industrial areas have totally taken over any possible remnants of the Rock Dove.

Feral Pigeons breed in urban areas throughout the county particularly near the centre of towns where the buildings (churches, public buildings, etc.) provide suitable nest sites (ledges, holes, etc.). They also nest in other structures such as motorway bridges.

Feral pigeons were not included in the field work for the 1993 atlas, so no comparisons can be made.

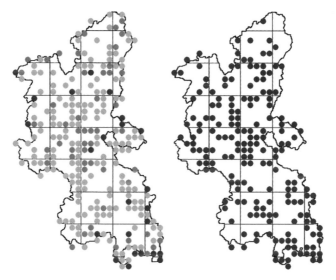

JER

Collared Dove
Steptopelia decaocto

Common resident.

The unprecedented rapid spread of the Collared Dove's range across Europe into the British Isles is well documented. The first breeding Collared Doves in Britain were recorded in 1955 with the first Buckinghamshire sighting in 1960 and breeding in 1961. For the next twenty years there was a steady increase in the local population, particularly in the more heavily populated southern part of the county. Even up until the mid 1970s numbers in north Buckinghamshire were regarded as low in comparison with the southern half of the county (MTNHS) and this is shown in the first atlas. However, the current survey does show a more even coverage across the county.

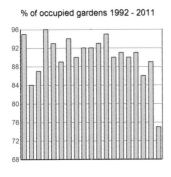

% of occupied gardens 1992 - 2011

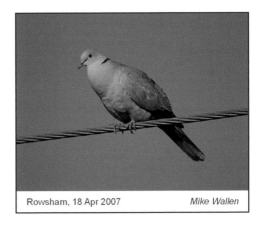

Rowsham, 18 Apr 2007   *Mike Wallen*

The Collared Dove's preferred habitat includes towns, suburbs, parks, large gardens and farms. In Buckinghamshire there were confirmed breeding records from most of the larger towns and villages. Some of the areas with no records are areas of unsuitable habitat, consisting largely of woodland or farmland with few breeding sites. Collared Doves often nest or roost in conifers and ornamental evergreen bushes which offer suitable shelter.

Breeding normally commences in March and may continue until September. Usually two eggs are produced with as many as 3-6 clutches being raised in one year. Nests of Collared Doves are not so easy to find as those of a Woodpigeon because the nesting trees are generally more dense. The easiest way of establishing confirmed breeding is perhaps by the presence of recently fledged birds.

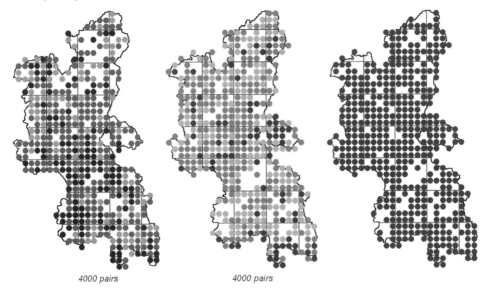

4000 pairs   4000 pairs

Following breeding, Collared Doves may gather in flocks with 100-200 being recorded annually while a maximum flock size of 500 was recorded in 1975. Dispersion from the breeding locality usually occurs the following spring when the birds are about one year old (BWP). The recovery of a bird originally ringed as a nestling near Aylesbury in May 1973 and found dead in Shropshire in February 1974 illustrates such a movement. Adult birds are thought to be more sedentary but there are some records of long distance travel: an adult bird ringed in the Netherlands in February 1971 was found dead near Aylesbury in January 1972.

JER

Turtle Dove
Steptopelia turtur

Rare and decreasing summer visitor.

Woodham, 3 May 2009   Tim Watts

The Turtle Dove perhaps shows the most dramatic decline in numbers of breeding birds in the 20 years since the previous Buckinghamshire atlas. In the first atlas the species was recorded in approximately 300 tetrads. Sadly this has dropped almost 90% to a mere 31 tetrads, with 10 of these of non-breeding birds and none of confirmed breeding. In line with this, populations estimates have dropped from 2500 to 20 pairs for this period. The distribution has also changed. Previously the most densely populated areas of the forests and woods on the Chilterns have been deserted and almost all of the possible and probable breeding records are to the north of the Chilterns. Turtle Dove is on the red list of Species of Conservation Concern.

Historically, a rise in the Turtle Dove population on a national basis in the 19th century was attributed to an increase in arable farming at that time (The Breeding Atlas). Numbers were steady during the period 1900 to 1940, but this was followed by another increase until the late 1970s. The Turtle Dove's status in Buckinghamshire was described in 1902 as 'a common summer bird' (H & R), while in 1920, H & J said they were 'not rare in well wooded places' with 'considerable numbers in the Thames Valley'. F & Y (1976) described them as common. During the 1980s there appears to have been a fall in the population with comments such as 'scarce' being used in the BBC annual reports. CBC data from Buckinghamshire and adjacent counties at the time supported these apparent changes.

In common with other seed-eating species associated with farmland, it has been affected by modern farming practices. Additionally, it is a prime target species for hunters as it passes through southern Europe to its winter quarters in West Africa where the breeding success in Europe appears to be influenced by cereal production in the wintering region (Eraud *et al.* 2009).

Typical Turtle Dove habitat consists of woodland, copses, tall hedgerows, areas of scrub and parkland. The nest site is not normally close to human habitation.

The breeding season begins shortly after the birds arrive. This is generally in May, but the earliest are typically seen between the second and fourth weeks of April. Birds may already be paired on arrival thus enabling breeding to start almost immediately. Two eggs are laid in a platform nest of fine twigs, grasses and moss. Young birds leave the nest from around the last week in June.

During September the birds leave Britain to winter just south of the Sahara Desert. The last birds may be seen in Buckinghamshire up until the first week in October.

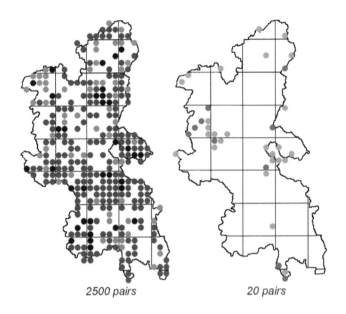

Migration dates

Earliest:	20 Mar
Ave earliest:	23 Apr
Ave latest:	16 Sep
Latest:	17 Oct

2500 pairs   20 pairs

JER

Ring-necked Parakeet
Psittacula krameri

Local but increasing introduced resident.

This species began breeding in the wild in Britain about 1969 and was admitted to the British list in 1983. The population gradually increased and by the early 1990s there were 500-1000 birds, mostly in Kent and the lower Thames Valley. Birds moved west along the Thames Valley and south into Surrey and the population rose to an estimated 5800 adults in 2001-2.

Little Marlow, 30 Mar 2011   *Jim Rose*

The first record in the county was of a pair producing three young at Dropmore in June 1974. The next records were of seven on several dates in 1976 (but not in 1977) in Marlow, one on 10 Oct 1977 in Medmenham, and one on 26 Jul 1982 at Stoke Mandeville. Records and numbers continued to increase and the first double-figure flocks occurred in 1993 at Dorney, Black Park and Coleshill. Birds probably bred in the county around this time but breeding was not confirmed until 1997 with two pairs at Dorney.

The maps show the extent of the increase in range since then. Birds have reached as far west as Henley and as far north as Beaconsfield although the core of the population remains the Dorney/Taplow area. The preferred habitat is parkland with large trees suitable for this hole-nesting species, They are often found within sight of the Thames and have bred on islands in the river.

Since 2003 large flocks have been seen going to roost to sites outside the county. The first record was 67 flying in small groups over Dorney on 23 March 2003. This was surpassed by 103 at the same site on 20 July 2005 and 250 flying north-east on 6 Nov 2009. There is no evidence of birds roosting in the county.

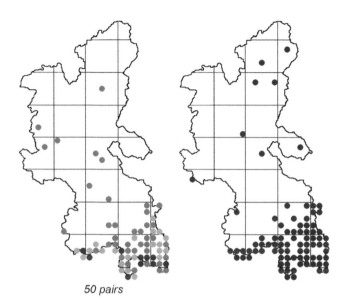

50 pairs

DMF

Cuckoo
Cuculus canorus

Uncommon summer visitor.

Calvert, 1 May 2009   Tim Watts

The Cuckoo was described by both H & R and H & J as common in Buckinghamshire in the early 1900s. They mentioned that Cuckoos needed hosts such as warblers and pipits in the county (H & R), and that in the Thames Valley eggs had been found in the nests of Marsh Warbler, Garden Warbler and Reed Bunting, in addition to those of the more usual foster parents (H & J).

The first atlas map shows them to be widespread, and the gaps, particularly in the north, are probably the result of under-recording. Since then there has been a substantial population decline in England and Wales which is reflected in the second atlas map. Cuckoo is on the red list of Species of Conservation Concern.

A number of reasons for this decline have been suggested. Dunnocks are probably the main host species in Buckinghamshire. Climate change has induced earlier breeding in Dunnocks so that Cuckoos may be arriving too late to parasitise this species. There is a very tenuous correlation between the distribution of Cuckoo in Buckinghamshire and those of Reed Warbler and Meadow Pipit, the next most frequent host species. Other possibilities are decreasing moth populations which may have reduced food supplies for adults and deterioration of the wintering habitat. Cuckoo is on the Species of Conservation Concern red list.

Cuckoos frequent a wide range of habitats and their distinctive, far-carrying call can be heard in towns, villages, farmland, woodland, reedbeds, and grassy downland slopes. The first survey shows a high percentage of probable breeding compared to the second but this is a result of a change in the breeding categories. Dunnocks are the main hosts in farmland, woodland and around habitations, replaced by Reed Warblers and Meadow Pipits in freshwater and heathland habitats respectively (Glue and Morgan 1972). Both are rather local species in Buckinghamshire and Meadow Pipits. Other species that are occasionally recorded as foster parents vary from Blackbird to Wren in size; and Robin, Pied Wagtail, Sedge Warbler and Reed Bunting have all been recorded in Buckinghamshire.

Birds tend to return to the same habitat in which they were raised and parasitise the same host species that fostered them. A female Cuckoo watches potential hosts, seeking out birds engaged in nest building. Eggs are usually laid in the afternoon at intervals of two to five days and the process takes as little as nine seconds. The breeding season of Cuckoos is synchronised with the host species and young may still be found in Reed Warbler nests as late as the last week of August.

A study using satellite-tracked birds has shown that adult Cuckoos leave Britain during June and July to travel to Congo via the Sahel region of Africa. The young birds leave a month later. The latest recorded dates in Buckinghamshire are usually from late August to early September but one at Hillesden was seen on 26 Sep 1994 and another on the very late date of 6 Oct 2004 at Broughton, Aylesbury. Ringed Cuckoos are infrequently recovered but two involving Buckinghamshire birds give some indication of timing and direction of departure in the autumn and, more importantly, the probable wintering area. These records are: Newport Pagnell (27 Jun 1965) to Loire, France (6 Sep 1965), and Marlow (27 Jul 1980) to Belgium (14 Sep 1980), and there is a record of a bird ringed just outside the county at Eton (23 Jun 1928) being found in Cameroon on 20 Jan 1930. The earliest arrival date is 14 Mar 1973 followed by 30 Mar 2000 but they more usually arrive from 7 April onwards, with more widespread reports from 17 April. A group of seven on Steps Hill on 3 May 1996 was exceptional.

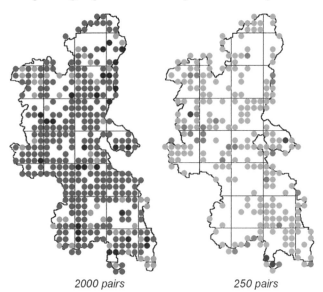

Migration dates	
Earliest:	30 Mar
Ave earliest:	11 Apr
Ave latest:	25 Aug
Latest:	6 Oct

2000 pairs   250 pairs

RAM

Barn Owl
Tyto alba

Uncommon resident.

Linford, 28 Dec 2008   *Mike Wallen*

H & R stated that the Barn Owl 'breeds commonly', but by 1920 H & J had modified this to 'by no means uncommon in suitable localities', and considered it decidedly less numerous than the Tawny Owl. Price thought it to be a fairly common resident but much less so than in former years. By 1976 F & Y found it to be uncommon. They remark that 'there has been a marked decrease in recent years but numbers appear to be building up again'. Possibly this apparent recovery owed something to a series of mild winters, but whatever the cause it was short-lived. In 1978 extensive felling of elms killed by Dutch elm disease took place and the following winter was hard, with prolonged snow cover. A sharp downturn in the Barn Owl's status in the county appears to date from this time, and the birds disappeared from many previous strongholds. This history closely followed the apparent national picture. Worst hit were the more built up and intensively farmed areas of central and S England (Shawyer 1987), of which Buckinghamshire seemed typical. Concern for the Barn Owl's future prompted a variety of initiatives such as surveys, nestbox installation and captive breeding schemes, although the last had very little effect on the wild population as many died quickly (Balmer *et al*, 2000). Success, ultimately, was dependent on fundamental improvements in habitat quality.

Barn Owls are typically birds of open farmland. Rough grassy marginal land, as along hedgerows or river banks, provide valuable hunting areas within this habitat. Unfortunately, roadside verges also fill the birds' feeding needs admirably, but expose them to a high level of risk from traffic. Not at all a woodland bird like the Tawny Owl, none the less the presence of woodland edge is a useful feature, though in the Chilterns much of this is on higher ground where the Barn Owl fares less well in winter.

The two breeding maps show a remarkable increase in range. From survival in a number of scattered pockets, Barn Owls are now quite widespread in the open country north of the Chiltern escarpment, particularly in the Vale of Aylesbury and the Upper Ray Valley. The various Stewardship Schemes, which encourage farmers to adopt more environmentally friendly practices, such as leaving wide fields margins, appears to have had a considerable positive effect on the county's Barn Owl population, as has had the provision of nestboxes in suitable habitat.

When conditions are good the Barn Owl has a greater capacity to respond with increased breeding effort than any other British bird of prey. Though three to five eggs are normal, many more are sometimes laid. H & R recorded clutches of nine and 11 in Buckinghamshire. It is also the only owl in Britain which is capable of rearing more than one brood in a season, despite a fledging period nearly double that of the Tawny. The potential breeding season therefore spans much of the year, but August is perhaps the peak month for fledging in the county. Well grown young Barn Owls can sometimes be detected even in a deeply concealed nest site by their loud snoring hisses. The young disperse after a few weeks, but not usually far. Three quarters of recoveries have been within 20 km of the ringing site (Winter Atlas).

Wintering Barn Owls roost in tree cavities or farm buildings. The latter are particularly frequented during hard weather, sometimes raising hopes that breeding will follow. Unfortunately such birds usually disappear with the return of milder conditions. East coast counties receive varying numbers of winter visitors of the darker continental race *T.a.guttata*, but there appear to be no records of them for Buckinghamshire. A fledgling, ringed at Wormsley on 15 Jun 1998 was found dead in Kent on 31 Oct 1998.

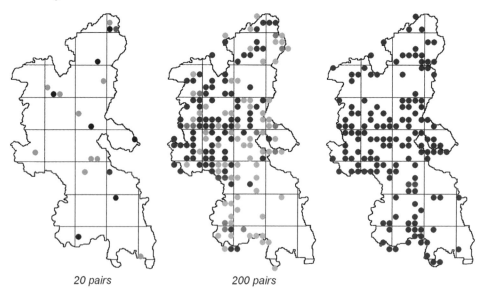

20 pairs   200 pairs

PJKB

Little Owl
Athene noctua

Uncommon introduced resident.

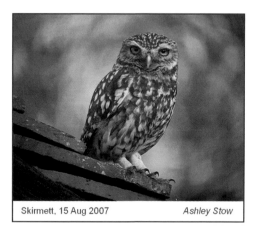

Skirmett, 15 Aug 2007   Ashley Stow

The plump outline and frowning face pattern of a Little Owl on a roadside perch is a familiar sight in Buckinghamshire today, yet the bird was unknown in the county a century ago. Following introductions into Yorkshire and Kent from Europe, large scale releases were made in the 1890s by Lord Lilford in Northamptonshire and by Walter Rothschild in Tring Park. The latter seem to have been unsuccessful, although the species now breeds there regularly. Presumably most of the first Buckinghamshire colonists originated from the Northamptonshire stock. H & R comment that `Every year cages full are sent over from Holland ... many have been liberated and bred, though they are decreasing in numbers." This theme, of an increase followed by a decrease, has been echoed by histories up to and including the Breeding Atlas, though the supposed timing of these changes varies. For an introduced species expanding into a vacant niche, such a sequence of events is perhaps to be expected, but there is clearly a subjective element in many accounts. Evidently, hard winters such as 1946/47 and 1962/63 had an adverse effect, and so, perhaps, did the pesticide problems of the 1950s and 1960s. Concrete facts and figures are scarce, and the effects of recent changes in agricultural practice on the Little Owl are poorly understood. An excellent Swiss study (Juillard 1984) could provide the basis for more detailed work in Britain.

In the first edition it was stated 'Within Buckinghamshire, more limited surveys over the past eight years suggest that over much of the county the Little Owl is the most numerous farmland bird of prey, and is maintaining its numbers.' This is no longer true. A study of the two breeding season maps show a marked decline in the former stronghold of the Vale of Aylesbury and the area now occupied by Milton Keynes. This is apparently partially compensated by an expansion into formerly unoccupied areas in the north of the county, but it is likely that these areas were initially under recorded.

Open farmland is the principal habitat in the county, subject to availability of nest sites and invertebrate prey. The former are not difficult for the birds to find, except in some areas devastated by Dutch elm disease, but prey availability may influence habitat choice. Although rodents form a substantial part of the diet, invertebrates are also of great importance to this small predator (Hibbert-Ware 1937-38). Vital items are earthworms, best obtained from grassland, and dung beetles, especially *Geotrupes* spp, for which the presence of stock is essential. Consequently, extensive areas of cereal or other arable farming are unlikely support high densities of Little Owls. A probable cause of the population decline is a trend away from stock farming.

Breeding may commence from early April, but most Buckinghamshire birds start at the end of the month or in early May. Breeding success can be adversely affected by cold weather in spring. Typical nest sites are narrow curving cavities in trees, with the eggs or young often hidden around a corner. Pollard poplar, abundant in parts of the Vale of Aylesbury provides many such sites, while willow, ash, oak, apple and the few remaining dead elms are all regularly used. Farm buildings, bale ricks, wood stacks, rabbit burrows and even a dense hawthorn hedge are some of the alternatives recorded in the county. Nest boxes are less readily taken here than by Tawny Owls and Kestrels.

Fledged by early July, the young disperse after four or five weeks, usually moving only a short distance. Most recoveries are under 10 km, and although occasional birds travel considerably farther, no such records involve Buckinghamshire. A high proportion of recoveries in the county are road casualties. Persecution seems rare.

Winter roosts, which may be used throughout the year by established breeding birds, are generally on ledges or crevices in trees, giving shelter and a good view. They are betrayed by characteristic brownish pellets, spangled with glossy fragments of beetle elytra, and often also by accumulations of prey, sometimes referred to as `larders'. Territories are established from February onwards, to the accompaniment of far carrying `kiew' calls, uttered by day as well as night. Data from S England (Glue and Scott 1980) indicate territory areas averaging from 35 ha (water meadows) to 38 ha (mixed farmland). Sites selected for nesting include some traditional cavities, used year after year, but changes are more frequent than with Tawny Owls and Kestrels. Consequently, breeding surveys of this species require extra effort in order to locate all new nest sites each season.

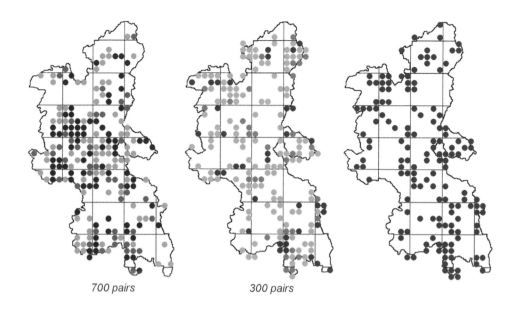

700 pairs   300 pairs

PJKB

Tawny Owl
Strix aluco

Fairly common resident.

H & R reported that the Tawny Owl was `common wherever there are large and old trees with hollows to breed in'. This essentially holds true today, but the loss of tree cover in the intervening years must have reduced numbers overall, although there was an increase in numbers in the first three decades of this century. Tawny Owls escaped the worst effects of the organochlorine pollution during the 1950s and 1960s, but the

Marlow Bottom, 21 Feb 2007   *Adam Bassett*

efficiency of modern rodenticides must have had an adverse effect through prey reduction. On the credit side, direct persecution is less than at the turn of the century, while active encouragement of the birds, for example by provision of nestboxes, has emerged as a positive factor.

However, the two breeding maps show a dramatic thinning of the range which is most noticeable north of the Chilterns, although the Chilterns themselves have also seemingly lost many birds. This may be a rather distorted picture of the Tawny Owl's distribution in the county largely due to the difficulties of covering all the woodlands adequately for a nocturnal species. Almost certainly the density in the Chilterns is considerably greater than in the Vale of Aylesbury where the population is patchy and dependent on scattered woodlands, thickets and hedgerows. Very open country is avoided, because the Tawny Owl hunts principally by dropping on to its prey from a perch, rather than quartering the ground. Nesting cavities could be a limiting factor, especially in commercial beechwoods where diseased growth is quickly eliminated, but old nests of squirrels, crows, Sparrowhawks and others provide alternatives which are probably under-represented by nest records. Chimney-type boxes installed in such woods have been readily accepted. In the Vale, cavities in ash, pollard poplar or dead elm are the usual sites. Kestrel boxes are also used, though interestingly very few are ever used by both species. Eighteen local Kestrel boxes have been used by Tawny Owls and 56 by Kestrels, but only one has been used successfully by both species, with failed attempts in another two. Tawny Owls occasionally nest in bale ricks, but never in farm buildings, though individuals often roost in barns, leading to many spurious reports of `Barn Owls'.

Being dependent on detailed local knowledge for hunting success, most established Tawny Owls are extremely sedentary. Breeding territories coincide closely with winter range, their size and boundaries depending from year to year on rodent numbers. In years of poor food supply, few pairs breed at all, and those that do tend to start later and have smaller clutches. The Tawny Owl is on average the earliest nesting British owl, with a mean starting date of 25 March (the Breeding Atlas). In 1985 at least one Chilterns pair started their large clutch of five eggs in mid February.

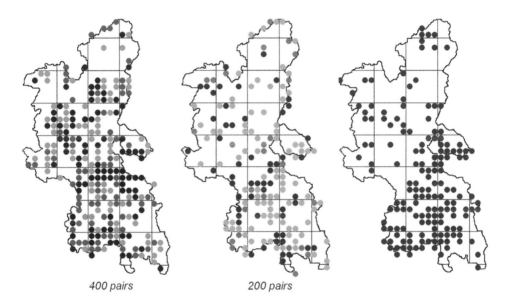

400 pairs   200 pairs

Monitoring of nestboxes and natural sites since 1980 has shown marked differences in breeding success between populations in the Chilterns and the Vale of Aylesbury. As might be expected, Chiltern birds are more successful on average, but this is not so in all years. Unseasonal weather can have a serious effect on success, as when several monitored broods were killed during heavy snow on 25-26 Apr 1981. Successful broods mainly leave the nest during May. Most consist of one or two young but three or four, and rarely five, may be reared in a good year. The presence of fledged broods is betrayed after dark by insistent `kewick' hunger calls. Full independence comes in the first autumn, during which time mortality is highest, with road deaths accounting for a high proportion of ringing recoveries in the county. Most young birds disperse no more than 10 km in their search for territories in which to establish themselves. During winter Tawny Owls roost by day in trees, with a liking for ivy-covered limbs. Occasionally their powers of concealment fail them, and noisy mobbing parties of small birds draw attention to their whereabouts. Courtship and nest cavity selection occur from December onwards, though some sites are chosen only just before breeding.

PJKB

Long-eared Owl
Asio otus

Rare resident and scarce winter visitor.

Early accounts depict this species as a regular, if not numerous, breeding bird in wooded parts of the county (H & R, H & J). Much later F & Y refer to these accounts as `old nesting records', and describe the Long-eared Owl as an uncommon resident, rarely recorded. It may in fact be much overlooked as it is highly nocturnal, and an immense amount of skilled fieldwork would be required to form an accurate picture of its distribution in the county. That said, it does appear to have decreased this century, perhaps as a result of competition with the Tawny Owl. Indeed, since 1992 there have only been three instances of confirmed breeding, near Brill in 1995, at Dorton in 1997 and in mid-Bucks in 2006. Ironically, it will also be less well recorded as a result of the decline in keepering, a reversal of the situation with many other birds.

Pitchcott, 18 Mar 2006   *Mike Wallen*

Songs and calls associated with territory establishment and courtship begin in late winter, and provide the best means of discovering this elusive species. Coniferous woodland is a favoured habitat for nesting, though by no means the only one, and quite small copses and spinneys may be utilised. A nest in the Vale of Aylesbury in 1975 was in a hedgerow poplar in open farmland (P. J. K. Burton). Typically this was in the old nest of a Carrion Crow, though those of Magpies and Sparrowhawks are also commonly used. This habit is a further factor in making proof of breeding difficult to obtain. Breeding starts somewhat later on average than the Tawny Owl, and most young fledge in late May or June. For several weeks after this the presence of the young may be revealed by their `unoiled gate' hunger cries. Thereafter they disperse randomly, and farther on average than Tawny Owls or Little Owls, with about a quarter of the birds ringed in Britain moving more than 100 km.

Birds from N Europe are more strongly migratory, and reach Britain in varying numbers each winter, sometimes almost on the scale of an irruption as was the case in 1986. The Winter Atlas mentions 26 foreign ringed Long-eared Owls recovered in Britain. One of these was a bird ringed at Vogelenzey in N Holland on 8 Jun 1932 and recovered at High Wycombe on 3 Nov 1932 while an adult female ringed at Buckland on 9 Dec 1995 was found dead in Koln, Germany on 27 Mar 1997. Probably some visitors stay in Britain to breed, so increased vigilance following such influxes may reveal nesting pairs in new localities.

Birds have been found wintering more frequently in recent years. A roost of up to 13 birds was found in the Chilterns in January 1991 while there was a roost of up to eight at Linford in Jan to Mar 1994 and seven at Dorton on 5 Dec 1994.

PJKB

Short-eared Owl
Asio flammeus

Scarce winter visitor and migrant.

Great Linford, 13 Nov 2011   *Jason Chalk*

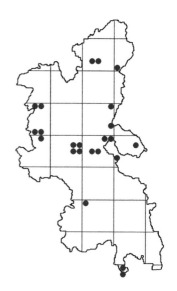

The status of the Short-eared Owl has probably not changed significantly since the days of Clark Kennedy. Small numbers appear in the autumn in suitable grassland habitats and may stay until the following early spring. Birds are usually alone but occasionally small groups are formed such as five on set-aside near Ford on 1 Feb 1997 and eight, again near Ford, on 9 Dec 2004.

The map shows that the Vale of Aylesbury and the Upper Ray Valley are particularly favoured. Here can be found areas of the rough grassland that the species favours, for example the Gallows
Bridge Farm reserve.

A very small number of migrants pass through the county in spring and autumn, some of which may be continental birds. There is one intriguing record of possible breeding. Two birds were seen in June 1980 and four in August at a site in the south of the county.

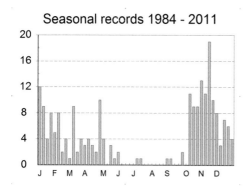

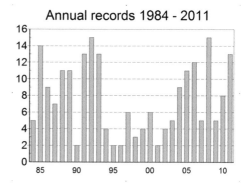

Nightjar
Caprimulgus europaeus

Irregular summer visitor and rare migrant.

Clark Kennedy described the distribution of Nightjars as partially distributed throughout Buckinghamshire but nowhere a numerous species. He gives Gerrards Cross as a site. H & J remarked 'in suitable places by no means rare.' They list a number of sites throughout the county from Newport Pagnell and Bletchley in the north to Burnham Beeches, Marlow, and Hambleden in the south.

The history of Nightjars since the Second World War is one of a steady decline. In 1944 about eight pairs were recorded in the area bounded by Beaconsfield, Dropmore, and Wooburn. Between 1948 and 1963 up to four pairs bred at Littleworth Common, one pair at East Burnham Common, and three pairs at Bockmer. Birds may also have bred at Dukes Wood near Gerrards Cross, Penn Street, and Black Park. Many of these sites are now unsuitable due to the growth of trees in the breeding areas.

In 1965 four pairs were discovered in the Brickhill Woods. This area remained a breeding site until the early 1980s when they seem to have died out. In the late 1970s birds were heard in Balham's Wood, near Stonor and may have bred for a few years.

The species is maintaining a very precarious existence in the county. The 1981 BTO survey produced only two sites in the county, while during the first mapping period Nightjars were only found in the Brickhills and at one site in the south. Since then breeding has been proved in only four years although birds have been heard churring in suitable habitat in a further eight years.

The primary habitat of Nightjars is heathland, a very rare and decreasing habitat in the county. They also utilise cleared woodland or recently planted conifer plantations, but this is a very transient habitat. The population decline in the county is parallelled by its decline in the country as a whole. As well as the reduction in habitat, this decline may also be linked to climatic change and degradation of the wintering areas in Africa.

Attempts are being made to improve the heathland habitats in the county. This habitat is continually threatened by invasive birch scrub and considerable work is required to maintain suitable conditions for breeding.

There are only three autumn records: 12 Sep 1982 at Downley Common, 15 Aug 1988 at Langley Park, while one was killed by a car by Wendover Woods on 19 Sep 1994.

DMF

Swift
Apus apus

Common summer visitor.

Clark Kennedy and all subsequent authors refer to the Swift as a regular or common summer visitor to Buckinghamshire, which it remains today.

The earliest arrival reported in the county is a single at Calvert on 12 Apr 2009. The previous earliest arrivals were on 14 Apr, in 1996 at Little Marlow and in 2007 at Startopsend. This is part of a trend for some summer migrants to arrive earlier. Mass arrival generally occurs in mid May when feeding flocks over water can be large; the

Kimblewick, 4 Aug 2012   *Richard Billyard*

flock of 1000 birds at Little Marlow on 28 Apr 1996 was unprecedented. More typically, on 11 May 1995 'thousands' were seen in the Colne Valley, with 1000 reported at Tilehouse.

The single-brood breeding cycle is very compressed, and the birds stay only three to three-and-a-half months before returning to Africa, south of the equator. There has been a considerable decline in the UK breeding population and the species has been moved from the green to amber list of conservation concern. There are a number of possible reasons for the decline. As the birds are almost entirely dependent on buildings for their nest sites, replacement of old buildings, which have openings to nest sites, with less suitable modern buildings maybe a major factor. Other possibilities are fewer flying insects and less favourable conditions in their African wintering areas.

The two breeding maps are not entirely comparable. The later map shows, by using grey dots, where birds were present but definitely not breeding, a category not recognised in the earlier map. Though they are seen throughout the county, breeding is not easy to prove - notwithstanding the assertion in the Breeding Atlas that `locating breeding Swifts is easy because of their noisy chases'. Moreover, among the adults of breeding age are younger non-breeders - some possibly even three years old - which practise nest making, and this in itself makes it difficult at times to prove breeding. It is significant that tetrads showing only possible breeding are three times as numerous as those showing proved breeding.

In the late summer some lakes and reservoirs attract quite large flocks. At Willen Lake more than 1,000 have been recorded. The main southward migration from the county usually starts in mid August. In 1976 most had left by the first week of August, which was considered early, but the good summer had obviously allowed the young to develop quickly. However, the following year the last birds were seen well into September. The latest reported was at Bletchley 2 Nov 1975, although Clark Kennedy noted one at Fawley on 22 Dec 1860. A more recent report is one over Steps Hill on 28 Oct 2004.

Few Swifts have been trapped and ringed in Buckinghamshire. One ringed at Weston Turville in May 1967 was recovered at Brazzaville, Congo in September 1968 and another, recovered when breeding at North Dean in June 1971, had been ringed as a nestling in Holland in June 1963 (BWP). Many local High and West Wycombe birds have been recovered in the same area, one after 11 years.

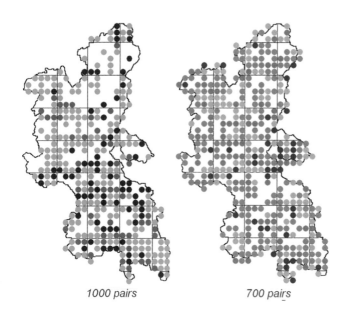

Migration dates	
Earliest:	12 Apr
Ave earliest:	21 Apr
Ave latest:	20 Sep
Latest:	2 Nov

1000 pairs   700 pairs

DBH

Alpine Swift
Apus melba

Very rare vagrant. All records are given.

2006: 1 on 8 Apr, Bergher's Hill.
2006: 1 on 16 Apr, Little Marlow then 18 Apr, Boulter's Lock, Maidenhead when it flew into
        Bucks airspace.
2008: 1 on 23 June, Stowe.
2011: 1 on 3 July, Taplow.

It is likely that only one bird was involved in the 2006 records although a number of birds were
seen in England at this time (Rose, 2008).

Kingfisher
Alcedo atthis

Local resident.

Broughton Trout Pools, 12 Sep 2009   *Mike Wallen*

Earlier this century H & R indicated that the
Kingfisher was generally distributed where
suitable habitat existed, and H & J wrote that
Kingfishers were once quite numerous but
reduced in numbers due to shooting,
particularly on the River Thames. According
to F & Y an increase occurred following the
cessation of shooting and the introduction of

220

the Protection of Birds Acts. The provision of new habitat, through the excavation of gravel pits, reservoirs, clay pits and canals, has also been beneficial to Kingfishers.

The present breeding distribution shows a very localised pattern around streams, rivers, gravel pits, lakes and reservoirs, where a plentiful supply of minnows, sticklebacks and bullheads may be found. This shows the specific habitat requirements of Kingfishers. In the extreme south of the county Kingfisher distribution follows the meandering of the River Thames, and a concentration may also be found at the Wraysbury gravel pits bordering the Thames in the county's south-east corner. The central part of the county shows a few isolated breeding records, associated with the River Thame and its tributaries in the west, and the Grand Union Canal and Tring Reservoirs in the east. Very few breeding sites are found in the northern part of the county, with the exception of the Milton Keynes area where the Grand Union Canal, Rivers Ouzel and Great Ouse, and the gravel pits associated with them provide more suitable habitat.

Two or sometimes three broods may be reared in a season extending from March to September. Adult Kingfishers chase the young from the breeding territory soon after fledging. Movements of juvenile birds take place mainly from July onwards, in no particular direction. The birds usually travel less than 10 km but occasionally up to 250 km (Morgan and Glue 1977). Birds ringed in the county in autumn have been recovered in Surrey and Essex (via Northamptonshire), while others ringed at Chew Valley, Avon (149 km) and Knaresborough, Yorkshire (250 km) have been found in Buckinghamshire in November and August respectively.

Three major factors affect Kingfisher numbers: severe winters, pollution, and waterways management. Cold winters can cause very high mortality when access to open water is restricted by ice for long periods. Between 1962 and 1982 the winters of 1962/63, 1978/79 and 1981/82 reduced Kingfisher numbers considerably (Dobinson and Richards 1964, Marchant and Hyde 1980, Taylor and Marchant 1983). In extreme conditions some Kingfishers escape by moving to the coast. However, the high reproductive potential of the species enables a rapid recovery from heavy losses.

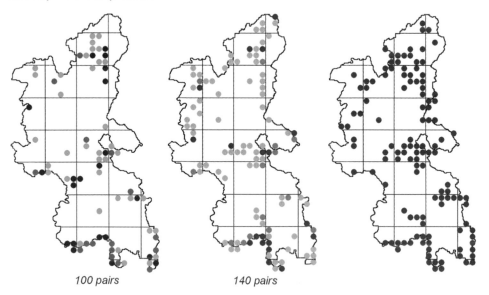

100 pairs   140 pairs

RAM

Bee-eater
Merops apiaster

Very rare vagrant. All records are given.

1866: 1 Dropmore.
1927: 1 in last week of Oct, Skirmett.
1976: 1 on 8 May, Buckingham.
1979: 1 on 27 Apr, Chalfont St Giles.
1997: 1 on 1 Jun, Chesham Bois.
1997: 5 on 28 Jul, Great Missenden.
2002: 1 on 15 Aug, Gerrards Cross.
2002: 4 on 11 Sep, Beaconsfield.
2005: 1 on 12 Jun, Princes Risborough.

The record of seven at Stoke Mandeville in June 1983 mentioned in Brucker et al. (1992) was never submitted to the British Birds Rarities Committee, and cannot be substantiated.

Roller
Coracius garrulus

Very rare vagrant. There is one record.

1938: 1 on 5 Jul, Great Missenden (Ferguson, 2009).

The bird was seen from close range in a garden. Given the wariness of this species there is a possibility that the bird was an escape although the record was accepted at the time by the editors of British Birds.

Hoopoe
Upupa epops

Rare vagrant. Has bred once.

Clark Kennedy gives an undated record for Chesham.

The first dated record is:

1760: 2 shot at Ford.

Between 1838 and 1957 there were a further 11 records, including successful breeding in a garden at Taplow in 1916. There were another 12 records between 1962 and 1969,

Horsley's Green, 15 May 2011   *Jim Rose*

18 records between 1970 and 1990 and 18 records between 1991 and 2011. The records since 1974 are shown on the graphs. Hoopoes have been found throughout the county, often in gardens.

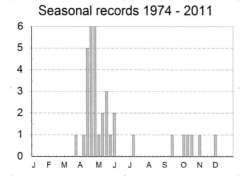

Seasonal records 1974 - 2011

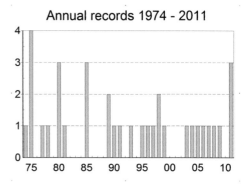

Annual records 1974 - 2011

Wryneck
Jynx torquilla

Scarce migrant which used to breed.

Clark Kennedy described the status of Wryneck as a 'common summer visitor', but there was evidently a reduction in the population by the early 20th century for H & J stated it was a 'regular summer visitor, but has recently decreased in numbers'. By 1947 Price wrote that it was a 'regular summer visitor, only breeding in the south-east'.

In the 1950s pairs bred at Penn, Marlow, and another site in the county. Small numbers of birds continued to be seen almost every year but there was no sign of breeding

Bacombe Hill, 20 Sep 2010   Mike Wallen

except for a bird emerging from a hole in the Thames Valley during 1973. It was assumed that Wrynecks as a breeding bird in Buckinghamshire were long past until 1985 when a pair bred in a coconut hollowed out by Blue Tits in a garden in Chalfont St Peter. They were seen in the same locality during 1986 and 1987 but breeding was not proved.

Wrynecks require trees with suitable nest-holes, and areas of grassland where they can feed on ants, their major food. They found these conditions in old orchards, parkland, large gardens, and in the areas of scrub and grassland which are typical of the Chilterns.

The local decline is part of a general decline throughout England, which, in turn, is part of a decline throughout Europe. It is likely that the reasons for the decline are associated with the destruction of orchards and ant-rich grasslands and the increased use of pesticides.

The graphs show the pattern of occurrence of migration during the years 1972-2011. During this period 62 birds were seen in 28 of the years. There is a tiny spring passage and a much larger autumn passage which peaks in the last week of August and the first week of September. It is likely that these birds are drift migrants from Scandinavia. Wrynecks have been found throughout the county, but the Chilterns seem particularly favoured.

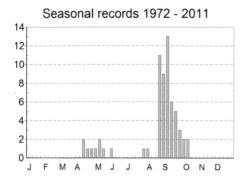

Seasonal records 1972 - 2011

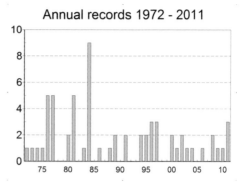

Annual records 1972 - 2011

DMF

Green Woodpecker
Picus viridis

Common resident.

H & R described this as probably the most
plentiful woodpecker in the county: `though
nowhere numerous'. They wrote, `it occurs
wherever there are old trees in which it can
nest.' H & J noted that Green Woodpeckers
became scarce on the lower ground in the
eastern part of the Thames Valley compared
with their status in the beech woods of the
western part.

Beaconsfield, 28 Jan 2010   *David Ferguson*

The first atlas map shows the species to be
widespread, though more numerous in the well-wooded southern half of the county. North of
the Chiltern escarpment, which shows clearly on the map, the records were much more
localised and the species was absent from much of the agricultural area lacking copses or
hedgerows with mature timber. The chain of deciduous woodland running from Oakley to
Middle Claydon, and the woodland areas of Brickhill Woods and Ashridge were centres of
Green Woodpecker distribution here. Most of the other scattered records related to farmland
breeding birds.

Green Woodpeckers have been expanding their range in the UK while BBS data shows that
the population index has doubled since 1990. This expansion is reflected in the second atlas
map which shows the species to be occupying most of the tetrads in the county and is only
notably absent from the urban areas of Milton Keynes and High Wycombe. It is likely that this
expansion is a result of climate change, in particular a series of mild winters since the 1990s.
In hard winters Green Woodpeckers are severely affected when they are unable to find food
in the frozen ground. Some local woodland CBC plots in N Buckinghamshire reflect this. For
example, following the cold winters of 1978/79 and 1981/82, the density of Green
Woodpeckers at Linford Wood (Milton Keynes) dropped from seven pairs per 1.1 sq km in
1978 to none in 1979, and at Howe Park Wood (Bletchley) birds were present in three out of
five years during 1970-1974, but not in either 1983 or 1984.

Green Woodpeckers are much less restricted to deciduous woodland than the other two

British species of woodpecker. Well timbered parkland, dry heath and well grazed chalk grassland are other favoured habitats of Green Woodpeckers, where they feed on the ground, especially on ants. Nest holes are usually excavated in deciduous trees (especially ash, oak, birch and beech) at varying heights up to 15 m. Elms accounted for 8% of nest trees recorded on BTO nest record cards, with no difference in usage before or after the onset of Dutch elm disease (Osborne 1982). Eggs are laid from early April to early June (most commonly during May), with young in the nest in June/early July. Green Woodpeckers may travel some distance from the nest to feed at favourite grassland sites.

Green Woodpeckers are very sedentary birds and there is no evidence of long-distance movements within this country or the Continent. The most notable local ringing recovery is of a bird moving 45 km from Cheddington to Little Barford (Bedfordshire).

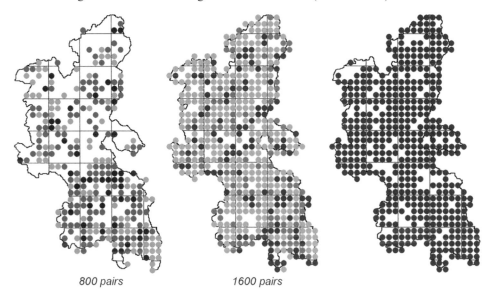

800 pairs   1600 pairs

RAM

Great Spotted Woodpecker
Dendrocopos major

Common resident.

Historical information on the Great Spotted Woodpecker in Buckinghamshire is rather sparse, but H & J noted that it was scarcer than formerly, being less rare in the south of the county. The results of the first survey show birds to be present in almost all the woods in the county. The second survey shows an even wider distribution with birds occupying relatively treeless areas of agricultural land.

These population changes are part of a national trend. By the early nineteenth century the species had all but disappeared north of Cheshire and Yorkshire. With the climatic amelioration that began in the latter part of last century a range expansion occurred, taking the species to the limit of suitable breeding conditions in N Scotland. The first National Breeding Atlas showed a widespread distribution in mainland Britain, and the population nationally has shown further recent increases. While the Common Birds Census index for woodland remained stable from

1

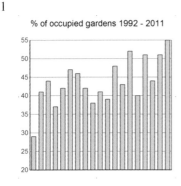

% of occupied gardens 1992 - 2011

Little Kimble, 3 Dec 2011   *Richard Billyard*

965-1971 it rose by 116% in the period 1972-1978. Osborne (1982) considered the most likely cause to be the greater availability of beetle larvae due to the spread of Dutch elm disease. The population then stabilised until the mid 1990s when it rapidly increased. The CBC/BBS surveys show an increase of 250% between 1995 and 2009.

Surveys conducted in the 1970s give a more detailed picture of the increase. At Linford Wood, Milton Keynes a density of 9.3 pairs per sq km was recorded in 1979 compared to 4.7 pairs per sq km in 1975. At Howe Park Wood, Bletchley the population increased from nil in 1971 to 16.7 pairs per sq km in 1983. The highest densities recorded in the county are from some W Buckinghamshire woodlands, where in 1984 15 pairs per sq km were found in old coppice and 20 pairs per sq km in high forest oak. These compare with an average density from a sample of national Common Birds Census plots in E England in 1983 of 8.3 pairs per sq km.

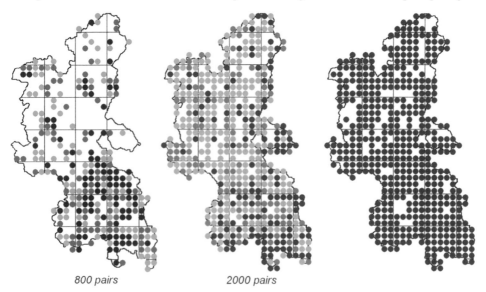

800 pairs   *2000 pairs*

RAM

Lesser Spotted Woodpecker
Dendrocopus minor

Scarce and declining resident.

The Lesser Spotted Woodpecker is described by earlier authors as 'fairly common in wooded areas', and all remark that it is commoner than generally thought. It is not easily seen, and is certainly under-recorded. This is largely due to its small size and its tendency to stay in the tops of trees. It is also very mobile within its local area. It may occur unexpectedly and rarely seems to be seen in the same place twice, except at nesting time.

BBC annual reports did not discuss the status of the species in the 1980s but the MTNHS report for 1979 mentioned records from 22 localities, which was three less than in 1972. In the north of the county the only records were from Milton Keynes and Stowe.

In 1978 it was suggested that the population had suffered a slight reduction and the loss of trees due to Dutch elm disease was put forward as a reason, a view repeated three years later. The first Breeding Atlas suggested that the consequences of Dutch elm disease were initially beneficial in providing an abundance of food in dead and decaying trees, though conceding that the eventual loss of trees might lead to fewer birds.

The first county breeding survey map showed only eight tetrads with proved breeding out of a total of 78, a reflection of the difficulty in locating breeding birds. Birds were thinly dispersed throughout the county with most in the central Chilterns and least in the Vale of Aylesbury and the north of the county. The later maps show that this species has suffered a considerable decline with birds only recorded in 15 tetrads in the summer and 21 in the winter. A peculiarity of these maps is that, with the exception of the Church Wood, Hedgerley and Burnham Beeches tetrads, no tetrad has records for both summer and winter. This may be the result of the large territories this species maintains.

The reasons for the decline are not clear. Possibilities are: predation by the increasing numbers of Great Spotted Woodpeckers; reductions in small-diameter dead wood which are suitable for foraging; and a fragmentation of their large territories due to loss of woodland and hedge trees such as elms. The species is on the red list for species of conservation concern.

100 pairs   20 pairs

The Lesser Spotted Woodpecker breeds from late April into June, and is single brooded. Both sexes excavate the nest hole which is usually in soft or decaying wood, sometimes even on the underside of a branch. It can be up to 20 m above the ground, adding further to the difficulty of proving breeding.

The BBC Garden Survey has mentioned individuals in a few gardens and even taking artificial food.

DBH

Woodlark
Lullula arborea

Occasional breeding summer visitor and rare vagrant.

Woodlarks bred regularly though rather sparsely in the middle and south of the county until 1961 when there was a last record of three birds on 16 Sep at Longdown Hill, Cadsden. The largest recorded flock during this period was one of 15-20 birds at Saunderton on 20 Nov 1949. There then followed a gap of 10 years before a pair was observed feeding young on 18 Jul 1971 at Bow Brickhill Woods.

During the next 21 years there were just four records of single birds.

1973: 14 Feb, Iver GP.
1988: 23 Feb to 8 Mar, Burnham.
1990: 30 Mar, Taplow.
1990: 21 Oct, Calvert.

In 1993 a bird was seen twice during the summer in Black Park and in 1994 a pair feeding young was discovered there on 2 May 1994. The site was an area of clear fell newly planted with black pines. The pair raised two broods of four and three and were last seen on 24 Sep. Since then up to five birds were present at Black Park every year until 1999 with breeding proved in 1996 when the original site was vacated because of the growth of the pines; instead the heathland was utilised. A single bird was seen here on 1 Jul 2007.

In 1997 four territories were present at Stoke Common after a devastating fire the previous year. At least one pair bred successfully. Up to three pairs were present every year until 2004 with confirmed breeding in 1998 and 2000. At a site in the north of the county, single singing birds were recorded in 1999 and 2000. One was singing in the early morning of 26 Jun 2011 at Farnham Common.

There have been two spring migrants:

1999: 1 singing on 23 Feb, Dancersend.
2005: 1 on 23 Mar, flew over Black Park.
2010: 1 singing on 13 May, Stoke Common.

and nine autumn migrants:

1994: 1 on 4 and 6 Oct, Drayton Parslow.
1998: 1 on 23 Sep, Steps Hill.
1998: 1 on 1 Nov, Little Marlow.
2008: 1 on 12 Oct, Ivinghoe Beacon.
2008: 1 on 4 Nov, Steps Hill.

2010: 1 on 10 Oct, Steps Hill.
2010: 1 on 2 Nov, Steps Hill.
2011: 2 on 14 Oct, Ivinghoe Hills.

These passage birds are probably moving between the Breckland, where they summer, and the south coast or the near continent where they winter.

In the last hundred years the population of Woodlarks in the UK has fluctuated considerably from a high in the early 19th century to a low in the 1880s. Numbers began to increase in the 1920s reaching a peak in the early 1950s. The steep decline since then resulted in possibly less than 100 pairs in the mid 1960s (Sitters, 1986). The population then rose with some fluctuations to an estimated 1500 pairs.

Woodlarks in Britain are at the north-western edge of their world range and are consequently sensitive to changes in climate which may be a factor in their fluctuating population. Their habitat requirements are quite precise: a mosaic of bare ground or short vegetation for feeding and tussocks of vegetation with disturbed ground for nest sites (UK BAP). Away from the few heathland sites in the county these requirements can only be met in areas of clear fell and young plantations, a transient habitat that is only occasionally visited by birders.

DMF

Skylark
Alauda arvensis

Common resident, migrant, and winter visitor.

Ivinghoe Beacon, 8 Apr 2008   Mike Wallen

The earliest accounts describe the Skylark as common. The first edition of *The Birds of Buckinghamshire* stated 'that Skylarks breed in almost every tetrad in the county'. The latter statement is no longer true. A large gap in the map in the north-east of the county is easily explained by the growth of Milton Keynes but the scarcity of records in the south-east and agricultural areas in the north are less straightforwardly explained.

After a long period of stability, Skylarks began declining nationally around 1980 so that the National Common Birds Census indices are now at about half the 1980 figures. There are a number of reasons for this decline. The birds prefer fields whose vegetation is short enough to walk through. In the breeding season this is found in newly-cut grass and spring-sown cereals. Autumn-sown cereals and oil-seed rape are only used in April, after which they become too tall. The change to winter cereals, which has become a common practice in the county, is thus detrimental to Skylarks. This change in farming practice has also reduced the area of stubble which is an important feeding habitat in winter. Spraying with herbicides is also a factor in the decline as this has reduced the amount of arable weeds which provide another important food source. It will be interesting to see what the effect of farm stewardship schemes in the county will have on the Skylark population.

In winter the resident population is augmented by visitors from NE Europe, though the lack of local ringing recoveries makes the source of the visitors only an assumption. During this period many birds form flocks. Flocks in excess of 100 birds are recorded almost every year, but flocks of over 250 birds are now uncommon. The largest recorded flock is one of 500-600 birds at Dorney Court on 20 Feb 1991, while there were 350-500 birds at Little Marlow on 10 Feb 1991 and 450 at Boveney on 26 Dec 1984. 400 near Finemere Wood on 26 Dec 2007 is the only comparable-sized flock of the new millennium.

Large movements during and after heavy snow are occasionally reported. On 31 Dec 1978 1000 birds flew SW over Marlow in 10 minutes, while on the following day a movement of 2500 birds per hour was recorded.

20,000 pairs   10,000 pairs

DMF

Sand Martin
Riparia riparia

Very local summer visitor and common migrant.

Sand Martins originally depended primarily on steep-sided river banks for nest sites, and their distribution in Buckinghamshire must therefore have been more restricted than it is today. Though nesting at sand and gravel excavations dates back at least to Clark Kennedy's day, the availability of this habitat has increased considerably in more recent times. Kennedy also alluded to breeding along the Thames and described the species

Caldecotte Lake, 28 May 2011   *Keith O'Hagen*

as `common everywhere during the summer months', but since he mentions no other colonies his assessment perhaps includes passage birds. H & R merely wrote of breeding `in suitable places' while H & J only mentioned birds at Tring reservoirs in summer, and knew of no nearby breeding site. Other pre-war reports note a few Thames breeding colonies and occasional breeding at pits elsewhere.

Fluctuations in population size are greatly affected by human activity, notably gravel digging and subsequent flooding and filling in. The extent of breeding, especially at major sites, has been only intermittently documented. No counts of more than 20-30 pairs were reported in the 1980s except for an estimate of at least 200 holes at a Newport Pagnell site in 1988. Colonies began to be recorded more regularly, although never annually, from 1999 and some sites were shown to have good numbers. At Little Marlow there were 128 nest holes in 1999, 86 in 2001, and 200 birds were present in 2010. At Warren Farm, near Chalfont St Peter, numbers varied from 37 to 91 nest holes between 1999 and 2002 while at Springfield Farm Quarry, near Beaconsfield, a working sand quarry where the owners take measures to protect the martins, numbers have reached a maximum of over 100 nest holes.

With the exception of the former chalk quarry of College Lake, breeding has always been confined to the south and the north-east of the county where the main gravel deposits lie. Some sites are used for many years while other colonies are short-lived. Sand Martins generally feed over (and breed beside) lakes or rivers, but sandpits some way from water are sometimes used. They also occasionally use other sites. For example, a colony at Olney used the masonry of the river bridge, and birds at the Stony Stratford Reserve have readily adopted metal pipes set into a concrete bank, designed to resemble natural burrows. Nesting may begin early in May, and as two broods are often raised, fledging dates often extend to mid August and even into September.

5000 pairs   5000 pairs

Migration dates

Earliest: 24 Feb
Ave earliest: 17 Mar
Ave latest: 1 Oct
Latest: 24 Oct

Gatherings of migrants begin to be reported in late July with peak numbers usually in August. The highest count of all was of 5,000 at Iver on 31 Aug 1963; several other flocks of 1,000 to 3,000 have been reported, but not since 1977. More recently, the largest number was at least 250 in an hour at Foxcote on 22 Aug 1980. Last sightings are usually in late September or early October, with the latest at Weston Turville on 24 Oct 1971.

Many Sand Martins have been ringed in the county, especially during the BTO enquiry in the 1960s. Much movement between colonies was recorded, with birds from Buckinghamshire moving to colonies as far as Durham and France. Although there were a few northward flights in summer, most dispersal was predominantly southwards. Birds from Ireland, N Scotland, Wales and many parts of England have been caught in the county, and Chichester reedbeds have provided a much used south coast staging post. Ringing also reveals that movements begin in early July, well before a build up in numbers is seen. Eight birds have been recovered in NW France in August, while one ringed in Shropshire in 1979 was controlled at Linford in August 1980 and found in Spain 22 days later.

The earliest arrival dates are 3 Mar 2008 at Little Marlow and 4 Mar 2000 at Linford. Arrivals in mid or late March are recorded in most years but larger numbers do not usually appear until mid April. Three unusually large spring gathering were reported in 1994: 700 each at Little Marlow on 4 Apr, at Caldecotte on 6 Apr and Willen on 8 Apr but these were eclipsed by 2100 at Little Marlow on 8 Apr 2008.

HM-G

Swallow
Hirundo rustica

Common summer visitor and migrant.

Familiar to Clark Kennedy in the 1860s, the Swallow was regarded as very common everywhere by H & R early this century. Despite decreases in recent years it has remained widely distributed to the present time.

Swallows traditionally prefer to nest in stables or cattle-sheds where they evidently benefit from the associated supply of insect food. They may therefore have been affected by changes in agricultural practice and, in

Radnage, 24 Jul 2011   *Gerry Whitlow*

earlier decades, by the disappearance of commercial and farm horses. However, all kinds of farm buildings and other sheds may be occupied, and also out-buildings and porches of houses. The last types of site are occupied on a small but quite wide scale in leafy suburban roads or even near the centres of small towns. In addition some industrial sites are utilised: at the Pitstone cement works pairs nest both in buildings and a tunnel entry well below ground level. Occasional pairs nest under bridges over a brook or canal. In favoured places a number of pairs may nest near each other. While the Swallow's occurrence at a local level is obviously influenced by its dependence on man-made nesting sites, there can be few full tetrads within Buckinghamshire with no potential Swallow homes, and further fieldwork might well have revealed birds in many of the blank squares. At all events the species can be seen to breed throughout the county; problems of access to private buildings frequented by Swallows may explain why only `possible breeding' was recorded in many tetrads.

In 1975 and again during the 1980s observers' comments on a drop in numbers, both of breeders and (latterly) of autumn flocks, were broadly in line with the national Common Birds

Census, which demonstrated a decline beginning in 1973 (with some revival between 1975 and 1978). A connection with a drought-related deterioration of the African migration route and wintering habitat must be suspected. In cold, wet or windy weather, which occurs all too frequently in spring, Swallows congregate over lakes where insects are still available - and the earliest returning migrants are usually seen at such sites. In some years large beds of reeds, or sometimes other tall reed-swamp vegetation, are used as roosts by migrant flocks. Occasional roosting sites used by small to moderate flocks were a mixed hedgerow (1966), a wheatfield (1968) and a water culvert under the M40 (1978). Late summer gatherings on telephone wires are a familiar sight. Nearly all nests are within buildings, or under archways, typically built against a wall or beam, sometimes supported by some form of ledge. In dry spells, a lack of wet mud can delay nest-building, although old nests are quite often re-used. In warmer than average springs a few birds begin laying in late April, whereas in cool years breeding starts several weeks later. Even then many pairs manage two broods, since fresh clutches up to mid August are normal (if not numerous). Third broods are only occasional: a pair at Iver must have embarked on theirs around 23 Sep 1965, the young flying on 28 October.

Actual southward passage movements are seldom reported. Passage is frequently though irregularly manifested in the form of feeding concentrations and especially of roosts, but ringing has shown that the turnover of birds at roosts is rapid, and probably many birds leave their nesting quarters, or pass through the county, without forming or joining a local roost (in 1923 a June-ringed nestling was already found in Hampshire in July). Reedbed roosts vary from a few individuals or family parties up to (in Buckinghamshire) occasionally 3,000 birds. A roost of c300 at Aylesbury SF on 27 Jul 1976 was rather early; roosts in August (even c2,000 birds at Weston Turville in 1966) are not infrequent, but more often the large numbers occur during September with, as a rule, a rapid fall-off towards the end of the month, although Weston Turville still had 1,000 birds on 1 Oct 1962, and c700 on 3 Oct 1970.

Ringing at roosts has provided ample evidence of birds from further north in England passing through the county, as well as some from Wales and as far as Perthshire, at least between mid August and late September. Two birds made unexpected reverse flights to Shropshire in the autumn of 1967. The thousands of swallows mist-netted locally have only yielded one southern English recovery in the same autumn (in Dorset), suggesting that many of them may not make another stop before crossing the Channel. There is one October recovery in France, of a nestling ringed at Bourne End in July 1950.

Cool autumn days can result in spectacular feeding concentrations, notably 3,000+ birds at Calvert brickpits on 17 Sep 1973 and several thousand over Haddenham village on 11 Sep 1985. On 22 Aug 1994, 2000 roosted in a field of maize at Drayton Parslow while, in the same year, 4000 passed through the Hambledon Valley on 24 Sep. There have been no large passages since 3000 in two hours passed over Broughton, Aylesbury on 18 Sep 1998.

A few late October Swallows (occasionally up to a dozen together) are recorded annually, and there are plenty of November records, from the 1860s to the present. Single birds were observed in the county on 11 Jan 1974, 2 Dec 1974, 1 Dec 1975, 5 Dec 2006, and 1 Dec 2008. A full-grown May bird from Weston Turville was controlled in the Transvaal on 19 Mar 1969, while one ringed in the latter province on 20 Mar 1970 was controlled at Chesham on 15 Aug 1970.

Contrasting with birds tarrying in South Africa are the earliest arrivals in Buckinghamshire: 13 Mar 2000 at Turville and 15 Mar 1981 at Linford. There are later March records (mainly in the last four days) from a number of years but sometimes the first sightings are in April, the most delayed being 13 Apr 1978. As a rule the species is not widespread until mid April, and generally late April, or occasionally early or even mid May, is the time of main arrival.

All-white or partial albino Swallows have been reported periodically. H & J describe a succession of mixed broods of white and normal Swallows reared by an Aylesbury pair from 1891 to 1895.

5000 pairs   *5000 pairs*

Migration dates

Earliest: 13 Mar
Ave earliest: 27 Mar
Ave latest: 3 Nov
Latest: 5 Dec

HM-G

House Martin
Delichon urbicum

Common summer visitor and migrant.

Great Kimble, 25 Jun 2011   *Richard Billyard*

It is probable that the status of House Martins has not changed markedly in the county since man began building and the martins moved from cliffs to artificial structures. Clark Kennedy wrote 'abundant' while H & J commented 'Common, though absent from many apparently suitable villages. Supposed to diminish steadily, but numbers fluctuate'. This is still an accurate statement. They noted that about a million(?) were seen over the river and pond at Great Marlow about 4-5 pm on 18 Sep 1896. The query is their's.

However, the maps suggest that House Martins have disappeared from much of the Chilterns. The reasons for this are not known but is unlikely to be due to under-recording. Most birds occur in small, apparently mobile colonies. This mobility means that the population at a particular site can vary widely from year to year, although the overall population probably remains stable. Their presence in suburbs depends to some extent upon the toleration of house-holders to the mess the nesting birds create.

Due to the mobile, colonial nature of House Martins, the population is unusually difficult to estimate. The figures of 9000 and 5000 pairs for the two surveys is very tentative.

The first birds usually arrive in the first half of April, though exceptionally early birds were seen on 19 Mar 1989 at Willen and 19 Mar 2009 at Tongwell. The main arrival is usually in late April early May. Birds begin leaving in late September and early October, though an abnormally tardy pair were still feeding young on 7 Oct 1950 at Marlow. The last birds may linger to the first week of November with the latest in recent years being a bird seen at Chesham on 24 Nov 1986. The latest of all was a bird at Hartwell on 5 Dec 1874 (H & J).

House Martins are familiar migrants, often associating with Swallows. They can occur almost anywhere on migration, but, like Swallows, they tend to congregate over open water in poor weather. Flocks of several hundred are common, although flocks of more than 1000 are rarely encountered. The largest flocks recorded are over 3000 birds near Denham on 9 Oct 1976, 6000 in the Hambledon Valley on 24 Sep 1994, and 3000 at Shardeloes on 2 Sep 1994.

There has only been one ringing record involving a bird travelling beyond Britain. A bird ringed in the county on 6 Oct 1974 was recovered in Herault, France on 15 Nov 1974. A bird ringed at Little Marlow STW on 21 May 1994 was recovered at Fishtoft, Lincolnshire on 3 June 1997.

Albino birds are occasionally recorded. The last was seen at Latimer on 25 Aug 1974.

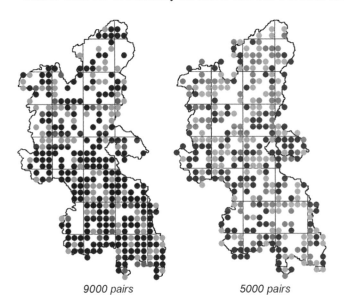

9000 pairs   5000 pairs

Migration dates

Earliest: 19 Mar
Ave earliest: 4 Apr
Ave latest: 28 Oct
Latest: 5 Dec

DMF

Red-rumped Swallow
Cecropis daurica

Very rare vagrant. There is one record.

2002: 1 on 29 Apr, Furzton Lake, Milton Keynes (Nicholls, 2004).

Richard's Pipit
Anthus richardi

Very rare vagrant. There are three records.

1967: 1 from 7 to 24 Oct, Dorney Common.
1990: first-winter from 28 to 30 Oct, Blue Lagoon, Bletchley.
1998: 1 on 8 May, Ivinghoe Beacon.

October is the typical month for this Siberian vagrant. Spring migrants are unusual.

Tree Pipit
Anthus trivialis

Rare summer visitor.

Steps Hill, 12 Apr 2006   *Mike Wallen*

Clark Kennedy described the Tree Pipit as 'a common summer visitor', although not as common as Meadow Pipit. Since then there has been a substantial decline which is still continuing. The first county breeding atlas recorded them as present in 82 tetrads (14% of the total) but by the second atlas they were only found in 16 tetrads. This decrease may well be habitat related. Tree Pipits occur within the county in open areas with bushes and scattered trees. They find the required habitat in young coniferous plantations and open areas of woodland. There has been a reduction in the planting of conifers and the management of broadleaved woodlands which has led to a reduction in the amount of favoured habitat. Although Tree Pipits winter south of the Sahara there is no evidence that conditions in the wintering areas have affected their populations.

The species was most common in the Chilterns, Brickhill Woods, and Bernwood Forest. In the Chilterns a few place names appear regularly in the records: Penn Woods, where birds were very numerous in 1974, Coleshill, Bradenham and Ashridge.

First arrivals occur between 2 and 16 April with the main build-up from mid to late April. Tree Pipits start to leave the breeding grounds in mid July. Last reports range from late August to mid October. There have been two interesting records involving locally ringed birds. Of two birds ringed as nestlings at Stoke Poges in June 1988, one was controlled at Alum Bay, Isle of Wight on 23 Aug 1988 and the other at Baldwin's Wood, near Wendover on 6 May 1990.

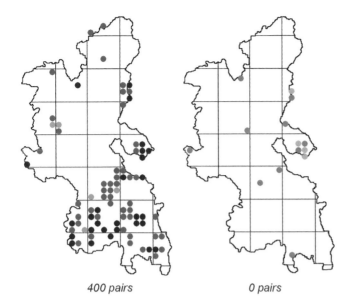

Migration dates	
Earliest:	15 Mar
Ave earliest:	9 Apr
Ave latest:	18 Sep
Latest:	19 Oct

400 pairs   0 pairs

DBH

Meadow Pipit
Anthus pratensis

Scarce resident and fairly common migrant and winter visitor.

Countrywide, the Meadow Pipit is common and numerous, but Buckinghamshire is not one of its strongholds in the breeding season. It is a bird which prefers open country, so the wooded Chilterns hold no attraction for it. Even the open areas of the Vale of Aylesbury have very few breeding pairs. This confirms

Gallows Bridge Farm, 22 Apr 2011   *Jim Rose*

the findings of F & Y, but Clark Kennedy and H & R suggest that the Meadow Pipit was much commoner and more widespread in the 19th century. The former noted it as one of the commonest resident birds and H & R reported it occurring especially in lowland pastures.

The two breeding maps show that birds are common in the Ivinghoe Hills area but are thinly scattered north of the Chilterns. Here the effect of the new town of Milton Keynes is clearly shown as breeding birds have vacated this area. In contrast, the far west of the county appears to have been colonised since the first atlas, although this may be a result of under-recording during the first survey. It is probable that the breeding population has not changed significantly since the mid 1980s. Based on a density of four pairs per tetrad, which is far below the national breeding density, the breeding population is estimated at 200 pairs.

This is in contrast to an estimate of `40 plus' pairs made in 1980 but many sites are infrequently visited by birdwatchers. Birds are sometimes present on sites that have only a transient attraction, such as waste ground by the John Lewis superstore at Booker.

There is a small passage in March and early April when flocks may exceed 100, but are usually in the 30-50 range. The autumn passage is more obvious and flocks may reach 200, usually in the Ivinghoe Hills. The largest passage was in October 1992 when 350+ were recorded passing through Little Marlow STW on 20th, and c2000 at the same site on 27th when 115 birds were caught and ringed using a tape lure. Another notable flock was 600 at Dorney Lake on 20 Sep 2007.

As can be seen from the map, Meadow Pipits are much more widespread in winter. There is no evidence that foreign birds winter in Britain (Migration Atlas). It is likely that most birds wintering in the county originate further north in Britain. Possibly the bird ringed as an adult in Chesham in January 1972 and recovered there in December 1973 was one such. The only other ringing recovery involves a bird ringed at Abberton in Essex in October 1957 recovered at Chenies in January 1960.

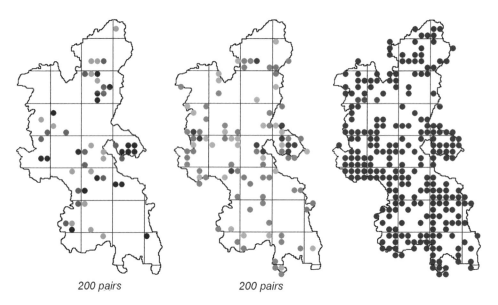

200 pairs   200 pairs

DBH

Rock and Water Pipits
Anthus petrosus and *A. spinoletta*

These pipits were split into two species in 1986. Hence for records prior to that it is not absolutely certain that the identification is correct. There is still quite frequent confusion between brighter examples of the Scandinavian Rock Pipit *A.p. littoralis* and Water Pipit in spring. Thus it would not be surprising if a number of birds recorded as Water Pipits in March or April were in fact Scandinavian Rock Pipits.

Rock Pipit
Anthus petrosus

Scarce vagrant.

There are three records prior to 1974:

1932: 1 on 16 Oct, Startopsend.
1960: 2 on 23 Apr, Newport Pagnell GP.
1970: 1 on several dates in Feb, Little Marlow.

Since 1974 there have been 80 records of 95 birds. The seasonal graph shows very well

Foxcote, 18 Mar 2012   *Tim Watts*

defined spring and autumn passages. It seems that most, if not all, spring birds are *littoralis*. Birds have been found at many of the well-watched sites in the county.

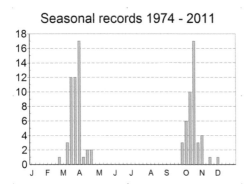

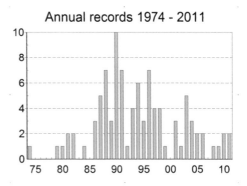

Water Pipit
Anthus spinoletta

Scarce vagrant and winter visitor.

There are four records prior to 1972:

1960: 1 on 18 Apr, Newport Pagnell.
1962: 1 on 25 Mar, near Chesham.
1971: 1 from 28 Jan to 11 Apr, Chesham.
1971: 3 on 30 Mar, Latimer Park.

Since 1972, there have been 48 records of 50 birds. They are shown on the graphs. Localities have included the margins of the usual lakes and Chesham cress-beds where wintering occurred from 1971 to 1977. The largest gathering was of three birds at Willen on 12 Apr 1986 and the three at Latimer noted above.

There is an interesting contrast with Rock Pipits. As can be seen from the graph, Water Pipits are mostly found from January to April, with a peak in April, while Rock Pipits are found in both spring and autumn, with a peaks in late March/early April and October.

Seasonal records 1972 - 2011

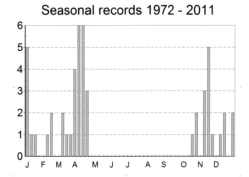

Annual records 1972 - 2011

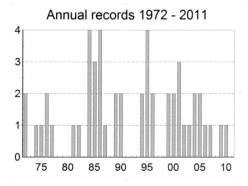

Yellow Wagtail
Motacilla flava flavissima

Uncommon and decreasing summer visitor and migrant.

It seems that the Yellow Wagtail has been in decline over many years. In 1947 Price stated 'The British race (*M.f.flavissima*) is a regular summer visitor, found in low-lying meadowland and near rivers' while in 1976 F & Y remarked 'Breeds in small numbers in low lying meadows near rivers'. BWP stated 'There has been a marked contraction in the

Caldecotte, 1 Apr 2010   *Keith O'Hagen*

range of this species in the country since 1930'. The 1993 Atlas concluded that there had been a reduction in number since 1976. Since the 1993 Atlas numbers have decreased further from an estimated 900 breeding pairs in 1993 to just 200 currently. This is clearly demonstrated on the maps where the main population, north of the Chilterns, is much thinner than previously.

The breeding habitats of Yellow Wagtails in the county are damp water meadows and marshy fields along river valleys. Chalky areas are avoided by this species (The Breeding Atlas) this being borne out by the maps where there are no birds breeding within the Chilterns. The population decline has been attributed to a loss of habitat because of drainage and conversion of pasture to arable. Also, the decline of cattle breeding has meant that the sight of Yellow Wagtails feeding on the insects disturbed by the feet of cattle is now an increasingly rare sight.

The species is usually recorded in the county between end March and the second week in October with the main movements normally in the last two weeks of April and between the third week of July and the end of September. The earliest recorded arrival date is 23rd March and an exceptional late record of 21st November was received in 1976 when an adult female was trapped at Weston Turville Reservoir. Larger flocks are more frequently recorded during the autumn migration when flocks of 50+ are not uncommon, but in recent years we have not got close to the 150+ recorded on occasion in the past. On 31st August 1980 up to 375 were recorded at a roost at Aylesbury STW. During the spring flocks tend to be somewhat smaller with up to 100 being recorded in years gone by. These days maxima vary between 10 and 50 birds.

Once our Yellow Wagtails leave us in the autumn they head southwards via SW France and Portugal before crossing into Africa and on to their wintering grounds in tropical Africa (BWP).

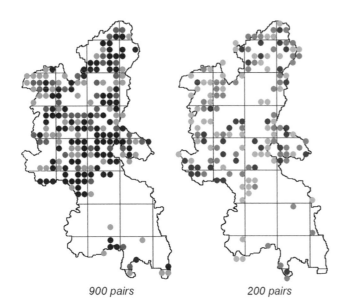

Migration dates	
Earliest:	23 Mar
Ave earliest:	1 Apr
Ave latest:	12 Oct
Latest:	29 Nov

900 pairs   200 pairs

Spanish Wagtail
Motacilla flava iberiae

In 1980 a male bird of this species was first seen on 25 May at Aylesbury STW after which it was seen paired with a normal female and observed carrying nest material. No young were seen. This sub-species normally breeds south west France, Iberia and the Balearics.

Syke's Wagtail
Motacilla flava beema

A bird showing characteristics of this sub-species was seen at Willen from 1 to 3 Apr 1983. This sub-species breeds in South East Russia.

Ashy-Headed Wagtail
Motacilla flava cinereocapilla

A single record of one at Weston Turville Reservoir on 16 Apr 1988. This sub-species breeds in Italy, central Mediterranean islands, southern Austria, and north west Yugoslavia.

Grey-Headed Wagtail
Motacilla flava thunbergi

Two records of this sub-species which breeds in Scandinavia and N Russia. One at Caldecotte on 4 June 1991 was perhaps a little late, while one at Linford on 18 April 1995 was considered to be a month early.

241

Blue-Headed Wagtail
Motacilla flava flava

A scarce passage migrant previously recorded on one or two occasions in most years, but since 2000 can be considered less than annual. The majority of records occur in the spring with many birds being seen during the last two weeks of April. The fact that less birds are reported in the autumn, may be partly due to the identification difficulties posed by birds in non-breeding and juvenile plumages during return passage. The vast majority of these records are close to the major water bodies in the north of the county.

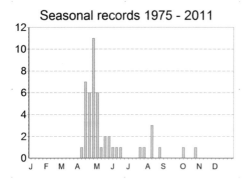

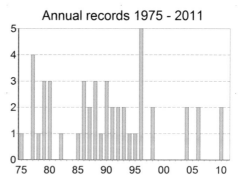

JER

Grey Wagtail
Motacilla cinerea

Local resident and winter visitor

There was a gradual expansion of breeding range into southern and eastern England, most noticeably from 1950 with breeding becoming regular in areas where it had previously been erratic (Marchant et al, 1990). Price (1947) described this species in the county as 'Chiefly a passage migrant in autumn and spring; a few remain for the winter, and some pairs remain for the summer'. In 1976 F & Y stated 'Breeds in small numbers by some rivers and lakes.

Shardeloes, 17 Apr 2011   *Jim Rose*

Numbers supplemented during the winter by visitors from the north. Numbers greatly reduced during the 1963 hard winter but now fully recovered'. In 1990 and on a country wide basis (Marchant *et al*, 1990), reported a decline following the hard winters of 1978/9, 1981/2 and 1984/5 and, although some recovery was made, it was estimated to be just 50 pairs in the first Birds of Buckinghamshire. Since then there has been a significant increase in numbers (an estimated 100 pairs) and an expansion of range in the county.

Grey Wagtails are essentially birds of fast flowing streams in upland and hilly country. In Buckinghamshire they are usually found by rather more slow moving streams and rivers but they do often pick territories containing faster flowing water such as narrows, weirs and waterfalls. The map shows a fairly wide distribution of Grey Wagtails that is no longer so restricted to the Chilterns as shown by the first survey. The dots on the map often follow the lines of the rivers, but also many sites where slower rivers and lakes are present. Grey Wagtails usually build their nest above water on a rock or ledge, in exposed tree roots, or in ivy growing on a tree or bridge.

During the winter Grey Wagtails are recorded rather more widely in the county, this being very much in line with the Winter Atlas (1986) which shows a much wider distribution with records received from most 10Km squares in Buckinghamshire and the surrounding counties. BWP (1988) suggests that British Grey Wagtails are usually resident with mainly local dispersion, with only 25% of ringing recoveries over 100Km. However the Winter Atlas states that some birds move south, sometimes even as far as France and Iberia to be replaced by birds from further north and occasionally even from the continent. There are however no ringing recoveries for this species from birds ringed or controlled in the county to support this.

In very hard winters when much of their habitat is frozen many Grey Wagtails may perish (The Breeding Atlas). This was noted in the severe winter of 1963 when numbers were 'greatly reduced' (F&Y). However some birds move into sewage treatment works and into towns where food is more often available (The Breeding Atlas). Sewage treatment works have previously accounted for many of the Bucks winter flock records for this species although flock sizes larger than six are rarely recorded. However as some sewage treatment works are modernised, so the attractiveness of these sites to this and other species is reduced. So it seems unlikely that the exceptional flock of 20 birds at Marlow STW on 15th August 1981 will be repeated.

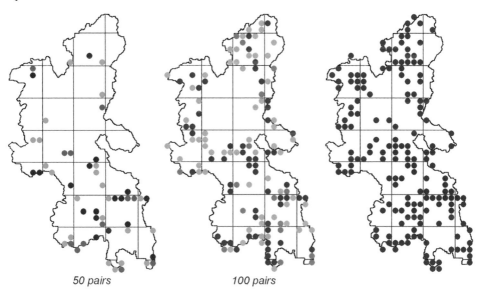

50 pairs   100 pairs

JER

Pied Wagtail
Motacilla alba yarrellii

Common resident and migrant.

Just after the turn of the century, H & R considered the Pied Wagtail to be `nowhere rare' in the county. At the time, the species was regarded as generally migratory but with single pairs seen in every month. Since then numbers have increased, possibly because of the spread of industry and urbanisation into areas which were previously woodland or farmland with few buildings.

Fawley, 16 May 2011   Ashley Stow

The Pied Wagtail breeds in a variety of habitats including farmland, quarries, gravel pits and industrial sites. It nests in crevices or holes in walls and embankments, on or under roofs and in buildings. Although sometimes associated with damp habitats, it may be found breeding more than 6 km from the nearest pond or river. The distribution of breeding records shows the bird to be present in most of the county, absent only from large tracts of woodland in the Chilterns and parts of the Vale of Aylesbury that are rural areas with few buildings and far from water. Since the first survey there appears to have been a decrease in the higher parts of the Chilterns and in Milton Keynes where the increased urbanisation seems to be inimical to pied Wagtails.

There are considerable differences in breeding densities. One suburban tetrad near Burnham had six breeding pairs; one covering mixed farmland near Dorney had five; and many Chiltern tetrads had only a single pair. This contrasts with some rural Scottish tetrads with up to 11 breeding pairs.

In Buckinghamshire the Pied Wagtail usually starts breeding from the second week in April, normally raising two broods and occasionally three. Roosts of all male birds from breeding pairs have been observed in May and June, but after the breeding season, from mid July, the birds begin to flock and to use the autumn reedbed roosts.

These flocks are augmented from mid September onwards by migrant Pied Wagtails from N Britain. Two records from Scotland (May and August) and two from Yorkshire (August) involving birds in Buckinghamshire in October and November are indicative of this. The recovery of a bird ringed near Buckingham in October 1976 and recovered on a ship in the Skaggerak off Denmark in March 1977 suggests that continental birds may also winter in the county. Most adults remain in S England for the winter, although first-year birds usually go further south to the Atlantic coasts of Portugal, France and Spain. Local breeding birds tend to make only short-distance movements, but some in their first winter also move to the Continent (Davis 1966); a Pied Wagtail ringed at Eton on 18 May 1923 was recovered at Tovias, Portugal during November 1923.

During severe weather up to three-quarters of wintering birds may migrate to areas with more clement conditions. The individuals which remain are hard pressed to find enough food and sometimes continue to feed in suburban areas for up to an hour after sunset. National Common Birds Census data show a drop of between 25% and 66% in the population after a severe winter. In winter, flocks of feeding birds may be found on agricultural or common ground where the cereals and grasses are less than about 40 cm tall. Although flocks numbering up to 200 are seen occasionally, groups of 10-20 are not uncommon.

A number of urban areas have held large roosts, particularly at Aylesbury (up to 500), High Wycombe (up to 300), Beaconsfield (up to 200), Haddenham (200), Chesham (150), Amersham (100) and Central Milton Keynes (100). The roosts at Dadford (up to 400) and Little Marlow STW (up to 500) and the pre-roost at South Iver (over 1000) no longer feature in the annual reports. The majority of the birds from south of the Chilterns roost 1 km outside the county, near Burnham; this roost also contains birds from Middlesex and Berkshire, and has held up to 3,400 birds (December 1982).

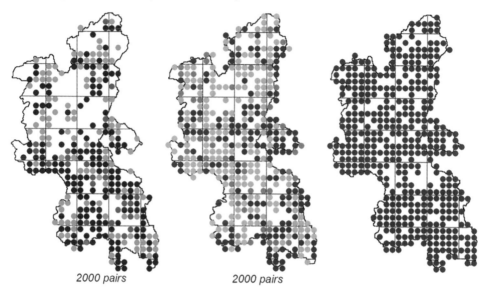

2000 pairs   *2000 pairs*

White Wagtail
Motacilla alba alba

The European race is recorded annually on spring passage, usually at wetland sites that birders frequent. The numbers have increased significantly since 2005 probably as a result of increased observer awareness. Much smaller numbers are recorded in late summer and autumn possibly because this subspecies is more difficult to identify at this time. A pair bred near Latimer in 1902 (H & R).

Startopsend Res, 26 Mar 2012   *Mike Wallen*

JK

Waxwing
Bombycilla garrulus

Erratic winter visitor.

Widmer End, 19 Mar 2011   *Mike Wallen*

The irregular irruptions of Waxwings are occasioned by an imbalance between the Waxwing population and the availability of rowan berries, their preferred winter food, coupled with weather conditions that allow them to cross the North Sea from their breeding areas in northern Europe.

Early records are strangely sparse. The first records are for the winter of 1849/50 when birds were observed 'in several parishes'. The second records, also given by Clark Kennedy, were in 1867 when an 'immense number' were shot in the spring of 1867 around Buckingham. Surprisingly, H & J do not give any further records for Buckinghamshire, but one is recorded in The Countryman for 1883.

Between 1921 and 1950 Waxwings were recorded only in 1921, 1944, 1945 and 1949. The largest flock in this period was one of 14 birds at Drayton Beauchamp on 8 Mar 1944. From 1951 to 1970 they were recorded in nine years. Notable flocks during this period were 19 at Aston Clinton on 8 Feb 1959, 20 at Amersham in January 1966, and up to 30 birds at Beaconsfield from 4 Dec 1970 to the end of the year. The records since 1973 are shown on the graphs. They show long periods when no birds were recorded at all and only small numbers until the invasion of early 1996. This peaked in February and March when flocks of up to 100 were recorded in Milton Keynes and much smaller numbers in many of the county's urban areas. A similar but smaller invasion occurred in 2001 but this was eclipsed by the huge, unprecedented invasions of 2005 and 2010/11.

Although there were three records in November and December 2004 there was no indication as to what was about to happen until mid January 2005 when a flock of 40 appeared at Walton Hall, Milton Keynes. Numbers here built up to 314 by 23 Feb. Three-figure flocks were recorded elsewhere in Milton Keynes and in Gerrards Cross while there were flocks of over 50 at Little Chalfont and High Wycombe. Smaller flocks were recorded throughout the county.

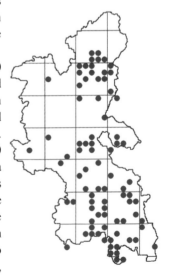

The invasion of 2010/11 began at the end of October 2010 and by the end of the year double-figure flocks were recorded in Milton Keynes, Aylesbury, High Wycombe and Amersham while 200 were present in Bletchley. By early 2011 birds had spread throughout the eastern and central parts of the county. Numbers dwindled in April and the last bird was seen on 20 May 2011. However there was an extraordinary record of a single bird at Medmenham on 13 Aug 2011. The invasions were part of a nationwide phenomenon caused by a shortage of berries in northern Europe. Nine colour-ringed birds were seen in the county, six of which had been ringed in Aberdeen the previous November when they arrived in the UK. Two others were probably ringed in Orkney (Parmenter & Collard,

2011). This invasion occurred during the period of the second atlas recording. The map clearly shows attraction the species has for conurbations, particularly Milton Keynes. Flocks are typically found on the berry-bearing trees of new housing estates and supermarket car parks, a striking contrast to their remote forest breeding areas on the edge of the Arctic.

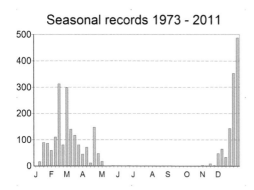

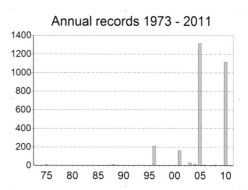

DMF

Dipper
Cinclus cinclus

Very rare vagrant.

There are old undated records for the River Chess and the canal near Drayton Beauchamp.

The first dated record is:

1894: 1 near High Wycombe

There were no more records until 1941 when a bird was seen from 4 to 11 May on the River Chess below Chenies. The next record came in 1966. Between that year and 1972 there were eight records, but then nothing until 1975. There followed four more records: in 1984, 1989, 1991 and 1994. Five of the 15 records were identified as birds of the continental Black-bellied race, *C.c.cinclus*. None were identified as the British race *C.c.gularis*.

Localities include Shardeloes, the River Chess, the Wendover Canal and the River Wye. Birds were seen between 13 Aug and 20 May but there is no pattern to the occurrences. The longest stay was achieved by a bird at Shardeloes from 5 Nov 1967 to 6 Mar 1968.

Wren
Troglodytes troglodytes

Caldecotte Lake, 30 Jul 2011   *Keith O'Hagen*

Very common resident.

The Wren's status in the county has not changed much since Clark Kennedy's day when he described it as 'abundant'. The gaps in the north of the county shown by the first breeding map are almost certainly due to under-recording. The two breeding maps show a noticeable increase in the number of 'possible' breeding tetrads from the first to the second atlas. This is due to the change in the category of a single record of a singing bird from 'probable' to 'possible'. This effect is most marked in skulking birds that have loud, distinctive songs such as Wren.

It is likely that the maximum population in the county has not changed significantly since Clark Kennedy's day but, due to its small size, the species is very susceptible to severe winters. Numbers then drop considerably, but equally they can recover quite rapidly.

Wrens normally produce two broods in a season between April and July. The nest can be almost anywhere, constructed in bushes or ivy with a dome and side entrance, or simply placed in a hole or crevice in a rock or a tree. In 1974 a nest in a squirrel's drey was reported from Great Kingshill.

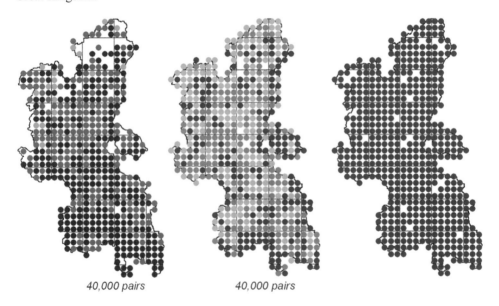
40,000 pairs   40,000 pairs

Outside the breeding season the Wren often remains territorial, but it is very adaptable. It is able to collect food from all kinds of small nooks and crannies and will even penetrate under the snow if necessary. In winter and especially on colder nights it roosts in holes, and it is then that many birds will huddle together. MTNHS records a roost of 42 Wrens in one Denham nest box in the cold winter of 1978/79.

248

Wrens use gardens quite extensively in winter. They were reported from 80% of the gardens in the BBC Garden Bird Survey. Natural food was preferred to that provided on bird tables.

Wrens have been ringed in the county in quite large numbers. There has been one continental recovery and two British long distance recoveries. A bird ringed in Lane End in October 1965 was recovered at Cageux, France in February 1968. A bird ringed at Moulsoe Wood in November 1982 was retrapped at Gibraltar Point in Lincolnshire in September 1983 and a juvenile ringed in Nottinghamshire on 7 Aug 1989 was retrapped in Aylesbury on 26 Jan 1992.

A melanistic bird was seen at Tilbrook on 31 Oct 1993.

DBH

Dunnock
Prunella modularis

Very common resident.

Comparison with old records suggest that the Dunnock's status has not changed significantly over the years, although CBC/BBS data show that there was a halving of the species' population between 1975 an 1985, a period when survey work for the first county breeding atlas took place. Nevertheless, the maps show that the species

Gallows Bridge Farm, 26 Nov 2010   *Rod Scaife*

is widespread throughout the county; the gaps in the north are almost certainly due to under-recording. The two breeding maps show a noticeable increase in the number of 'possible' breeding tetrads from the first to the second atlas. This is due to the change in the category of a single record of a singing bird from 'probable' to 'possible'. This effect is most marked in skulking birds that announce their presence by their songs such as Dunnock.

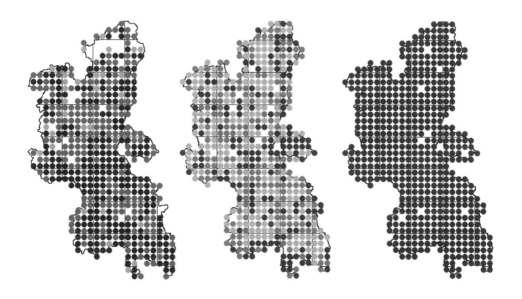

They are very common in woodland borders, farmland, hedges, rural and suburban gardens; and they will even penetrate into urban areas if there are suitable bushes. In the winter, the BBC Garden Bird Survey found it in 89% of gardens, with a maximum of 11 birds at any one time. Natural foods were used about as much as foods which were put out, and the birds normally remained on the ground to take bits that had fallen rather than fly up to a table.

A highly sedentary bird, the Dunnock often remains in the same territory throughout the year. In spite of a large number of Dunnocks being ringed in the county, all recoveries and retraps show only very local movements. A total albino raised a brood of four at Prestwood in 1972.

DBH

Robin
Erithacus rubecula

Very common resident.

Gallows Bridge Farm, 7 Dec 2010   *Rod Scaife*

The British national bird is found throughout the county. The scarcity of records in parts of the north of the county shown by the first breeding atlas is likely to be due to under-recording rather than a complete lack of birds. The Robin is tolerant of most habitats which offer a reasonable amount of cover, be it scrub, hedge or wood. So, although it is found most commonly in woodland, it is probably best known because of its adoption of gardens, both rural and suburban, and town parks. Its status does not seem to have changed at all since Clark Kennedy's time.

Breeding territories are set up around March and breeding continues until midsummer, with perhaps three or even four broods. Territories are held around the year, however, the sexes holding separate ones through the autumn and winter.

During the winter, Robins often visit bird tables, tending to be aggressive to other birds wanting to feed. The BBC Garden Bird Survey showed the species to be in the top five of garden visitors and feeders on artificial food. It was seen in all gardens in the second year of the survey, one garden having eight simultaneously. Robins showed a marked preference for the food provided on bird tables. Their adaptability, however, was shown one summer when a bird was seen to have learnt the knack of plucking tadpoles from a garden pond (D. B. Hamley).

There are three interesting recoveries of birds ringed in the county. One bird ringed at Frieth in June 1964 was recovered in December 1965 at La Chevrolire, Loire Atlantique, in France; another ringed at Drayton Beauchamp in October 1979 was retrapped five days later in London and found dead at Ashford, Surrey in April 1980. Finally, a first-year ringed near Grendon Underwood on 22 Sep 2007 was found dead in Warwickshire on 19 Dec 2007, a distance of 69 km.

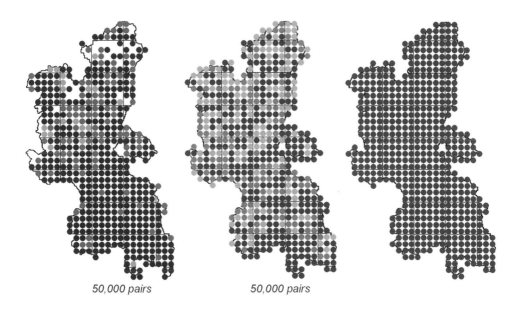

50,000 pairs   50,000 pairs

DBH

Nightingale
Luscinia megarhynchos

Rare and declining summer visitor.

Nightingales have been declining since H & J stated that "they were generally absent from the hills and drier beech woods, but were found in many places in the low-lying fertile districts". While the habitat preferences are still valid, 'many places' would now be considered far too optimistic.

The 1976 BTO survey found 64 singing birds in 21 sites. As 12 former sites were not visited it was considered that the true total may have been about 100 birds. The survey was repeated in 1980 when 72 birds were found, 16 of them in just two sites. Again the true total was considered to be around 100 birds. The first survey map shows records in 23 tetrads, four of them with only possible breeding. As this probably represented the true picture it can be considered that a slight population decrease had taken place. Since then the decrease has accelerated. A third national survey, held in 1999, produced just 10 singing birds. The survey for the second atlas resulted in birds being found in only 14 tetrads some of which were likely to be migrants.

In Buckinghamshire, Nightingales are virtually confined as a breeding species to the discontinuous band of woodlands stretching from Bernwood Forest on the Oxfordshire border to Salcey Forest on the boundary with Northamptonshire. These woods are mostly pedunculate oakwoods with a hazel shrub layer, the primary habitat of Nightingales in Britain. The population decline has several causes. The first is the cessation of coppicing as a woodland management practice. It has been shown (Studdart and Williamson 1971) that Nightingales prefer coppicing on a twelve to twenty-five year cycle with the five to eight year old stools providing the most suitable habitat. Only three of the Buckinghamshire Nightingale woods are managed with conservation in mind; elsewhere coppicing ceased during the Second World

251

War. The second cause is the increasing deer population (Fuller *et al*, 2005). Roe and Muntjac populations have increased in Buckinghamshire which has resulted in more intensive browsing in Nightingale habitats. This in turn has resulted in a woodland structure consisted of an open canopy and a ground layer of coarse grasses which is unsuitable for Nightingales. Another factor may be that the migration stop-over points and the wintering areas in Africa may have degraded to the point where they can no longer support British Nightingales. The species is on the Birds of Conservation Concern amber list.

The first Nightingales are usually heard during the last week of April, with the bulk arriving in early May. The earliest record is one singing at Kingswood on 4 Apr 2003. A few birds are seen most years in spring at sites where they do not breed, for instance Black Park and Dunsmore. Signs of autumn passage of this unobtrusive bird are very rare. One was trapped on Steps Hill on 14 Jul 1985 and another was seen in a garden at Wescott on 28 Jun 1991. One was singing on the very late date of 9 Aug 1998 at Calvert while one was seen on 20 Aug 2009 on Steps Hill. The only significant ringing recovery is of a bird ringed at Portland Bill on 10 Sep 1955 which was recovered at Newport Pagnell on 27 Apr 1956.

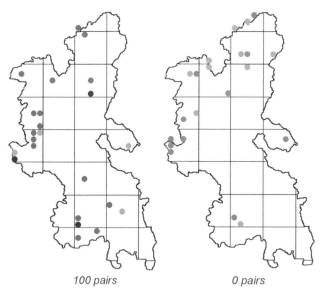

Migration dates	
Earliest:	4 Apr
Ave earliest:	21 Apr
Ave latest:	-
Latest:	20 Aug

100 pairs   0 pairs

DMF

Bluethroat
Luscinia svecica

Very rare vagrant. There are two records.

1969: 1 ringed on 31 Aug, Aston Clinton SF.
1983: female on 21 May, Great Linford GPs.

These are typical dates for this European species.

Black Redstart
Phoenicurus ochruros

Irregular summer breeder and scarce migrant.

There are 10 records prior to 1972:

1909: female or male of the year 11 Jun, near Wooburn.

1938: 1 in Oct, Olney.

1961: single birds 5, 25, 26 Oct believed to be 2 different birds, Stoke Park.

1965: 1 male on 22 May, Marlow nurseries.

1965: 1 male on 13 Aug, Sands, High Wycombe.

Milton Keynes, 2 Mar 2006   *Mike Wallen*

1965: pair with 3 juveniles, seen on several dates up to 22 Sep, Booker, High Wycombe. It seems likely that they bred in the area. The male seen at Marlow and Sands may have been the male of this pair.

1965: 2 on 10 Oct, Frieth.

1969: female Mar, Chesham SF.

1969: 1 on 18 Mar, Princes Risborough.

1970: 2 on 10 Apr, 1 on 11 Apr, High Wycombe.

The records of migrants between 1972 and 2011 are shown on the graphs.

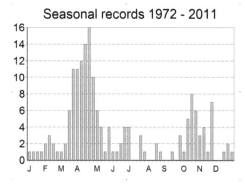

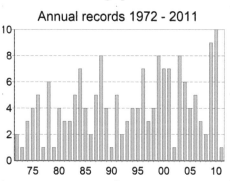

There have been five further attempts at breeding, four of which were successful:

1973: nest containing two eggs found in old brick kiln at Newton Longville Brick Pits but was subsequently deserted.

1975: four young fledged at Bradwell on 25 Jun.

1978: female with two recently fledged young 18 Jun at Pitstone.

1982: successful breeding in mid-Bucks.

1983: unsuccessful breeding Bletchley.

1996: attempted breeding at Pitstone cement works with unknown success.

1997: five young fledged near High Wycombe.

Black Redstarts first bred in Britain in the 1920s on the south coast and in London. They gradually spread until there are now rather less than 100 pairs as far north as Northumberland. In many places, including Buckinghamshire, they are erratic breeders. They prefer industrial sites, which birdwatchers tend to avoid, so they may well be under-recorded. Derelict factories are a favourite habitat. During the first atlas survey they were recorded in two tetrads - in SP91H where it was confirmed to have bred, and SP84V where the species was present.

The graphs show a concentration of records in the early spring. The birds may be found throughout the county, but the centre appears to be particularly favoured.

Common Redstart
Phoenicurus phoenicurus

Rowsham, 26 Aug 2011   *Mike Wallen*

Uncommon but increasing migrant; former summer breeder.

It is evident from earlier accounts that Redstarts have always been local in the county. H & J described them as 'generally not rare, but appears to be scarce in the Chilterns and uncommon in beech woods, though more frequent in the neighbourhood of rivers.' They give as river localities the Ouse near Newport Pagnell, Castlethorpe, the Chess, and the Thames. It is likely that they nested at these sites in pollarded willows. Parkland sites they mention are Stowe Park, Chequers, and Mentmore, and other sites given are Buckingham, Aylesbury, Burnham Beeches, and Amersham.

Since then the population slowly decreased until it is now extinct in the county. In 1946 12 pairs were found nesting in pollarded willows between Long Crendon and Waterperry in Oxfordshire, but they are no longer present. Up to six pairs bred at Burnham Beeches in 1960 but there have been no records since 1987. Up to five males were present at Ashridge in 1982 and three or four males in 1993 but there have been no records since, except for a male in 1999. At least six territories were held in Brickhill Woods in 1976, four in 1988, but the last breeding record was in 1997. Other sites have included Ravenstone Woods, where three pairs bred in 1960, Black Park, Stockgrove, where four pairs bred in 1964, Cublington, and Coombe Hill.

Redstarts nest in tree-holes but two unusual nest sites were found in 1967. A pair bred near Marlow in a gravel bank, even though suitable tree-holes were present nearby, and on the Oxfordshire border a pair nested below the floorboards of a gypsy-type caravan.

The site in Burnham Beeches comprised mainly ancient beech trees, but the other major sites were areas of pedunculate oak wood within large mixed woods. Restarts have to compete with other hole-nesting species, some of which are increasing in numbers. It is thought that, although Redstarts do not take readily to nest-boxes, provision of artificial nest-sites helps the birds as it reduces the competition from other species. None of the major breeding sites has any nest-boxes, and this may be a factor in accounting for the extinction. It is also known that Great Spotted Woodpeckers predate hole-nesting birds so the increase in this species may also be a factor.

It is interesting that Redstarts and Wood Warblers, which are usually found together in the sessile oakwoods of western and northern Britain were also found together in Buckinghamshire, even though both species were rare in the county. Ashridge and the

Brickhill Woods were the principal sites for Wood Warblers, while the third important site for Redstarts, Burnham Beeches, appears to have lost both its Wood Warblers and Redstarts at about the same time.

There are small passages in both spring and autumn. In the eight years between 1983 and 1991 66 birds were recorded in the spring between 3 Apr and 7 May, and 38 birds in the autumn between 12 Jul and 29 Oct. The records since 1992 are shown on the graphs. The increase in records is almost certainly due to increased observer interest. Birds are most frequent at the migration hot-spots of the Ivinghoe and Quainton Hills but birds have been found throughout the county. In the record-breaking late summer of 2011 up to nine were present at Quainton and six at Rowsham. A male remained at Rowsham from 27 Jun to 26 Jul 2011 while it moulted. The sequence of records at this site, which has no obvious attraction for migrants, can be attributed to one very active local observer. It makes one wonder how many birds are missed.

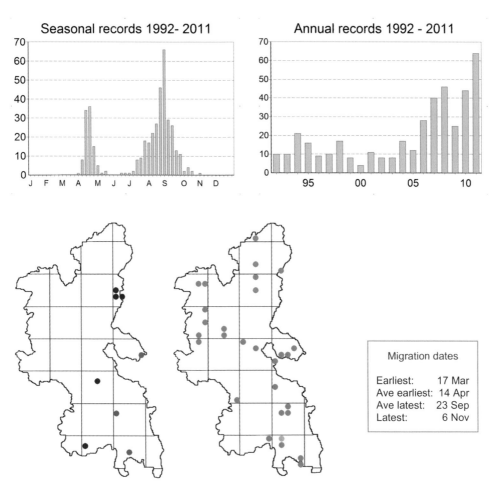

Migration dates	
Earliest:	17 Mar
Ave earliest:	14 Apr
Ave latest:	23 Sep
Latest:	6 Nov

DMF

Whinchat
Saxicola rubetra

Uncommon migrant; no longer breeds.

Clark Kennedy described the status of Whinchat as 'sparingly distributed' and gives Dorney Common and Chesham as sites. H & J were more detailed. They wrote 'somewhat locally distributed, and rare or absent from the hills or drier districts, but regularly breeding along the Thames Valley, though not in any numbers, also by Ouse, Chess, in the Vale of Aylesbury, and in the north of the county.' Price wrote 'regular summer visitor, breeding in small numbers'.

Ivinghoe Beacon, 2 May 2011   *Mike Wallen*

None of these statements is now correct. By the late 1950s breeding was restricted to the escarpment near Ivinghoe and probably Westcott. In the 1960s there were pairs at Haversham, near Kimble, and Calvert. By the mid-1970s breeding had become restricted to just three sites, but in 1978 breeding was not recorded. One or two pairs have bred since but the last positive breeding was at Aylesbury SF in 1983. During the first atlas period, breeding was proved in SP61W and SP71X, and probable breeding recorded in 1985 in SP70T, while birds were present in six other tetrads. Two adults and five immatures were seen at Hardmead on 21 Aug 1995 which may have been locally breeding birds.

There has been one wintering record: two birds were discovered at Jubilee River on 24 Nov 2002 and one bird remained until 25 Jan 2003. This is one of the few records of birds wintering in the UK.

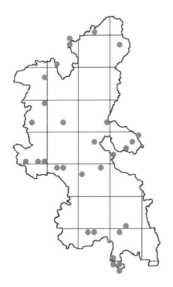

Migration dates	
Earliest spring:	16 Mar
Ave earliest spring:	22 Apr
Ave latest spring:	15 May
Latest spring:	-
Earliest autumn:	-
Ave earliest autumn:	3 Aug
Ave latest autumn:	9 Oct
Latest autumn:	11 Nov

The decline in the population of Whinchats in Buckinghamshire is part of an overall decline in lowland England which seems due to the degradation of its favoured habitat. Whinchats prefer weedy uncultivated land such as neglected fields, road-verges, and railway embankments. Now fields are largely cultivated, roads have become busier, and railway embankments are overgrown.

Whinchats are regular passage migrants through the county. Spring passage occurs between mid-April and the end of May while autumn passage is from the end of July to the end of September. The spring passage usually consists of single birds, or two together, but parties in the autumn, which are swelled by young birds, may be larger. The biggest congregations recorded are 17 birds at Dorney on 1 Sep 1982, and at least 16 birds at Little Marlow on 21 Sep 1980. The map shows the locations of spring migrants between 2007 and 2011. Regular sites are the Ivinghoe Hills, the Quainton Hills and Dorney, but they can occur almost anywhere where there is suitable habitat.

There has been one ringing recovery. A bird ringed at Mentmore on 7 Sep 1965 was recovered in Logrono, Spain on 16 Oct 1965.

DMF

Stonechat
Saxicola torquata

Scarce migrant and winter visitor; has bred.

Ivinghoe Beacon, 20 Oct 2011   *Lucy Flower*

H & J described the status of Stonechats as 'Now rather local but one or more pairs nest on most of the commons, where gorse abounds.' They remark that a few pairs nest in the south of the county and give Burnham Beeches as a locality. Price wrote 'a scarce summer visitor, breeding in small numbers. Some remain for the winter.'

Since then there were no confirmed breeding records until 1995 when two pairs successfully raised three broods between them at Stoke Common. A pair successfully bred at the same site between 2000 and 2003. Stonechats have suffered a substantial decline in inland counties due in the main to fragmentation of habitat. The species prefers heathland but will use areas of waste ground, particularly if gorse is present, a habitat which has become scarce in the county because of ploughing. This fragmentation of habitat has tended to isolate the Stonechat populations and thus render them susceptible to being wiped out during severe winters. During the first atlas period the species was recorded in only one tetrad, SP80I, where breeding was considered to be probable.

Stonechats are regular and increasing winter visitors. During the early 1970s 8-17 birds were seen annually but there was a large influx in Oct and Nov 1976 when birds were found at 45 localities, including seven birds at Little Marlow. Since then numbers fell, reaching a low of only three birds in 1987. The following year saw an increase to nine birds, and in 1989 and 1990 c16 birds were seen in both years. By 2008 up to 50 birds were wintering. Birds usually arrive during October and leave in February. There is also a very small passage in March and September.

A female present during February 1992 at Aylesbury SF had been colour-ringed as a nestling the previous June near Donaghadee, Co. Down, N Ireland. The bird reappeared at its birthplace on 11 Apr 1992 where it mated and laid eggs.

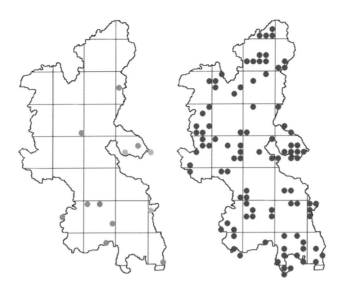

DMF

Northern Wheatear
Oenanthe oenanthe

Local migrant.

Ivinghoe Beacon, 22 Apr 2010   *Mike Wallen*

Wheatears have declined as a breeding species in the county since the beginning of the century. H & J wrote 'apparently less frequent than it used to be.' They mention as breeding sites Coombe Hill and Whiteleaf Cross, but also that it had ceased to breed on Ivinghoe Beacon 8-10 years previously and at Halton 20 years before. Price described the status as 'a regular summer visitor, breeding in small numbers.' Since this was written there has only been one confirmed breeding record. A pair reared seven young at Hartigan's GP, near Broughton, Milton Keynes in 1954. On 29 July 2007 a juvenile was seen being fed by an adult on Quainton Hills. It seems likely that breeding took place locally.

The reduction in the Wheatear population in Buckinghamshire is part of a general decline in south inland England where breeding Wheatears are now extremely rare. The decline is certainly due to habitat loss. Wheatears breed in open country with short grass, a habitat that was plentiful in the 19th century when sheep grazing was commonplace. Since then the numbers of sheep have fallen considerably, and rabbits, which also help to keep the grass short, have been decimated by myxomatosis. Furthermore, much of the grassland has been ploughed, particularly since the Second World War.

A strong double passage occurs through the county. The spring passage usually begins in the third week of March and ends in mid-May. The autumn passage begins in mid-July and continues to mid-October. Small numbers of the larger and brighter Greenland sub-species are annual. The map shows the distribution of spring records between 2007 and 2011.

258

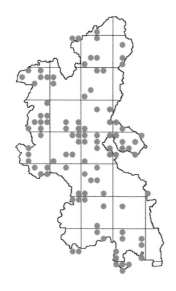

Migration dates	
Earliest spring:	6 Mar
Ave earliest spring:	18 Mar
Ave latest spring:	23 May
Latest spring:	-
Earliest autumn:	11 Jul
Ave earliest autumn:	1 Aug
Ave latest autumn:	18 Oct
Latest autumn:	10 Nov

Wheatears may be found at suitable localities throughout the county but certain places seem favoured. In recent years these include the Ivinghoe Hills, Lodge Hill, the Quainton Hills and Dorney. The largest congregations recorded are c25 at Lane End on 24 Apr 1963, 20+ at the same locality on 4 May 1967, 20+ at Westcott between 9 and 19 Sep 1974, 21 at Downley Common on 5 Apr 1987 and 20+ at Broughton/Kingston on 26 Apr 1992. There have been two November records: one at Willen on 4 Nov 1978 and one at Drayton Parslow on 2 Nov 1999.

There have been three records of single birds in June: 19 Jun 1974 in N Bucks, 28 Jun 1987 at Pitstone cement works, and 15 Jun at High Wycombe.

DMF

Black-eared Wheatear
Oenanthe hispanica

Very rare vagrant. There is one record.

1992: male on 25 Apr, Chearsley (Rose and Wallen, 1993).

This bird, one of the few to be recorded in an inland county, was a pale-throated male of the eastern race *O.h.melanoleuca*.

Ring Ouzel
Turdus torquatus

Very local migrant.

There are old undated records for the middle of the county. The first dated record is:

1840: 1 shot, Risborough.

Between 1862 and 1960 only 10 birds were recorded, while between 1961 and 1971 17 birds were seen. Since 1972 the frequency of recording had increased markedly with 389 birds being identified. These last records are shown on the graphs.

Quainton Hills, 6 May 2007   *Mike Wallen*

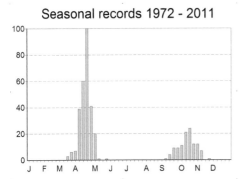

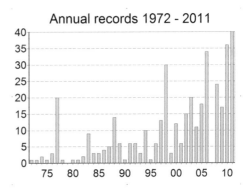

The largest flocks were all seen on the Ivinghoe Hills. There were seven birds on 9 Apr 1977, eight on 17 Apr 1988, 11 on 20 Apr 2003, 14 on 11 Apr 2006 and eight on 17 Apr 2008. Most of the records have been on the Chilterns escarpment, an increasing number on the Quainton Hills due to increased observer coverage and rather fewer in the north of the county. There have been only seven records for the south. The seasonal graph shows a brief spring migration with a marked peak at the end of April. Fewer birds are seen in October although numbers are increasing, again probably due to increased observer coverage. There are two records of birds seen in gardens: a male in Milton Keynes on 27 Mar 1996 and another male at Walter's Ash on 30 Mar 2009.

Blackbird
Turdus merula

Very common resident, migrant and winter visitor.

All the early accounts describe the Blackbird as one of the commonest species. Blackbirds diversified from their natural woodland habitat to towns and villages during the 19th century and are now found throughout the

Radnage, 24 Jul 2011   *Gerry Whitlow*

county. They reach their highest population densities in suburbs with mature gardens where there can be over 250 pairs per 100 hectares.

It is probable that Blackbirds breed in every tetrad in the county and that the gaps are due to under-recording. The estimated population of 70,000 pairs makes the Blackbird the second most numerous breeding bird in Buckinghamshire. Large areas of the county are a mosaic of woods and towns and villages that are very favourable to the species. The only threat to the population comes from the removal of hedges and from changes in farming practices. Spring tillage is helpful to Blackbirds as it enables the birds to find food more readily during the breeding season. Winter cereals, which are commonly planted in the county, have the effect of reducing the area tilled during spring and this may have an adverse effect on Blackbird populations (O'Connor and Shrubb 1986). This may be balanced by the change from hay to silage which involves many cuts during a season and thus increases the amount of time when the vegetation is short enough to be available as feeding areas.

Blackbirds were recorded in 99% of the gardens participating in the BBC Garden Birds Survey, which, with Blue Tit, is the highest percentage recorded. A maximum of 22 birds have been seen at one time.

The local population is augmented in winter by birds from elsewhere. Up to 50 birds have been recorded in October in places such as Campbell Park and the Ivinghoe Hills. Most ringing records outside the county have been from other parts of S England, although a bird ringed at Weston Turville Res on 30 Aug 1964 was recovered in Dyfed on 4 Nov 1965, another bird locally ringed on 8 Dec 1974 was recovered on 14 Jan 1977 in Co.Fermanagh, a juvenile ringed at Aston Clinton on 9 May 1995 was recovered in S Yorkshire on 11 Apr 2006. An adult ringed on Fair Isle on 30 Mar 2001 was controlled on 16 Dec 2001 at Cheddington.

26 locally ringed birds have been recovered abroad. All were winter visitors to the county but only seven were recovered in the breeding season. Of these, two were found in Germany, and one each in the Netherlands, Belgium, Denmark, Sweden and Finland. A further seven birds were recovered in March, when the birds could have been migrating. Two were found in the Netherlands, and one each in Germany, Belgium, Denmark, Finland, and Norway. The remaining 11 birds were recovered in autumn or winter. Three were found in the Netherlands

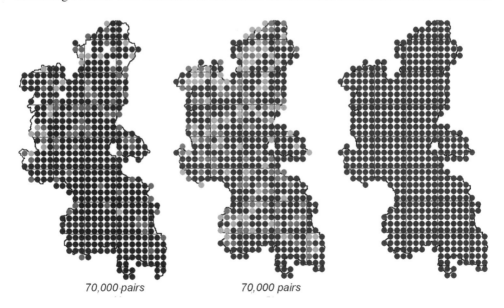

70,000 pairs   70,000 pairs

and Germany, two each in France and Sweden and one each in Finland and Iceland. It seems from this that Blackbirds are not particularly faithful to their wintering areas. A juvenile ringed in Belgium on 19 May 1998 was controlled at Drayton Beauchamp on 1 Feb 1999. An adult ringed in Sweden on 19 Mar 2003 was controlled at Cheddington on 30 Dec 2003.

DMF

Fieldfare
Turdus pilaris

Common winter visitor.

The status of Fieldfares appears not to have changed since Clark Kennedy wrote 'regular winter visitant'.

Marsh, 14 Jan 2012   *Richard Billyard*

The earliest autumn record is of a single bird at Willen on 17 Aug 1983, three weeks before the next earliest bird, one at Middle Claydon on 7 Sep 1981. Birds are not usually noted in any numbers until October, and sometimes not until November. The timing of departure of birds from their Scandinavian breeding grounds is dependent upon the abundance of rowan berries. Very large flocks are not usually present in Buckinghamshire until the new year, but an exceptionally large flock of c15,000 birds in the Haddenham-Aston Sandford area was recorded on 18 Nov 1981. Movements of birds during the winter are very variable and are dependent upon the availability of wild fruit crops and the weather. This is reflected in the considerable variation in the maximum numbers that are recorded each year. For instance the largest recorded flock size in 1980 was 500 birds, but the following year saw the huge flock at Haddenham. Feeding flocks of more than 1000 birds are recorded in most years, and flocks greater than 2000 birds are not unusual.

Only two feeding flocks of more than 10,000 birds have been recorded: the one already mentioned, and another in the same locality on 23 Feb 1990. Although the map shows Fieldfares present throughout the county, numbers tend to be lower in the south.

Fieldfares roost communally, usually in trees. The largest roost recorded in the county was in Bernwood Forest which regularly held in excess of 10,000 birds. On 25 Mar 1984 15-20,000 birds were estimated to be present. However, birds have not been recorded at this site since 5000 were noted on 10 Mar 1988.

Birds begin to leave the county in April and are usually gone by the end of the month. The latest records are of single birds near Chinnor, but within the county on 4 Jun 1993 and at Broughton, MK on 28 May 1978. There are two early summer records. A bird was present in Amersham from 28 Jun to 3 Jul 1978, and another bird was seen at Moulsoe on 12

Jun 1990, but there were no indications of breeding. A bird seen at Marlow on 3 Aug 1992 could have been an early arrival or summering bird.

12 birds ringed in Buckinghamshire have been recovered, seven in the summer and six in the winter. Three of the summer recoveries were in Norway, two in Sweden, and two in Finland. Five of the winter recoveries were in France and the other was in Belgium. It seems that Fieldfares do not necessarily return to the same wintering areas, and indeed that they can move considerable distances during a winter, as shown by a bird which was ringed at Calvert on 26 Jan 1986 and recovered in Finistere, France on 3 Apr 1986. The ring of a nestling ringed in Karelia, Russia on 8 Jun 1974 was found at Denham on 24 Jun 1988.

A partial albino with a white head and neck was seen at Cublington in January 2010.

DMF

Song Thrush
Turdus philomelos

Common resident, migrant and winter visitor.

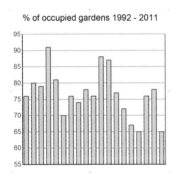

% of occupied gardens 1992 - 2011

Shardeloes, 20 July 2011   *David Ferguson*

Evidently the status of Song Thrushes has changed considerably since 1920 when H & J described it is 'even more numerous than Blackbird' because there is no doubt now that Blackbirds are much the commoner birds.

This change in relative numbers is part of a national trend. The Song Thrush population began declining during the 1940s which can be explained in part by a succession of winters which had an above average number of days when the ground was frozen (Baillie 1990). The decline has also been attributed to changes in farming practices (O'Connor & Shrubb 1986). The area of land which is tilled in spring has been reduced owing to the preponderance of winter cereals, so that birds breeding in farmland now have a smaller area in which to feed during the breeding season. Removal of hedges, which is an important nesting habitat, is also another factor.

CBC and BBS data shows that Song Thrush numbers declined rapidly until the mid-90s and then began to slowly rise. It is likely that Stewardship schemes have had a positive effect. The county population in the 1970s may have been around 30,000 pairs, falling to 15,000 pairs in the mid-1980s, and falling again to perhaps 12,000 pairs in 1990 but since then there has been an increase to an estimated 20,000 pairs.

The graph of percentage of gardens recording Song thrushes shows a different situation. The graph shows widely fluctuating percentages, but with an overall downward trend. It is well known that Song Thrushes eat snails. It is possible that the use of slug pellets has had an adverse effect on Song Thrush populations either through direct poisoning or by causing a reduction in mollusc populations.

In winter the population is augmented by birds from other regions. It also seems that Buckinghamshire birds winter in other parts of Britain and in Europe, possibly in response to freezing conditions. No British ringing recovery of a locally ringed bird has been made further north than Shropshire, but birds have been found as far east as Lincolnshire and as far west as Devon. There have been five foreign recoveries, four in France and one in Spain. All were recovered between October and February.

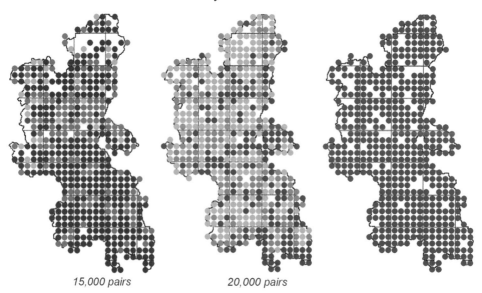

15,000 pairs   *20,000 pairs*

DMF

Redwing
Turdus iliacus

Common winter visitor.

Aylesbury, 15 Jan 2012   *Martin Ansley*

The status of the Redwing has changed little since H & R wrote 'Fairly common, sometimes very numerous'. H & J wrote 'On 11th March 1906 a flock estimated to be 38,000 were spread thickly over eight acres of grassland near Skirmett,' and 'In 1918 Redwings were generally very scarce. Hartert saw none until March'. In 1976 F & Y gave the Redwing's status as 'common winter visitor with numbers varying from year to year.'

This has not changed. The largest flock recorded in some years is only 150 birds, but in others flocks of over 1000 birds are common.

264

The largest recent flocks were of 5000+ birds at Ford/Bishopstone on 17 Dec 1977 and another of 4000 birds at Hughenden on 21 Dec 1989. This annual variation is due to birds not regularly wintering in the same area or even the same country. Birds which come to Britain one year may winter in Italy the next. Similarly the numbers of Redwings in the county are rarely the same throughout a complete winter. When few birds have been recorded in the first half, an increase can usually be expected towards the end of the winter.

The first Redwings normally arrive in Buckinghamshire in late September. Many of these early records are of birds heard calling while flying over at night but on 12 Oct 1997 an astonishing passage took place shortly after dawn. 18,000 flew over Steps Hill in six hours, 4000 flew over Marlow in two hours, 3000 were counted in two hours near Salden Wood, 1000 flew over Whitchurch and 1000 over Freith/Rockwell. Few of these birds stayed in the county. In 2004, again shortly after dawn, 10,000 birds flew over Steps Hill on 9 Oct and 3000 on 18 Oct 2008. Although the peak arrival is in early October, 100 flew over Steps Hill on 9 Sep 1994.

Redwings commonly roost with Fieldfares and other thrushes. Gatherings of 200-300 are fairly common, but roosts of up to 2500 have been found at Bacombe, Wendover, 2000 at Shenley Wood, Bletchley, and at Lady Villiers Gorse, Drayton Parslow. During severe weather most birds usually migrate with the remaining few frequently succumbing to the cold.

5000 flew west over Marlow on 21 Nov 1993 after snow. At these times some birds move into gardens to feed. The cold winter of 1854, according to *The Field*, destroyed Redwings and Fieldfares by tens of thousands. H & J also state 'In the cold winter of 1917 all or nearly all Redwing which were in the county at the time perished. Redwings were then scarce in 1918 and were probably as common as before the 1917 frost in 1919'. Most are gone by early April, and the average latest date is 20 April.

There are two records of Redwings in summer: one shot at Harleyford on 28 Jul 1871 (H & R), and one at Old Wolverton on 16 Aug 1983. The latter bird was thought to have been present for some time as it was in heavy moult.

Redwings ringed in the county have been recovered in Italy (two birds), Belgium (two), France (two), and one each in Sweden, Germany, Spain, and Portugal.

A white bird with pale buff head and shoulders but a normal supercilium was seen at Tilehouse on 22 Jan 1990.

JK

Mistle Thrush
Turdus viscivorus

Common resident.

Early writers described the status of Mistle Thrushes as common, although H & J also remarked that it was not in any great numbers in the Thames Valley. The situation has probably not changed as Mistle Thrushes can be found throughout the county although not in any great numbers. They favour wood edges, farmland with hedges, and urban and suburban areas. Open areas for feeding are essential. In urban areas this is provided by parks and sports fields, while elsewhere farmland is used.

Coleshill, 25 Nov 2009   *Ashley Stow*

Nationally there has been a slight decline, although this has not been obvious locally. To some extent, Mistle Thrushes are dependent upon the area of land which is tilled in spring for feeding during the breeding season. With the trend towards winter cereals this area has decreased. On the credit side the change from hay to silage, which is cut earlier, has probably been beneficial as short grass suitable for feeding is available during this species' early breeding period.

The map shows several large gaps in the north of the county, which are probably due to under-recording. The gaps are larger than those on the Song Thrush map and may be caused by the much smaller Mistle Thrush population, which results in the birds being harder to find. There is no reason to suppose that Mistle Thrushes do not occur in every tetrad in the county.

The species has been recorded in 25% of the gardens participating in the BBC Garden Birds survey with a maximum of five being seen at one time.

Post-breeding flocks can be quite large although the only 50+ flocks reported are c72 over Coleshill on 31 Oct 1989, 80-100 at Stokenchurch on 1 Sep 1993, 50+ at Kingston on 27 Jul 1993, 50+ at Eythrope on 10 and 24 Aug 1996. Large winter flocks are unusual but there were 45 birds at Great Missenden on 25 Feb 1981.

Buckinghamshire Mistle Thrushes seem remarkably sedentary. Of the 34 ringing records involving birds either ringed or recovered in the county in only three cases had the birds travelled more than 10 km.

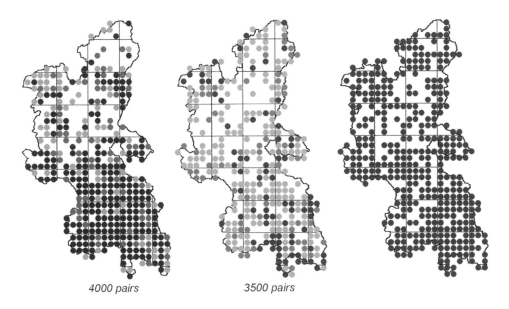

4000 pairs   3500 pairs

DMF

Cetti's Warbler
Cettia cetti

Very local resident and rare migrant.

Calvert, 28 Apr 2010   *John Sheppard*

The first record was an adult trapped on 22 Jul, 1967 at Weston Turville Res. It was retrapped on 29 Jul and 9 Sep. This was only the third British record. The significant increase in a resident English population, which took place in appropriate habitat initially close to the south-east and south coasts in the 1970s and 1980s was not reflected in the number of records in the county. While physically secretive, this is a rather vocal species, so the lack of records is probably a pretty accurate indication of its absence. There was a second record, at Linford GPs in 1977 and the third was back at Weston Turville Res. in the winter of 1985/6. Between 1989 and 2001 the species was recorded in seven years at one or two sites per annum, during which time there was no serious indication of breeding, although this was known to be taking place in adjacent counties. However from Mar to Jun 2002 a male was clearly holding territory at Caldecotte Lake. The following year there was a similar situation, but this time at Willen Lake, with two males singing regularly in September. Breeding probably took place at Willen Lake in 2004, with birds at two other sites. Precisely the same happened in 2005, but the two other sites were different to those of the previous year. Birds were present at five sites in 2006 and four in 2007, before breeding was eventually proved at both Linford GPs and Weston Turville in 2008, as well as the species being noted at six other sites. Again eight sites were favoured in 2009 and in 2010 Cetti's Warblers could be seen or, more often, heard at thirteen sites throughout the county, with six occupied in the breeding season, of which four held more than one male. Rather surprisingly, while the breeding season map indicates a more general distribution based, as one would expect on gravel pits and other water bodies, all of the certainly occupied territories in this last year were in mid-Bucks and northwards.

The shift from initial to steady, but very limited occurrence seems to have taken place rather slowly, but the apparent definite colonisation has actually taken place very quickly indeed, and presumably relates to some unknown tipping point.

20 pairs

AVH

Grasshopper Warbler
Locustella naevia

Scarce summer visitor.

In the nineteenth and early twentieth century the Grasshopper Warbler was, much as today, considered to breed sparsely though widely in Buckinghamshire. Combining past and current information in 1920, H & J knew of only ten places where it had occurred, including three which were on or just outside the county's present boundaries. However, the species was probably more under-recorded then than it is now. Numbers appear

Steps Hill, 1 May 2009   Mike Wallen

to have fluctuated over the years. The older statements, though very vague, suggest at least one period of decline earlier this century. Thus Clark Kennedy's `not very plentiful' in 1868 and H & R's `generally distributed' in 1905 contrast with H & J's `rather rare' in 1920, while Sage (1959) writes of a `decrease during recent years in Hertfordshire'. The MTNHS reports show birds present in a good many places during the 1950s, without commenting on abundance. By

1964 the species was 'widespread in all suitable localities'; and increases were recorded over the following three summers, with numbers remaining high to at least 1969. In 1972 and subsequently a marked drop was noticed. The 1973 report attributed this to the local maturation of conifers, with consequent habitat loss, but both the rise and subsequent decline locally corresponded closely to changes in annual numbers of migrants at coastal bird observatories (Riddiford 1983), suggesting that the local changes were in fact part of a nationwide pattern. Since the first survey, the Buckinghamshire range has contracted slightly, partly because of the construction of Milton Keynes. The original population estimate of 100 pairs may have been optimistic and that the new estimate of 50 pairs is more accurate.

The Grasshopper Warbler inhabits low scrub and rank herbage, in both dry and damp situations. Thus it may be found in areas of rough, tussocky grass, as in damp and neglected fields, or where such herbage is interspersed with low brambles and bushy growth on waste or common land. This can include chalk downland, if not heavily grazed, and field hedges and ditches. Song is sometimes heard, and breeding perhaps takes place, in growing crops. A locally important habitat is provided by forestry plantations and felled but regenerating woodland, where there are young trees and tangled undergrowth. Plantations have been available on a larger scale and more regular basis in recent decades than formerly, and they acquire sizeable populations of Grasshopper Warblers for the few seasons when they offer ideal conditions. How far such new sites may compensate for scrubland lost through intensification of agriculture, and sometimes urbanisation, is however not known.

First clutches are often begun around mid May and there may be two broods. Nests are notoriously difficult to find. It is therefore not surprising that breeding was only proved in four tetrads, while many of the 'probable' breeding records may simply relate to reeling males. Since the birds sing mainly around dawn and dusk, it is likely that some birds were missed, but against this must be set the frequent reports of birds reeling on just one or two dates, apparently during pauses on their migration. Also, as the maps was compiled over several years it may exaggerate the distribution in one year because some sites may only be suitable for a year or two.

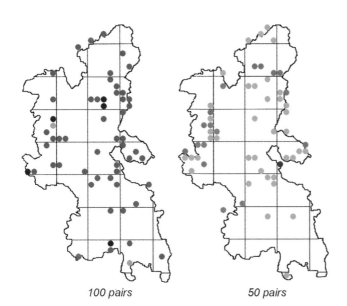

100 pairs   50 pairs

Migration dates

Earliest:	4 Apr
Ave earliest:	17 Apr
Ave latest:	21 Aug
Latest:	25 Sep

There is rather little information on departure dates. Though nests with young in August are not exceptional, the annual reports list few late summer records. There were at least five birds (not all reeling) at one breeding site on 16 Aug 1986, and occasional birds are seen or mist-netted at non-breeding sites in August and early September. The latest records are 25 Sep 1999 at Stoke Common, 19 Sep 2002 at Steps Hill and 15 Sep 2010 at Calvert landfill.

The earliest spring arrival date is 4 Apr 2002 at Drayton Parslow. In many years the first bird is recorded between 11 and 22 April, but in 1974 and 1977 none was noted until 28 April. It may be assumed that most local birds arrive during late April or early May, but precise information on this very secretive species is hard to gather and the arrival of females must go very largely unnoticed.

HM-G

River Warbler
Locustella fluviatilis

Very rare vagrant. There has been one record.

1997: 1 singing from 15 to 16 Jun, Linford (Andrews & Wallington, 1998).

Aquatic Warbler
Acrocephalus paludicola

Very rare vagrant. There are two records.

1990: 1 on 2 Aug, Blue Lagoon, Bletchley. Probably also on 3 Aug.
1990: 1 on 26 Aug, Botolph Claydon.

It is of course remotely possible that the two records refer to the same bird. The dates are typical for this European species.

Sedge Warbler
Acrocephalus schoenobaenus

Local summer visitor.

Willen Lake, 1 May 2010   *Keith O'Hagen*

Past accounts, back to Clark Kennedy's time, are essentially in accord with present-day observations in describing the Sedge Warbler as generally distributed along large and small watercourses, as well as by pools and lakes. It is also found in drier sites.

The species exploits a wider variety of more or less luxuriant vegetation than the Reed Warbler, and the map shows it to have a slightly wider distribution. Since Sedge Warbler pairs are quite strongly territorial, concentrations like those often formed by Reed Warblers do not occur. The national Common Birds Census shows the breeding population to have been high in the mid 1960s but to have declined markedly from 1965 to 1975, the decrease coinciding with drought conditions in the African wintering range, and then slowly increased. A comparison of the maps shows that the construction of Milton Keynes has removed a number of sites and that the Thame and Lea Valleys have fewer occupied tetrads which suggests that adverse local conditions have counteracted any national increase.

While most pairs breed within about 100 m of water, single pairs or small loose groups can occur by tiny pools or wet ditches, which may even dry out during the summer, and birds can then quite easily escape detection. Some birds settle well away from water, though often still in its general vicinity. Birds heard singing in completely dry sites, including gardens, probably include wandering males, but there is evidence of nesting at times in young plantations and on farmland. Apparent breeding in rape fields has been observed in neighbouring counties (Bonham and Sharrock 1974). Clearly some breeding sites are transient in nature, affected perhaps by waterway management and farming. The waste ground around gravel pits, for instance, is often ideal while it remains at the open scrub stage. At the same time there are some long stretches of watercourse which lack suitable vegetation and hold no Sedge Warblers.

Breeding generally starts in mid May, though sometimes earlier, and second or repeat clutches can be found up to mid July. While some birds live up to their names by building in sedge tussocks in marshes, and a few build in Reed Warbler fashion among reed stems, far more nest in brambles or other shrubs and in herbage such as nettles and willowherb. They are usually in extensive areas of herbage, but sometimes by hedges. Once a pair is breeding the male sings very little, and the parents sometimes contrive to approach and leave the nest entirely under cover. They become more conspicuous again when tending fledged young.

Autumn passage usually gets under way towards the end of July or even in mid month. It is mainly observed in wetland areas, though not exclusively (eg a bird was found dead in the centre of Medmenham on 8 Sep 1976). Evidence of the substantial numbers that can be involved is provided by the 128 birds, at least 90 being juveniles, which were ringed at one site in the last week of July 1963. Passage probably reaches its peak in August but diminishes markedly thereafter. Nevertheless, 10 birds were still noted in the MTHNS area on 19 Sep 1976 and two were observed at one site on 13 Oct 1974. The latest county record is of a bird at Willen on 22 Oct 1989.

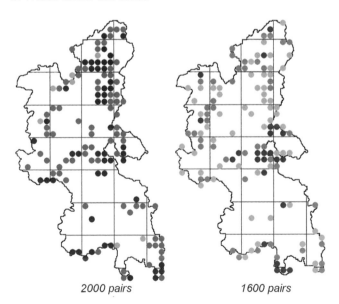

2000 pairs   1600 pairs

Migration dates	
Earliest:	31 Mar
Ave earliest:	9 Apr
Ave latest:	23 Sep
Latest:	22 Oct

Several ringing recoveries illustrate the timing and direction of autumn movements. A nestling ringed at Newport Pagnell on 19 Jun 1977, had flown 65 km south-east to Essex by the end of the following month. A juvenile ringed on 21 Jul 1963 was on the Sussex coast on 16 August, one ringed on 25 Jul 1965 was already in SW France 16 days later, and a later juvenile reached Sandwich Bay, Kent within five days of being ringed on 5 Sep 1964.

The earliest records are 1 Apr 1998 at Stony Stratford, 2 Apr 1961 at Weston Turville and 3 Apr 1999 at Willen. More usually the first report comes during the second week of April. At Weston Turville early arrivals typically remain hidden in *Phragmites* beds, uttering only infrequent and subdued snatches of song. Major influxes or passage movements occur between mid April and early May, depending on the season, and can continue into late May.

HM-G

Marsh Warbler
Acrocephalus palustris

Very rare vagrant which has bred. All records are given.

1931: bred Chalfont Park.
1956: 1 on 18 May, Shardeloes.
1960: 1 singing from 20 to 26 Jun, near Wendover.
1974: 1 on 26 May, Weston Turville Res.

Reed Warbler
Acrocephalus scirpaceus

Local summer visitor and migrant.

Early this century the Reed Warbler was `abundant where reed abounds'. The rivers Thames, Ouse and Colne, and the Tring and Weston Turville reservoirs received specific mention, as well as ponds with osiers. Since then, the additional habitats provided at new waters, mostly formed during mineral extraction, have allowed further areas to be colonised.

Little Marlow, 4 May 2006   *Julia Eyles*

The Reed Warbler's distribution is fairly strongly bound up with that of the reed. Yet even where reeds are present, pairs often breed in a variety of other riparian herbage as well as in willow and sallow scrub. Wandering birds sometimes sing in gardens or farmland, but no nests in such habitats have been recorded in the county. Nearly all the tetrads where the species was found contain some wetland. As a rule, Reed Warblers breed colonially, the densest concentrations apparently occurring in vigorous, recently formed stands of reed. In limited patches of suitable habitat such as the short strips of reed scattered along the smaller rivers, colonies are necessarily much smaller, and single pairs may be found. These pockets probably constitute the nearest Buckinghamshire possesses to a natural Reed Warbler environment.

Bigamy is known in this species, and instances have been suspected at Weston Turville Res, with occupied nests only two or three metres apart (H. Mayer-Gross). The species is also regularly parasitised by the Cuckoo, but with no noticeable impact on numbers. As well as sharing with the host species such hazards as predation, young Cuckoos in nests over water can drown on fledging; this has been witnessed once and suspected on other occasions (H. Mayer-Gross).

It is clear that Reed Warblers in Buckinghamshire are heavily dependent on man for the provision and preservation of their main breeding areas. Colonies quickly establish themselves wherever suitable plant growth develops at newly dug waters, whereas operations to straighten stretches of river inevitably eliminate Reed Warbler sites, at least in the short term.

The male Reed Warbler has a readily recognisable song, and as the species has a long breeding season (the first birds laying before mid May and the last broods fledging in early September), location is usually straightforward, although the odd isolated pair may have escaped detection.

The two maps show some changes in distribution. North Milton Keynes is now more sparsely occupied, presumably a result of increasing urbanisation, while several sites in the Thames Valley have been colonised, in particular the Jubilee River. NE Buckinghamshire has the highest density of occupied tetrads, closely associated with the meanderings of the Great Ouse, whose tributaries the Ouzel, Claydon Brook and a small brook at Bradwell provide further pockets of habitat to the south and west. Beside the Great Ouse lie the Newport Pagnell and Great Linford gravel pits. The former especially, with associated riverside reeds, has long formed a stronghold although the second survey did not record any birds in the Gayhurst area, a former colony.

In mid county there are colonies at College Lake and at the large Marsworth Reservoir colony which just extends into Buckinghamshire. The population at the major colony at Weston Turville Res was put at 34 pairs in 1985, 52 in 1986 and 48 in 1993, although it had been an estimated 100 pairs in 1962. In part at least, this reduction was due to maturation of vegetation. At the Wotton Lakes reedbeds the last estimates of population were of 25 pairs in 1977 and again in 2011.

The Reed Warbler's lifestyle makes it particularly amenable to ringing studies, and a wealth of interesting recoveries is to be found in the annual reports, especially since 1963. A selection of these, along with fuller ringing data from Weston Turville Res and north Buckinghamshire, amplifies and illuminates the picture of migratory movements obtained by visual observation. There are numerous records of adults and young birds returning to the same breeding colony, and also of birds breeding in colonies at some distance from their birthplace. While most of the latter concern youngsters, there are occasional instances suggestive of adults changing colonies. For example, one ringed at Colnbrook on 6 Jun 1968 was controlled at Weston Turville Res on 24 Jun 1973, and one ringed at Wilstone Res, Hertfordshire on 19 Jun 1980 was controlled at Weston Turville on 18 Jul 1983. A few others have been proved to reach at least six years of age, including one ringed in Spain on 11 Sep 1967 found breeding in the county in 1972 and 1973 and one ringed as a pulli at Weston Turville which was controlled in Berkshire on 1 Jun 1999. Finally, one again ringed as a pulli at Weston Turville on 18 Jun 1990 was controlled at Wilstone on 1 Jul 2001.

Most records of 'autumn' migration come from reedbed breeding sites, but some birds stop on passage at other localities, even well away from water. Being unobtrusive, such birds are more often than not detected during mist-netting, though occasionally they are found dead.

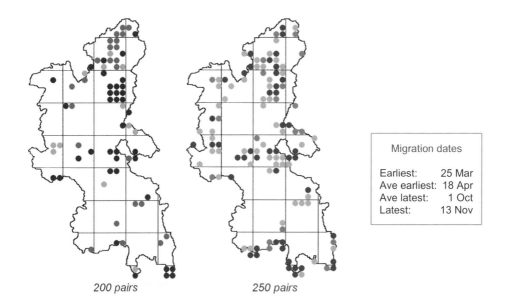

200 pairs	250 pairs

Migration dates

Earliest:	25 Mar
Ave earliest:	18 Apr
Ave latest:	1 Oct
Latest:	13 Nov

Visual observations of passage have been recorded from mid July, for example in 1963, and in several seasons the population at Weston Turville Res has been found to be markedly diminished during early August (H. Mayer-Gross). Small numbers, however, remain well into September. Late records include nine in October since 1967. There are two November records, both in 1977. One was seen at Oakley on 2 Nov 1977 and one was killed against a window at Marlow on 13 Nov 1977.

Ringing indicates that August is the peak passage month for locally bred birds. There appears to be an initial rather random dispersal, including many juveniles travelling a few kilometres west, but all longer August and September movements have been in directions between south and east. The earliest long movement from within Buckinghamshire was two pulli ringed at Weston Turville Res in June 1993 and controlled in France in August. Another was a juvenile ringed at Linford in July 1994 was controlled in Spain the following month. September recoveries, both short and long distance, are still quite plentiful, though more of them involve juveniles which might have journeyed from their birthplace before being ringed. A 1985 recovery concerned an adult ringed at Weston Turville Reservoir on 1 August which reached Portugal by 2 September, and three more birds ringed in the county were recovered in Iberia between 29 September and 12 October, while one ringed as a nestling was taken in Portugal as late as 8 December - if the finder is to be believed. Better progress was shown by a juvenile still at West Wycombe on 15 Aug 1964 which had reached SW Morocco on 25 September.

The first spring arrivals have nearly always appeared between 11 and 24 April; the earliest post-war date was 9 Apr 1961, though there is a record in the Handbook for 5 Apr 1909. In 1962 no bird was seen until 28 April. Observations indicate large-scale arrivals from the second week of May onwards, with birds at least sometimes still arriving early in June. A Weston Turville bird at least two years old was still in Morocco on 6 May, a Newport Pagnell bird of similar age had reached Portland, Dorset in its northward journey on 16 May, and four birds caught between 11 and 19 May were still between seven and 30 km from their breeding colonies.

HM-G

Great Reed Warbler
Acrocephalus arundinaceus

Very rare vagrant. There have been two records.

1946: 1 singing on 27 Apr in Bucks section of Marsworth Res.
2008: 1 singing on 11 May, Willen.

Willen Lake, 11 May 2008   *Keith O'Hagen*

Icterine Warbler
Hippolais icterina

Very rare vagrant. There have been two records.

1997: 1 singing on 14 Jun, Aylesbury SF (Glue, 1998).
2008: 1 singing on 14 Jun, Longwick.

Blackcap
Sylvia atricapilla

Common summer visitor and migrant; uncommon winter visitor.

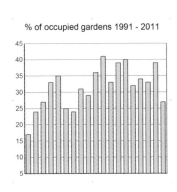

% of occupied gardens 1991 - 2011

Caldecotte Lake, 13 May 2011   *Keith O'Hagen*

Clark Kennedy found the Blackcap to be generally dispersed, more numerous than the Garden Warbler but not so common as many other warblers. The species was described as common in suitably wooded localities by H & R and H & J. None of these writers mentioned anything about overwintering, but F & Y in 1976 knew of `several' wintering records. In contrast to most other warblers, numbers have been maintained since the 1960s and have risen markedly on farmland (Common Birds Census).

The breeding season maps show the species to have spread into the less densely wooded parts of the county where it was previously absent. Blackcaps breed in most types of woodland, spinneys and scrub, and also not uncommonly in mature gardens. They require undergrowth or bushes and so are absent from dense conifers and closed-canopy beechwoods. Scrub, both low and tall, mixed with large trees is especially favoured.

The dispersal of local birds begins in July, and more visits to rural gardens and other non-breeding areas are recorded from then. The timing of the main passage is hardly mentioned in local reports. `Surprisingly large' numbers were ringed at Weston Turville Res in late July 1965, and movement certainly extends through August and generally well into September; for example, 20 or more birds were seen on Steps Hill on four occasions between 1997 and 1999, the largest being an impressive 100 on 2 Sep 1999.

In most years occasional migrants are seen into October, even late in the month. All such occurrences, perhaps significantly, have been since 1972 and could involve winter visitors arriving from continental Europe. However, some birds are very likely to be passage migrants, as there are breeding season ringing recoveries in Cheshire and Cambridgeshire of birds ringed in the county in September 1963 and 1981 respectively.

The first definite record of a wintering bird in Buckinghamshire is of one in Rectory Wood, Amersham on 22 Jan 1932. Although the MTNHS area produced single records in the early months of 1946, 1952 and 1953, regular wintering in the county apparently began considerably later. One bird was seen in November 1963, there were records between November and February in four of the next eight seasons, including five birds in 1969/70, and since 1972/73 birds have seen every winter. Numbers have slowly and rather erratically built up, sometimes producing 30 reports a winter by the mid 1980s. The winter map shows that birds are quite widespread south of the Chiltern escarpment but much more local to the north. Although most reports are from gardens it is likely that there are many undiscovered birds in the wider countryside. The true totals must be substantially greater. Prior to 1992 the BBC Garden Survey recorded Blackcaps in 8% of gardens. The graph shows the situation since when occurrences have risen to over 30%.

Snow and Snow (1988) have shown that various wild berries are taken while they are available in the autumn, and the birds move more into gardens from late December onwards when the berry stocks have dwindled. It is thought that bird tables play a key role in enabling this new wintering population to survive the coldest months (Berthold and Terrill 1988). Studying mainly scrubland in Buckinghamshire and adjacent parts of Hertfordshire, Snow and Snow saw 24 males and 26 females during four winters and consider that the frequently recorded preponderance of males arises through their `defending' garden feeding stations, and keeping the less aggressive females away. The actual numbers may well be about equal. There are instances of birds remaining up to 27 March, and there is circumstantial evidence of a few remaining into April, with a hen feeding on ivy berries on 18 Apr 1984 very likely being the same bird seen feeding there 10 weeks earlier (B. K. Snow).

Problems arise in distinguishing early summer arrivals from wintering individuals. Thus a number of `arrivals' were recorded between 5 and 12 Mar 1977, whereas in 1965 a small spate of mid March records was attributed to wintering birds on the move (MTNHS reports). Since rather few Blackcaps reach the south coast observatories before April (Riddiford and Findlay 1981) it seems likely that most March records are of late wintering birds, either local or passing through from the south-west, the main wintering area in Britain (Leach 1981). In many years first `arrivals' occur in late March or early April but widespread arrivals, initially mainly of males, usually do not begin until the second, third or even fourth week of April.

Adults ringed in the county have been recovered in S Spain in March and November, and Morocco in January, April (2) and September. Finally, there has been one record of a bird ringed abroad: an first-year female ringed in Koblenz, Germany on 12 Aug 1995 was controlled at Aston Clinton on 22 Mar 1996.

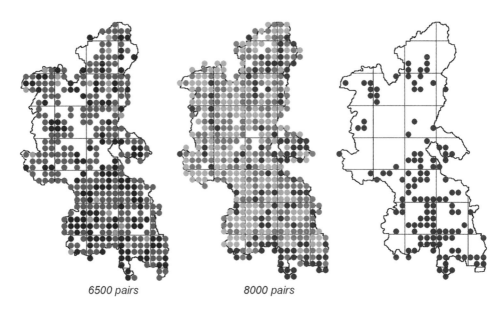

6500 pairs   8000 pairs

HM-G

Garden Warbler
Sylvia borin

Fairly common summer visitor.

A bird with no strong distinguishing features, the Garden Warbler tends to be under-recorded; but the older accounts, from Clark Kennedy onwards, agree with current assessments in considering it not particularly common but generally distributed in suitably wooded habitats throughout the county.

Both annual and longer term fluctuations have been observed. The national Common Birds Census registered a marked decline

Caldecotte Lake, 30 Jul 2011   Keith O'Hagen

during the 1970s, initially in the more marginal farmland habitats but later also in woodland, followed by a recovery in the 1980s which has since levelled off. The maps show that the species has spread into the far south and parts of the west and north, but has disappeared from parts of the Chilterns.

The Garden Warbler primarily inhabits woodland and spinneys, particularly clearings and margins or where the wide spacing of trees permits undergrowth to flourish. Bush scrub is also utilised, provided some taller shrubs or trees are present in the vicinity. With the same proviso, the thorny thickets which often develop for a few years in young conifer plantations are also favoured. Despite its name, the bird seldom nests in gardens, except ones containing sizeable patches of wilderness, though it may visit them on passage.

As with many other warblers, very little has been published about the local breeding population's departure. The 1963 and 1964 MTNHS reports indicated light passage taking place in late July, with August being the main passage month. This is supported by two ringing recoveries. A juvenile caught at Weston Turville Res on 30 Jul 1965 was found in the Cote d'Or, France on 10 Aug 1966, and a juvenile ringed at Marlow SF on 16 Jul 1988 was found in S France on 3 Sep. Another bird ringed at Marlow SF on 22 Aug 1987 was recovered in Ghana on 6 Dec 1988, indicating the wintering quarters.

Last sightings are usually in the second half of September but there are three October records: 1 Oct 1979 at Amersham, 11 Oct 1985 at Chesham and 13 Oct 1999 at Oakley.

Dates for the earliest spring arrivals are quite variable, in most years falling between 9 and 30 April. An exceptional record was of a bird seen along with some other migrants at Newport Pagnell GP on 13 Mar 1977, almost seven weeks before the next bird was reported that year. The second earliest sighting, on 2 Apr 1960, was also at Newport Pagnell. On the other hand the first birds in 1972 were not noted until 1 May, and in 1976 not until 7 May. Except in very forward seasons, the main influx of local breeders probably takes place in the first half of May.

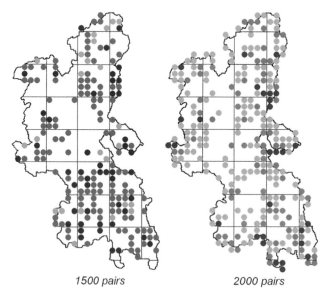

1500 pairs   2000 pairs

Migration dates	
Earliest:	13 Mar
Ave earliest:	19 Apr
Ave latest:	21 Sep
Latest:	21 Oct

HM-G

278

Lesser Whitethroat
Sylvia curruca

Rowsham, 19 Aug 2011   *Lucy Flower*

Fairly common summer visitor.

The Lesser Whitethroats which fell to the Rev. Mr Lightfoot's gun at Bulstrode, and were illustrated by Latham in 1787, were the first to be recorded in Britain. Authors from 1868 onwards have described the species as widespread though not very abundant, and so it remains today. Even though it is less conspicuous than the Whitethroat, statements indicating that prior to 1969 it was less numerous are surely correct. In the absence of numerical data, not too much weight should be attached to H & J's comment in 1920 that the Lesser Whitethroat was much more plentiful in Middlesex than adjoining parts of Buckinghamshire, unless there were habitat differences to account for the variation.

CBC/BBS results show that Lesser Whitethroat numbers dipped in 1970, rose to a peak in 1985, dipped again in 1997 and rose again to their 1966 level in 2010. Observers' comments on annual changes in abundance in MTNHS and BBC reports have often, but not always, concurred with the CBC/BBS findings. Breeding pairs are scattered enough to be counted easily, provided the song is known, and sometimes they are sufficiently numerous to give quite good counts. Thus at least eight males were singing near Great Kingshill in 1960, and nine nests in the Haversham - Linford area in 1983 indicated flourishing populations there.

While habitat requirements overlap considerably with those of the Whitethroat, the Lesser tends to prefer taller bush vegetation and its territories mostly contain scattered trees. It is therefore found along reasonably dense or bushy thorn hedges on farmland as well as in bush scrub, whether on waste land, in overgrown gardens, or in young deciduous or coniferous plantations.

CBC work, quoted in the Breeding Atlas, indicates that the highest density of breeding pairs occurs on chalk downland, given that the scrub community is at an ideal stage. This was evidently the case on Steps Hill, where at least some of the census study was carried out, and may in part explain the presence in a high proportion of Chiltern tetrads. However, even allowing for the bird's avoidance of open farmland where hedges are either cut very low or have grown into open tree-lines, it is likely that the first atlas survey considerably under-recorded the species in some parts of the county.

The two maps show some interesting and inexplicable changes. The species has become quite localised south of the Chilterns escarpment but appears more widespread in the Vale of Aylesbury and in the north, although this increase may be a consequence of under-recording during the first atlas. There is, however, an impression that the range has shifted northwards.

As the summer progresses, and certainly by mid July, the species becomes more widespread, appearing in rural and riparian scrub for example. This spread doubtless begins with local post-breeding dispersal, but later records may well involve an increasing proportion of passage migrants. Some annual reports, mostly from the 1960s, include brief details of passage movement, primarily from ringing work. Passage in late July can be quite strong, as shown by the 25 birds ringed in a week at Weston Turville Res in 1966. August is generally the main passage month, with 20 birds recorded at the same site on various single days. Movement continues into September, and in 1963 peak counts of around 20 birds were noted between 9 and 15 September at Weston Turville. In some years the final sighting is soon after mid September, though there are some late September observations. Even later records refer to 14 Oct 2000 and 12 Oct 2006 both at Broughton, Aylesbury, and a very tardy bird at Medmenham on 22 Oct 1973.

The earliest date for a spring migrant is 4 Apr 1999 at Wotton Lakes. In most years the first bird is recorded between 12 and 28 April. First records as late as 3 May 1970 and 6 May 1965 may indicate genuinely delayed migration or perhaps emphasise how easily Lesser Whitethroats are overlooked. In 1962 the species was reported, presumably on the basis of birds ringed, as 'numerous on spring passage' at Weston Turville Reservoir, and in 1968 various observers commented on newly-arrived birds not staying. Otherwise the annual reports do not mention spring movements, apart from noting early May as the time of main arrival at breeding sites. A bird ringed at Weston Turville on 2 Sep 1961 was recovered in Lebanon on 22 Mar 1962 during its return from the East African wintering area.

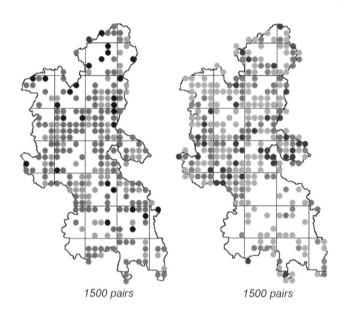

Migration dates

Earliest:	8 Apr
Ave earliest:	20 Apr
Ave latest:	29 Sep
Latest:	8 Nov

1500 pairs   *1500 pairs*

HM-G

'Desert' Lesser Whitethroat
Sylvia curruca halimodendri/minula

Very rare winter visitor. There are two records.

2009: 1 on 20 Dec at Tattenhoe, Milton Keynes.
2009: 1 from late Dec to 10 Apr 2010, Haddenham.

The Haddenham bird was ringed on 23 Jan 2010. Biometrics and photographs were taken but these did not fit neatly with any of the races. Lesser Whitethroat taxonomy and identification criteria are not fully understood so acceptance of this record has been placed on hold by the BBRC (Collard, 2011). Both birds were photographed.

Haddenham, 22 Jan 2010   *Mike Wallen*

Common Whitethroat
Sylvia communis

Common summer visitor.

Kimblewick, 24 Jul 2011   *Richard Billyard*

In 1868 Clark Kennedy wrote that the Whitethroat was one of our commonest warblers, and in 1905 H & R went further, calling it `one of the commonest birds in hedgerows, gardens, woods and commons'. One might in passing question whether gardens or mature woods really were particularly favoured habitats, but the species certainly continued to be abundant into the 1960s, when it was still possible to find nests in similar numbers to those of the ubiquitous Willow Warbler. However the population returning in the spring of 1969 proved to have fallen drastically from the level of previous years - by 70% on four local census plots. Since then it has slowly increased but is still about one-third of the numbers prior to the 1969 crash. Even so, this remains a reasonably common species. The population crash is attributed to the great deterioration of habitat produced by prolonged drought over the Whitethroat's winter quarters in the Sahel region of tropical Africa.

The preferred breeding habitat is essentially lowish bush scrub interspersed with rank herbage. In Buckinghamshire this occurs most widely in the guise of hedgerows on less intensively managed farmland and by country roads, with thick flanking vegetation on a verge, ditch-bank or field-corner forming a well-nigh essential feature. This type of landscape, as the Breeding Atlas points out, has only existed since the agricultural enclosures of two centuries ago, whereas ancestral territories may have been restricted to woodland clearings; these were still on occasion utilised by Whitethroats when numbers were high, eg on Ashridge. Patches of wasteland, both small and large, eg on cuttings and embankments and around chalk quarries, are also classic Whitethroat habitat, as is such bushy common land as the county contains. Breeding also takes place in young plantations. During dispersal or on passage later in the summer, birds often visit gardens and wetland sites where none breeds.

The relative sparsity of first atlas registrations in parts of south Buckinghamshire, which generally had good observer coverage, probably reflected a genuine scarcity there, especially in wooded areas lacking much suitable Whitethroat habitat. By the second atlas some infilling had taken place but birds were still at a lower density compared to the north of the county, where the farmland contains many Whitethroat territories.

Past annual reports contain no information on the timing of the main autumn departure, but it is likely that movement takes place chiefly during late July and August. A juvenile ringed a Weston Turville on 7 Aug 1961 was recovered in Portugal on 21 Sep 1963. Most last dates occur in the last week of September but there are seven October dates, the latest being a bird at Dorney Lake on 8 Oct 2010.

There are several winter observations. The 1936 OOS Report records a bird a St Leonards on 17 Nov 1936 (and one in W Oxfordshire two days later!), while a bird was ringed on 11 Dec 1982 at Little Marlow SF and remained for a week.

Arrival dates for the first spring migrants are generally in the third week of April but in the 13 years since 1998 there have been three years when the first bird was recorded on or before the 5th.

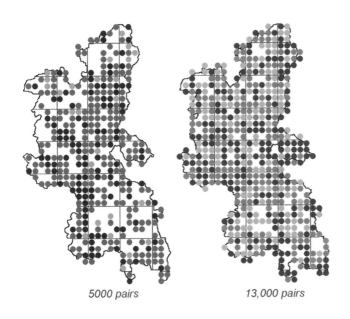

Migration dates

Earliest: 2 Apr
Ave earliest: 16 Apr
Ave latest: 25 Sep
Latest:13 Oct

5000 pairs   13,000 pairs

HM-G

Dartford Warbler
Silvia undata

Very local occasional resident and very rare vagrant and winter visitor.

Clark Kennedy mentions breeding, but, as his area covered both Buckinghamshire and Berkshire, it is not clear whether any took place in the county.

There were two records before birds were discovered in suitable breeding habitat:

Black Park, 3 Aug 2003   Jim Rose

1993: 1 female on 1 and 31 Jan near Slough
        STW where it was wintering (Barker 1994).
1998: 1 female from 25 Nov to 9 Jan 1999, Steps Hill.

In 1999 birds were found in two of the few heathland sites in the county, Stoke Common and Black Park. Birds were recorded up to 2008 but were only proved to have bred in 2003, 2004 and 2005 although they probably bred in 2006.

There were four records of birds away from these sites:

2005: 1 from 23 Jan to 28, Sarratt Bottom.
2007: 1 singing on 11 May, Fulmer.
2008: juv on 10 Oct, Turville Court.
2010: 1 on 7 Apr, Steps Hill.

Yellow-browed Warbler
Phylloscopus inornatus

Very rare vagrant. All records are given.

1966: 1 on 9 Oct, Holmer Green.
1992: 1 on 11 Oct, Little Marlow.
2003: 1 on 19 and 21 Oct, Water Eaton.
2004: 1 from 4 to 14 Apr, Woburn GC.
2006: 1 on 21 Oct, Dinton.

The 2003 and 2004 records were part of a large influx into inland England. It is possible they refer to the same bird.

Wood Warbler
Phylloscopus sibilatrix

Willen, 24 Apr 2006   *John Callaghan*

Rare passage migrant; former summer visitor.

It appears that Wood Warblers have always been local in the county. H & J described them as occurring in the Chilterns and Brickhills, but being scarce in the Thames Valley. Price described the status as 'a regular summer visitor in small numbers'. An increase was noted in the late 1960s, but since then the species slowly declined and is now extinct as a breeding species.

During the first atlas period, birds were found regularly at Ashridge and Brickhill Woods, where they bred in mature deciduous pedunculate oak woodland. 12 singing males were present at Ashridge in 1980 but this fell to only one in 1987. Numbers rose to four in 1988 but there was none in 1990 after the storm of October 1989 which felled around 10,000 trees in the Ashridge Estate and changed the appearance of much of the area. Two birds were singing in 1991 and in 1992 a pair raised four young. A pair was seen the following year but they were not known to have bred. Since then no birds have been recorded at this site except for a bird singing for a few days in May 1998.

Numbers in the Brickhill Woods fluctuated between one and three singing males 1980 and 1989 after which they were not recorded every year. The last record in the area was of a bird singing between 23 and 31 May 1999 at Rammamere Heath. Wood Warblers did not breed regularly in Chesham Bois Woods even though there was confirmed breeding at this site during the first atlas period. Most of the records on the first atlas map are almost certainly of passage birds.

Passage numbers, always small, have declined in a line with the dwindling British population. Only 15 birds were recorded between 1994 and 2008, 13 in April and May and two in July and August. Most were found in the northern half of the county.

The one ringing record is of a bird ringed as a nestling at Burnham on 12 Jun 1924 and recovered at Potenza, Italy on 23 Sep 1924.

DMF

Chiffchaff
Phylloscopus collybita

Common summer visitor and migrant; a very few winter.

In 1868 Clark Kennedy mentioned the Chiffchaff's early arrival and late departure but made no comment on its abundance. It was probably common then, as writers early this century certainly found it in suitable localities.

Chiffchaffs suffered a population crash in the 1970s probably due to drought conditions in their wintering area on the southern edge

Prestwood, 21 Jun 2011   *Richard Billyard*

of the Sahara. This low population continued during the period of the first atlas survey and then rapidly increased. This increase may be a result of a warming climate and to more sympathetic woodland management. The two breeding maps show that there has been a considerable range expansion since the mid 1980s with birds now occupying almost all tetrads in the county.

Chiffchaffs are birds of woods, spinneys and woodland scrub, so long as the canopy is sufficiently open to permit the continuance of a field layer of bramble, nettles and similar rank herbage for breeding. They are thus particularly associated with clearings, rides and margins, with nests often to be found beside paths or boundary ditches. In woodland sites they can outnumber or entirely replace Willow Warblers. Breeding regularly takes place in young plantations and sometimes by bushy hedgerows or in gardens, but usually when there are tall stands of trees nearby. Low brambles are a typical site for the domed nest, generally placed 15-30 cm above the ground, though other rank vegetation is also used.

Tall field hedges, gardens and riparian scrub are more extensively visited during migration. The wintering records come mainly from lower-lying wetland areas with willow scrub and thick bush cover, or cress beds; a January bird at Marlow GP was seen feeding on a manure heap, presumably taking insects. There are, however, occurrences in less sheltered habitats, as at The Lee, 195 m above sea level.

Singing males are particularly easy to locate, and as they take little part in nesting duties they continue singing through the summer. Song is also frequently heard in spring and late summer from passage migrants and even wintering birds from distant populations, so 'probable breeding' registrations which simply indicate a singing bird must be viewed with caution. On the other hand since nests are well hidden and breeding females generally inconspicuous (though observers familiar with the 'hweet' call can readily locate them), the map will on balance give a fair indication of breeding distribution.

Remarkably for a migrant, the Chiffchaff often begins laying in the third week of April and further nesting-starts, either repeats or second broods, continue until early July. After breeding, adults moult completely before moving south.

Autumn passage is strong during August, perhaps particularly in the latter half, and continues through September, with small numbers of birds still regularly observed in early and even mid October. Movements revealed by ringing, mainly of full-grown birds, which fill out this picture include two from Weston Turville to Dungeness, Kent (26 Sep 1974) and Spain (30 Sep 1968). Initial north-eastward movements were shown by three birds handled in summer in Berkshire and Wiltshire, and in September in Buckinghamshire. A 1923 nestling from Dorney was found in Portugal in October 1924. Two wintering areas used by birds from the county are indicated by recoveries of July-ringed individuals in S Spain in November and Mali in February.

The first record of a bird found in winter in the county was one at Weston Turville on 3 Jan 1961. It was nine years before the next when three were found in the Chess Valley in Dec 1970 but after this numbers slowly increased with two winters standing out, 1974/75 and 1982/83, the latter producing some 25 birds. The winter map shows that birds are now sparsely scattered throughout the county, although, as this map is a cumulation of four years work, it almost certainly gives an exaggerated view of the distribution in any given winter.

The winter birds are considered to be of European origin, although a wintering bird has yet to be controlled (The Migration Atlas) but a minority have in fact shown plumage typical of some populations of the `Siberian' Chiffchaff *P. c. tristis* and the northern European *P.c.abietinus*. Winter records are well distributed from November to February. After this it becomes increasingly difficult to distinguish the birds from spring arrivals, though a few individuals are known to have sojourned well into March, with one until 10 April (1975). It is not known whether a *tristis*-type bird singing at Taplow on 14 Apr 1986 had wintered locally, but it seems likely. It is probable that recent mild winters have contributed to this change in behaviour of some Chiffchaffs, as is apparent with Blackcaps.

Observations in early March of birds which could be returning breeders are infrequent. In most years the first such migrants appear during the second to fourth weeks of that month. In 1977 birds were already `at many localities' on 13 March and widespread arrivals later in the month are common, but major influxes in the first half of April are also observed. A bird ringed at Lane End on 29 Aug 1965 was controlled near Dorking, Surrey on 16 April the following year, presumably travelling north; and a male at Maple Cross, Hertfordshire on 7 Apr 1984 was en route to Drayton Beauchamp where it was controlled that summer.

5000 pairs   20,000 pairs

HM-G

285

Willow Warbler
Phylloscopus trochilus

Common summer visitor and migrant.

The Willow Warbler was well known to Clark Kennedy in 1868 and early this century it was described as generally distributed, H & R considering it as common as the Chiffchaff. This probably did less than justice to its status since it breeds in a wider spectrum of habitats than the other species, and there is little reason to think that it was not then, as it has been until recently, the commonest warbler in the county.

Caldecotte Lake, 10 Apr 2011   *Keith O'Hagen*

Willow Warblers primarily frequent various types of scrubland. They require an open, initially not too tall, field layer such as grass, weeds, bracken or heather in which to breed. These conditions are frequently provided by chalk downland, young plantations and regenerating woods, the surroundings of lakes and pools, heathland, and banks of railway lines. The bird also breeds in taller open woodland, old orchards, farmland spinneys, and tall hedge-lines with broad grassy verges. Pairs sometimes find large rural gardens attractive, and unsuspected nests can on occasion get pulled up in the course of weeding. During post-breeding dispersal and migration gardens are visited more extensively, as are riparian habitats. Many birds feed near water when newly arrived.

The two maps show a massive decline throughout the county although the south appears to be the most affected. This is in line with trends within the UK as a whole as numbers have increased in Scotland but declined in England and Wales. The obvious explanation is climatic warming but other factors are reduced woodland management which has led to a decrease in the young growth conditions that the species favours, and over grazing by deer (Fuller *et al*, 2005).

Nesting often commences about the second week of May. As a rule there is just one brood; nests with eggs which are found in June are presumably replacements. Willow Warblers are easily located by their song and call notes; sitting birds are not uncommonly flushed by chance from well concealed nests; and adults can often be watched carrying nest material or food for their young.

It may well be that singing birds quite frequently encountered in July and even later are already on passage. Adults undergo a complete moult before setting out for their African wintering grounds. Willow Warblers begin to migrate earlier than Chiffchaffs, though the passage of the two species overlaps considerably. Movement begins about mid July and is heaviest later that month and through August. There are several ringing recoveries, including a nestling from Lane End which had reached the E Kent coast on 2 Aug 1966 when no more than ten weeks old. A bird ringed at Moulsoe Old Wood in May 1983 was controlled well down the French coast on 22 Aug 1983, and a juvenile of uncertain origin which was caught near the Thames estuary in Essex on 9 Aug 1981 was controlled near Ashley Green on 5 Sep 1982. Two birds ringed at Weston Turville went rather off course: an adult ringed on 25 Jul 1966 was found in Lincolnshire 17 days later, while a juvenile ringed on 27 Aug 1966 was re-caught on Heligoland off NW Germany 15 days later.

Passage tails off rapidly in early September and in some years no birds are observed after mid month; but there is a scattering of October records, the latest in Buckinghamshire being at Hughenden on 20 Oct 1956.

The observation of one at Stoke Poges on the extraordinary date of 4 Mar 1959 may well be erroneous. The next earliest was 15 Mar 2003 at Linford. First arrivals during the last ten days of March have been noted in at least twenty years since 1949, but in quite a few seasons the initial sighting is in the first week of April or even later (eg 11 Apr 1975). Up to this point only a few males are involved. Major influxes, sometimes in waves a week or two apart and evidently comprising both passage birds and local breeders, usually occur between mid and late April. Nestlings ringed in the county have been intercepted when returning in later springs in Spain (1 Apr 1966), France (30 Mar 1968) and Dorset (20 Apr 1985), while a bird ringed on the Hampshire coast on 15 Apr 1977 covered the 150 km to Stowe within about 24 hours. In contrast to these birds, one ringed at West Wycombe on 11 Aug 1956 was still only at Portland Bill, Dorset on 21 May 1957, suggesting that it might have belonged to a northern, late-breeding population.

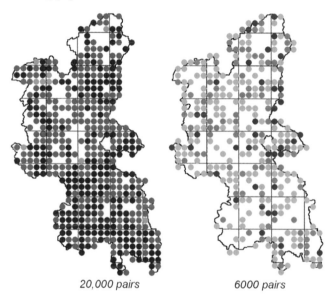

20,000 pairs   6000 pairs

Migration dates

Earliest: 13 Mar
Ave earliest:30 Mar
Ave latest: 29 Sep
Latest: 16 Oct

HM-G

Goldcrest
Regulus regulus

Common resident and winter visitor.

Prestwood, 4 Oct 2011   *Richard Billyard*

Last century and in the early 1900s Goldcrests were regarded as not very widespread breeders, though frequently seen in winter. Since in 1883 the siting of a nest in ivy was (mistakenly) regarded as exceptional, it may be that scattered pairs breeding away from conifers were less often detected in the past than now. However, conifer woods constitute by far the most important habitat, and with the maturation of the relatively extensive plantings of the last few decades the numbers of breeding Goldcrests have multiplied; and this presumably also applies to wintering birds. The birds only begin to move in when the trees reach a moderate height.

Few species can have benefited more from afforestation. Norway spruce plantations must hold a high proportion of the Buckinghamshire breeding population. Scots pines are also utilised, but stands of larch only rarely. All conifers, including exotic types from huge redwoods to smaller cypresses, will attract Goldcrests in virtually any situation, whether it be mixed woodland, small clumps, or scattered trees in parkland or gardens. Isolated pairs are quite often encountered in churchyard yews. Nesting also occurs, though at generally low densities, in deciduous woods, tall scrub and timbered hedgerows, especially where ivy is present. It is likely that habitats containing few or no conifers are occupied mainly when the species is at high abundance.

The distribution maps reflects the bird's habitat preferences well, showing presence in nearly all tetrads over the generally well wooded country from the Chilterns southwards, but a more patchy distribution in the predominantly open areas to the north. Comparison of the two maps shows a slight range expansion that may be due to a succession of mild winters. Although a few records could have involved lingering winter visitors, it seems likely that the species bred in most tetrads in which 'possible' or 'probable breeding' was registered.

Apparent influxes are quite often recorded in the autumn. There is a single observation of an influx on 4-5 Sept 1965, but most arrivals have been recorded between 3 Oct - 3 Nov. It is hard to guess at the numbers involved though counts of 40-80 birds at single sites are not infrequently mentioned, particularly on Steps Hill. These birds are generally presumed to come from N Europe, but ringing evidence hints that at least a few could be of N British stock. The Winter Atlas also mentions long-distance southward dispersal of British Goldcrests. On the other hand Gladwin and Sage (1986) consider the winter flocks in Hertfordshire to consist of locally bred birds.

From autumn to spring the species is much more widespread than when breeding, and individuals may be observed feeding in gardens or hedgerows, as well as in woods. Numbers are reported to remain high during the winter in some years, but exceptionally cold spells often cause dramatic losses. This was first documented in the county after the severe frost of early 1917, when Goldcrests became rare and were only 'beginning to reappear in small numbers' in 1919. Comparable reductions were noted after arctic weather early in 1947 and 1963, followed by recoveries. In the latter case MTNHS members recorded increases up to at least

1966, though the national Common Birds Census showed that numbers in fact kept rising until the mid 1970s. After 1975 numbers dropped somewhat but remained moderately high before plummeting again in the rather severe winter of 1985/86. The sharp 1981/82 cold spell had caused only a small reduction, suggesting that only certain features of winter weather (probably including glazed frosts) pose a particular threat.

There are hardly any records concerning return migration. A flock of 50 at Farm Wood, Wooburn Common on 7 Feb 1998 possibly falls into this category, and one observer reported a passage movement at the end of March 1967.

Ringing has tended to confirm that local birds are resident, with not infrequent retrapping of individuals where they were ringed (one was caught when at least five years old), whereas movements of even a few km are only occasional. A young male on passage at the Calf of Man on 24 Sep 1975 was controlled at Stony Stratford in January 1976.

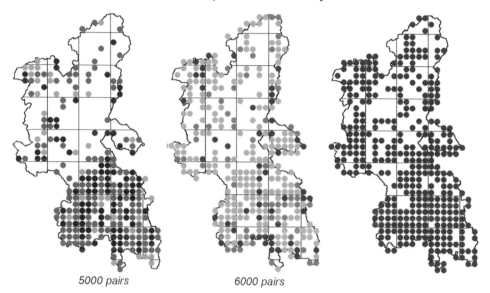

5000 pairs   6000 pairs

HM-G

Firecrest
Regulus ignicapilla

Local summer visitor and scarce migrant and winter visitor.

Prior to the establishment of a breeding colony in 1971 there were just five records:

1860s:1 killed, Great Marlow.
1941: 1 in Mar, Gerrards Cross.
1967: 1 adult on 9 Sep, Great Kingshill.
1969: 1 on 6 Apr, Latimer Park.
1969: 1 on 21 Apr, Oakley.

Aylesbury, 11 Mar 2008   Ken Plows

In 1971 at least two pairs bred in Wendover Woods, an event that was part of a range expansion in southern England, where it had previously been known only from the New Forest (Batten, 1971). Firecrests have bred every year since 1971 at this site in numbers varying between 46 singing males in 1975 to just two in 1978 with an average of around 10 pairs. The birds breed in a mature Norway Spruce plantation, part of which was destroyed by the storm of January 1990.

Since 1972, when a male was observed defending territory in N Buckinghamshire, Firecrests have steadily expanded their breeding range in the county. Sites include Cliveden, Ashridge, Chesham Bois Wood and Brickhill Woods. This range expansion is part of a national trend; the species has spread from its New Forest enclave as far as mid-Wales and north Norfolk and this in turn is part of a range expansion and population increase in Europe. Even though more sites have been found in the county it is still possible that the bird is under-recorded as the song is unfamiliar to many birders and is so high-pitched that many older birders cannot hear it.

Breeding birds normally appear at the end of April or in early May and are gone by October. It is not known if they leave Britain in winter, but the small passage at south coast ringing stations indicates that they may do.

There is a small passage in the county between March and May, and again in September. They have been seen in a number of sites in the county as far north as Willen, but they are most frequent in the Chilterns. During migration they inhabit a wider range of habitats than when they are breeding. One bird seen in a Chiltern beechwood was singing from the only large holly in the wood.

Since February 1976 birds are seen in winter with increasing frequency although most records are in the southern half of the county. Like Goldcrests, they are more catholic in their choice of habitat at this time and are just as likely to be in broad-leaved trees and bushes as in conifers although there seems to be a preference for holly at this time of the year. It is probable that the increased number of wintering records is due to increase in the European population and also to increasing observer awareness.

5 pairs   40 pairs

DMF

Spotted Flycatcher
Muscicapa striata

Uncommon and decreasing summer visitor and migrant.

The old accounts speak of Spotted Flycatchers being abundant (1868) or common (1905 and 1920). While it would be unjustified to infer too much from such generalisations, they perhaps hint at a decline in abundance over the intervening period. Indeed, Fraser stated in 1967 that some observers had noted a decrease. CBC/BBS data shows a steady decrease to the early 1990s when the rate of decrease lessened but is still continuing.

Hughenden, 25 Jun 2009   *Mike Wallen*

This decrease is not confined to the UK but is Europe-wide so it is likely that conditions in the African winter quarters or on the migration route are major contributors to the decline. All Spotted Flycatchers winter south of the equator and most in the southern hemisphere. It is likely that most UK bird winter in the west of the continent. Another factor is likely to be the lack of large flying insects, the species' main prey, which is a determining factor in the decline of several species. The two maps show the decline has resulted in a thinning of breeding sites which is spread evenly over the county.

Generally thought of as birds of larger gardens, churchyards, orchards and parkland, Spotted Flycatchers also occur quite widely in tree-lines, clumps of trees in farmland, and larger woods with clearings. The preference is for sites with mature trees. While many territories are in quite dry habitats, birds do seem to like breeding near ponds or larger waters, drawn by the prolific insect life found there. As a rule territories are thinly scattered or isolated, though under ideal conditions densities of 10 pairs per sq km have been recorded in the past.

This species returns and breeds later than most. On first arrival birds are generally conspicuous, but quite often they soon move on even from seemingly suitable places. However, if they do settle they can become remarkably unobtrusive during the early stages of breeding despite their flycatching habits. Eggs are laid from late May onwards and there may be two broods. As the young mature, the parents react more noisily to human approach, and fledged broods are conspicuous. If a family party `appears' in late summer, with young feeding independently, it may be uncertain whether the brood was reared locally. Clearly the odd breeding pair can easily be missed unless a tetrad is quite thoroughly covered, and local knowledge strongly suggests that the species was under-recorded. However, since open treeless country is avoided, the lack of records for some largely farmland tetrads probably reflects a genuine absence of birds. This is especially so as, with numbers declining, isolated pockets of suitable habitat may not always attract occupants. It is doubtful whether, during the fieldwork period, any tetrads were so totally urbanised as to offer no scope for a Spotted Flycatcher territory, though this might now be the case in parts of Milton Keynes until the young trees there mature.

Departure from breeding sites is virtually undocumented, but observations of birds on passage (not necessarily of local origin) are fairly frequent, occasionally beginning about 25 July and extending throughout August and sometimes well into September. There are several reports of 12-16 birds in one place, and an unprecedented one of about 70 along a fence near Hughenden on 25 Aug 1980. While final sightings are often in the last third of September, there are records in the first week of October for five different postwar years (three birds in 1987), with the latest date being 28 Oct 2005 when two were seen at Shardeloes. Two nestlings ringed in Buckinghamshire have been recovered during migration in Portugal, one in 1968 in its first autumn, the other on 4 Oct 1972 when it was five years old.

In many springs odd birds turn up well before the majority. The earliest Buckinghamshire dates are 17 Apr 1962 and 20 Apr 1975, both from the north of the county. More commonly the first arrival is seen during the first third of May, though it may occasionally be even later. Most birds probably reach the county during the second half of May. A 1955 nestling was found dead 88 km from its birthplace in June 1963 at Crowborough, Sussex, where it may well have bred in the intervening years.

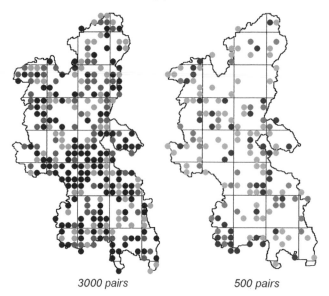

3000 pairs   500 pairs

Migration dates	
Earliest:	19 Apr
Ave earliest:	4 May
Ave latest:	28 Sep
Latest:	28 Oct

HM-G

Red-breasted Flycatcher
Ficedula parva
Very rare vagrant. There are two records.

1943: 1 on 4 May, Boddington Wood, Wendover Woods.
1970: 1 male on 5 Jun, Statnalls Wood, Pitstone.

Only about 5% of records of this East European flycatcher have been recorded in spring. These two records are therefore rather unusual.

Pied Flycatcher
Ficedula hypoleuca

Scarce migrant. Has bred twice.

The first record is of breeding. A female was killed sitting on six eggs in the 1870s at Berry Hill, Taplow (H & J). There were then a further 10 records to 1966, plus a pair that bred near Ashendon in 1968. There have been 119 birds recorded since 1972, including a pair which was observed prospecting a tree-hole at Medmenham in late May 1976. The only other semblance of breeding was a male singing in Little Linford Wood from 12 to 14 May 1996. 46 have been recorded in the north of the county, 43 in the middle, and 40 in the south. Apart from the breeding records there have only been two multiple occurrences: three birds together in Milton Keynes on 23 Aug 1983, two exactly ten years later again in Milton Keynes, and two at Little Marlow on 16 Aug 2004. Migrating birds rarely appear in woodland; scrub on Steps Hill, willow carr at Shardeloes, parks and gardens are more favoured.

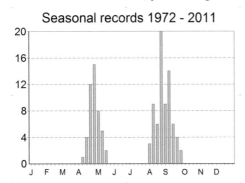

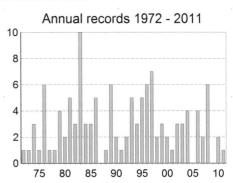

Bearded Tit
Panurus biarmicus

Rare winter visitor.

The records prior to 1972 are:

1959: 1 on 15 Sep, Claydon Brook, near Winslow.
1959: 4 in early Nov, Bucks edge of Marsworth Res (later wintered in Herts).

The records since 1972 are shown on the graphs. There have only been two records since 1994: a female at Wotton Lakes on 18

Walton Lake, 7 Nov 2010   *Keith O'Hagen*

Oct 2002 and four at Walton from 5 Nov 2010 to 11 Jan 2011. This dearth of recent records is inexplicable given that the national population is increasing. The birds are restricted to reedbeds so sites such as Weston Turville Res, Newport Pagnell GP and Walton have been favoured. Records have been confined to the autumn and winter with the remarkable exception of a female that was trapped at Weston Turville on 25 May 1986 and was retrapped shortly afterwards at Poole Harbour. Another ringed at Weston Turville on 15 Jan 1994 was retrapped at Icklesham, Sussex on 3 Jul 1996, a distance of 138 km.

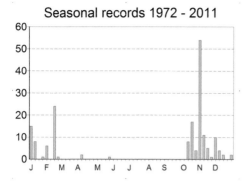

Seasonal records 1972 - 2011

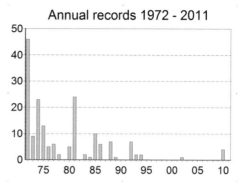

Annual records 1972 - 2011

Long-tailed Tit
Aegithalos caudatus

Common resident.

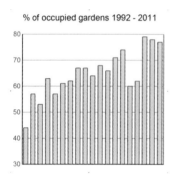

% of occupied gardens 1992 - 2011

Calvert, 17 Nov 2005   *Mike Wallen*

The Long-tailed Tit was recorded as common or very common in Buckinghamshire by Clark Kennedy and other earlier authors. The first breeding map shows birds to be widespread south of the Chiltern escarpment, scarce in the Vale of Aylesbury but more frequent further north. The absence of records in the far north is almost certainly due to under-recording. By the time of the second survey birds had become much more widespread in the northern half of the county. Being very small, Long-tailed Tits have a high surface area/body mass ratio which makes them susceptible to cold winters. It is likely that the series of mild winters since the 1980s has helped the Long-tailed Tit population together with an increasing use of garden feeders. It is estimated that the county's population has doubled since the first breeding survey.

Long-tailed Tits have a preference for woodland edges and larger hedgerows. Virtually any type of woodland is acceptable but deciduous woods with an open canopy seem to be the most preferred.

The species starts nest building early, in March. The nest is so elaborate that it takes a long time to build and eggs are not usually laid until mid April. After breeding, family groups of anything up to 12 birds are often obvious and noisy as they move along hedgerows.

With the approach of autumn, Long-tailed Tits are more prone to leave the hedgerows and woodland borders and move towards the inner parts of woods. They often join up with other small birds which flock together and form the noisy parties so characteristic of woodlands in winter. Although they tend to be less often seen in gardens than many other small birds their occurrences are increasing. The BBC Garden Bird Survey graph shows a steady increase up to the 2011 level of 77% of gardens recording the species. A substantial number sampled food provided on tables and in feeders. Up to six have been seen on one peanut feeder with four others waiting their turn, and this was during a fairly mild winter. Flocks can occasionally be quite large; one of 64 was seen in Stockgrove Park on 23 Feb 1983, 60-70 at West Wycombe on 2 Jan 1997, 100+ at Emberton on 22 Oct 2000, and 70 at Linford on 28 Oct 2006.

Though there is no indication of migration, there may be some short movements to escape severe weather. A six-year-old bird was found at Weston Turville.

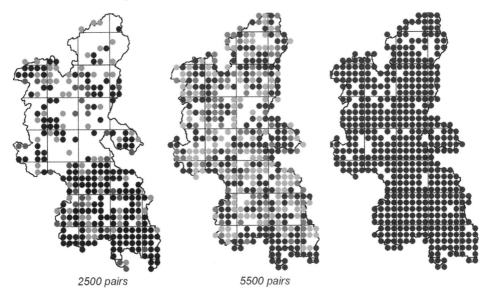

2500 pairs   5500 pairs

DBH

Great Tit
Parus major

Very common resident.

The Great Tit is a very common bird in Buckinghamshire and widespread in the country as a whole. CBC/BBS data shows that there has been a steady increase in the population since the 1960s.

It is a woodland bird, preferring deciduous trees, but it is also found in conifers. Mature suburban gardens are also a favoured habitat. It is likely that Great Tits breed in every tetrad in the county and that any gaps are due to under-recording.

After fledging, the family group remains together for a while before the juveniles disperse. The adults continue to hold territory longer than other tits before joining flocks as autumn draws on. These flocks may also contain other species of tit, Goldcrests and Nuthatches - even warblers early in the season.

With the coming of winter there is a shift in their diet from insects to vegetable matter. A favourite is beech mast, so the Chilterns are ideal country. However, gardens are also used extensively and most, especially rural ones, will probably have a couple of pairs. The BBC Garden Bird Survey graph shows an increase since 1991. It is consistently in the top six most common species. It is clear that supplied food is the main attraction.

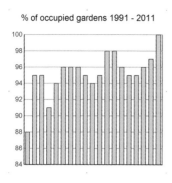

% of occupied gardens 1991 - 2011

Beaconsfield, 16 Feb 2005   *David Ferguson*

The Great Tit is generally sedentary in the British Isles. A few of the continental race are known to cross the Channel but there are no positive records as far inland as Buckinghamshire. There are, however, many recoveries of locally ringed birds, almost all of only very short range. The longest are: one ringed in Sheringham, Norfolk in July 1983 and found in Moulsoe Old Wood the following March (160 km); one ringed near Diss, Norfolk on 11 Mar 1999 which was trapped at Grendon Underwood on 6 Jan 2001 (159 km), one ringed at Tylers Green on 24 Jan 1981 found at Benhall, Suffolk on 12 Feb 1984 (158 km); and one ringed in Margate on 21 Apr 1975 which was found dead six days later at High Wycombe (154 km). Others have come from or gone to Essex, Gloucestershire and Wiltshire, and the counties adjacent to Buckinghamshire.

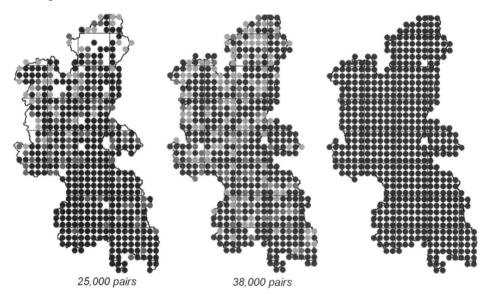

25,000 pairs   38,000 pairs

DBH

Blue Tit
Cyanistes caeruleus

Very common resident.

Since Clark Kennedy's time the Blue Tit has been one of the commonest and most widespread birds in the county, as elsewhere in Britain. Numbers fluctuate a little, largely as a consequence of particularly cold winters.

The maps show that Blue Tits occur throughout the county; the gaps in the north in the first breeding survey map are almost certainly due to under-recording. They occur wherever there are trees. They will use

Ivinghoe Beacon, 14 Nov 2005   *Mike Wallen*

almost any hole for their nests and take readily to nestboxes. There is one record in the county of a pair using the latch hole in an iron gate-post.

After fledging, Blue Tits join up with many other small birds to roam the woods, and they are often the most numerous species in autumn flocks. However, they will move into gardens very early on and become increasingly common during the course of the winter. It is remarkable how many Blue Tits will visit a garden. The Winter Atlas suggests that 200 may visit a favoured bird table in a day, with over 1,000 during the course of a winter. A MTNHS report confirms this sort of number, with 300 birds being trapped in a Stony Stratford garden in the 1975/76 winter. In this case over 60% were adults, which is the reverse of the normal situation. The BBC Garden Bird Survey found the Blue Tit to be the commonest bird in percentage of gardens visited with a maximum of 30 at one time. Peanuts were the main attraction although there was also a fair amount of foraging for natural food.

Most birds seem to be sedentary, only a few having been recovered some little distance away. A bird ringed in Great Brickhill in March 1973 was recovered in December 1975 in Boston, Lincolnshire (120 km), one ringed in Stewkley in April 1958 had reached Maltby in S Yorkshire by October 1959, and others have moved to Sussex, Nottinghamshire and Somerset, the south-west being the direction favoured by two thirds of the longer distance ones reported. There is also a record of a seven-year-old bird in Oakley.

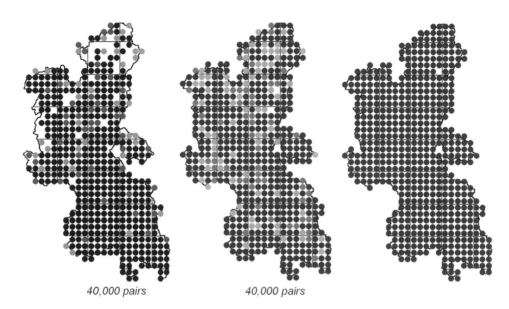

40,000 pairs   40,000 pairs

DBH

Coal Tit
Periparus ater

Common resident.

Early accounts suggest that the Coal Tit was widely dispersed though not as common as Blue, Great or Long-tailed Tits. Much the same applies today.

It is a widespread and well established woodland bird. Unlike other tits it is largely insectivorous and its beak is best adapted to extracting insects from conifer needles rather than deciduous trees. A preference for

Beaconsfield, 30 Nov 2010   *David Ferguson*

conifers may account for the concentration of records in the south of the county. A comparison of the two breeding maps show some minor changes in the distribution. Since the mid 1980s gaps have appeared in the distribution in the Chilterns while more have been found in the north, particularly in the north-west of the county although this may be a consequence of under-recording during the first atlas.

After the breeding season Coal Tits join other tits, Goldcrests, Nuthatches and other birds in flocks roaming the woodlands. Other than this they are highly sedentary. F & Y mention a bird trapped in West Wycombe being retrapped there seven years later, while a fully grown bird ringed at Great Brickhill in December 1977 was retrapped there in 1978, 1979, 1983 and 1984. Both these seven year-old birds are near the record age known from British ringing.

Coal Tits in winter will appear in gardens if they are not too far from woods. Between 1987 and 1991 the BBC Garden Bird Survey recorded the birds in 62% of gardens. Between 1992 and 2011 this had increased to 73%. There is a preference for artificial food, with peanuts

298

clearly an acceptable alternative to natural foods which in winter include beech mast and other seeds.

A recent awareness of the identification features of the nominate European subspecies has shown that these birds are occurring in the county. Two were seen on Steps Hill on 9 Oct 2005 while eight were present together at the same site on 27 Sep 2008 with singles appearing up to 1 Oct.

3000 pairs   3500 pairs

DBH

Willow Tit
Poecile montana

Very rare resident.

As this species was only recognised as separate from the Marsh Tit in 1897, nothing can be determined about its status until relatively recently. Price and F & Y describe the Willow Tit as 'locally fairly common', but they then allude to identification difficulties. The first atlas map shows it was patchily scattered throughout the county and appeared to be more widespread than the

Linford, 11 Jan 2012   Jason Chalk

Marsh Tit in the NE Chilterns, the Milton Keynes area and NW of Buckingham. The population was estimated at 200 pairs.

The second atlas maps show a dramatic decline. Since the end of the survey in July 2011 there has only been one indication of local breeding, a first winter bird at a feeding station at Linford in November 2011. The winter map shows a slightly wider distribution with records in the southwest of the county. This may be because Willow Tits are slightly easier to see in winter, but the difficulty of separating then from Marsh Tits make many records suspect.

The decline in Buckinghamshire is part of a national decline which is particularly severe in the south of England. The reasons are not understood although many explanations have been proposed. Willow Tits breed in open damp woodland and scrub where, unlike other tits, they excavate a nest hole. For this they need soft or rotting wood, which may explain their preference for damper areas. Climate change may be having two detrimental effects on Willow Tit population. First, the warming summers may have a drying effect on the preferred habitat, and, second, it is possible that Willow Tits have been unable to synchronise their breeding season with the earlier emergence of their insect food. Because they excavate their nest holes in soft, rotting wood they are susceptible to predation by Great Spotted Woodpeckers which are increasing in numbers. Great and Blue Tits have also been observed usurping Willow Tit nest holes (Fuller *et al.* 2005), A final and compelling explanation is the destructive grazing of an increasing deer population which has changed the scrub and ground layers of their preferred habitat (Newson, 2011).

They are less likely to join mixed species flocks than other tits, and adults usually seem to remain on their territories for longer (the Winter Atlas). It has been suggested that beech mast is not part of the winter diet, in contrast to the Marsh Tit, because its bill is thinner and less powerful. This would make beech woods less attractive to the species in winter.

In the mid-1980s the BBC Garden Bird Survey showed they were found in 5% of gardens, with up to three birds seen at a time. The only recent garden record is one near Buckingham in January 2011.

Ringing records show that Willow Tits are very sedentary. Two Buckinghamshire recoveries involved the oldest birds reported to the national ringing scheme at the time. One ringed at Tring, Hertfordshire in May 1966 was retrapped at Weston Turville in April 1975, and another ringed at Weston Turville in May 1976 was retrapped there in May 1985.

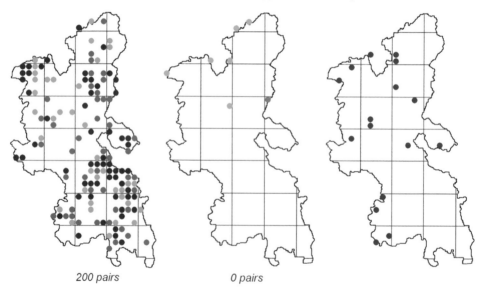

200 pairs   0 pairs

DBH

Marsh Tit
Poecile palustris

Uncommon resident.

The Marsh Tit is not associated with marshes. It is essentially a bird of deciduous woodland and is found primarily in the more heavily wooded areas of the county, especially the Chiltern belt. F & Y described it as `fairly common in wooded areas', which perhaps indicates a decline in the species' fortunes as they are now rather thinly distributed within their favoured habitat. It should also be noted that earlier statements must be treated cautiously because they are likely to include Willow Tits, which were not identified as a separate species until 1897.

Linford, 11 Jan 2012   *Jason Chalk*

There are a few clues which suggest there was a decline in numbers between Breeding Atlas, when fieldwork was carried out between 1968 and 1972 and the first county breeding atlas. In the fieldwork for the Breeding Atlas breeding was proved in all the county's 10-km squares, except one in which probable breeding was recorded. The first county breeding atlas showed that this was no longer the case. Several boundary 10-km squares had no records at all, and four or five would now only qualify for probable or possible status. The national Common Birds Census showed an overall 12% drop in 10 years.

Between the first and second county breeding atlases there have been some minor changes in distribution and a slight and probable insignificant fall in the estimated population. The maps show that Marsh Tits have spread in the Ivinghoe area but disappeared from parts of the Chilterns and the Burnham Beeches area. The colonisation of the area north-west of Buckingham may be an artifact of under-recording during the first atlas.

The apparently stable nature of the Buckinghamshire population is in contrast to the national situation where Marsh Tits are considered to be in decline. The birds are apparently dependent upon a diversity of seed-bearing trees and shrubs and a well-structured ground layer. This can be affected by reduced woodland management and browsing by an increasing deer population (Fuller *et al.* 2005). The species is on the red list of conservation concern.

Marsh Tits begin prospecting for nest sites about March. They are hole nesters and will occasionally use nest boxes although they prefer natural sites. Breeding can be difficult to prove.

Unlike most other tits, paired adults remain together on their territories throughout the winter. Unpaired birds roam more widely in mixed parties, and are joined by the members of a pair when the party crosses their territory (the Winter Atlas).

The birds usually remain in woodland during the winter. However, the BBC Garden Bird Survey shows that they will visit gardens, but usually only those near woodland. They were recorded in 8% of gardens, with no more than four birds present at a time. They showed a marked preference for the food provided and could hold their own against the other smaller tits.

They are very sedentary birds and although over 100 have been ringed in the county, no recoveries of note have been reported. National records show that over 85% of recoveries are within 4 km of the ringing sites.

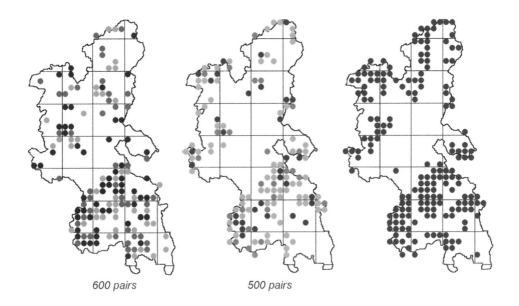

600 pairs   500 pairs

DBH

Nuthatch
Sitta europaea

Fairly common resident.

There is no indication from early records that the status of the Nuthatch has changed much, if at all, in the county over the past 100 years. H & R and H & J note that it was especially common in Burnham Beeches.

The maps show quite accurately the distribution of woodland in the county. The only exception is that the large complex of Bernwood Forest was not occupied by Nuthatches during the first county atlas survey period.

Beaconsfield, 13 Oct 2009   *David Ferguson*

The woods of the Chilterns provide well for its needs in terms of food and nest sites. It favours beech, oak, yew and hazel, as the fruits of these trees supply much of its diet. In MTNHS and BBC reports it attracts little comment, except where it turns up in some less usual place; for example, one at Weston Turville Reservoir in 1983 was the first recorded at this well-watched site.

Nuthatches are often heard in summer when they can be surprisingly hard to see, but they are more obvious in winter, when they join mixed flocks roaming the woods and can appear at feeding stations. The BBC Garden Bird Survey reported them in an average of 22% of gardens. They mainly came for the artificial food, especially peanuts which they are very adept at extracting from holders. They fly off to wedge the nuts into a crevice to be hammered into edible portions, in a very similar way to dealing with their natural food of acorns, beech mast and hazel nuts. They also regularly use bird baths.

Ringing in the county has provided no noteworthy recoveries, but the Nuthatch is the most sedentary of British birds. Only two recoveries of more than five km are known (the Winter Atlas).

An unusual individual was a bird without eye-stripes which frequented a garden in Lower Hartwell in 1985/86.

500 pairs   800 pairs

DBH

Treecreeper
Certhia familiaris

Fairly common resident.

The Treecreeper is a widespread species but probably under-recorded due to its good camouflage and small size. Rather unusually, under-recording was also noted by H & R. The comments of these and other authors also suggest that its status in Buckinghamshire remained much the same until the mid 1980s.

Prestwood, 23 Mar 2011   *Richard Billyard*

A comparison of the maps shows that there has been a reduction in the distribution within the county from 239 to 194 tetrads between the mid 1980s and 2007-2011. Given that coverage was greater during the second atlas this reduction is significant. National CBC/BBS data show a slight decline in population during this period. Combining this data gives an estimated population reduction from 2000 down to 1300 pairs.

Following dispersal in the late summer the adults tend to remain on their territory through the autumn and winter. It is not normally gregarious but will join mixed flocks of tits and Goldcrests roaming the woods. They are not common in the BBC Garden Bird Survey and none was seen to take artificial food. Between 1987 and 1991 they were recorded in 13% of the gardens but since then the percentage has fallen, with fluctuations, to around 5%, No more than two have been seen at a time.

The bird is no great wanderer. F & Y mention one ringed at Lane End in March 1964 recovered in Thame 18 days later, the 16 km movement being at the time the greatest distance of any national ringing recovery. Another ringed as a juvenile on Steps Hill on 15 Jul 1990 travelled 12 km to Bittam's Wood, near Wendover where it was trapped on 23 Jul 1990.

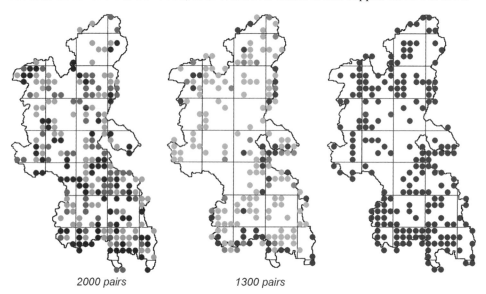

2000 pairs   *1300 pairs*

DBH

Golden Oriole
Oriolus oriolus

Rare vagrant. Has bred.

The first record is by Clark Kennedy, who stated that a nest was found at Burnham, but gives no details.

All other records are given:

1861: bred at Stoke.
1879: 1 male shot on 19 May, Stoke Mandeville.
1901: reported to have bred in the middle of the county.
1925: 1 female on 9 Sep, Haddenham.
1933: 1 on 25 May, Burnham.
1933: 1 in May, Stowe.
1936: 1 in Apr, Beaconsfield.

1949: 1 on 1 Aug, Burnham.

1972: 1 on 30 Apr to first week of May, Ivinghoe.

1979: 1 male heard on 17 Jun, Linford Wood, Little Linford.

1983: 1 male on 5 Jun, Ellesborough.

1988: 1 adult female on 22 and 25 May, Wendover Woods.

1989: first-summer male from 9 to11 Jul, Cholesbury.

1993: adult male on 15 May, Stewkley.

2001: 1 (probably 2) males on 25 May, seen while driving near Little Horwood.

The increase in the number of records since 1972 may be related to the establishment of a small breeding population in East Anglia in the 1970s while the lack of records since 2001 may be related to its decline.

Red-backed Shrike
Lanius collurio

Very rare vagrant. Formerly a local summer visitor.

Astwood, 20 Sep 2005   Ken Plows

H & J, writing in 1920, described the population as "rather local and less common during the last 12 years than it used to be". The birds must have suffered a substantial decrease since Clark Kennedy"s time, who wrote that the species was "numerous and breeds abundantly". Sites mentioned ranged from Buckingham and Newport Pagnell to the Thames Valley, where it was described as local. By 1947 they were "breeding in small and decreasing numbers" (Price).

During the 1950s the population had decreased to 3-6 pairs around High Wycombe and Farnham Royal. In 1959 a bird was seen at Wolverton and in 1960 a pair bred at Halton, but in the following year three of the sites near Wycombe were built on. In 1963 there were pairs at Little Chalfont and Haversham, and birds were seen at Gerrards Cross and Bletchley. Only one pair bred in 1968, none in 1969, although one bird was seen, while in 1970 two pairs bred near High Wycombe and Princes Risborough, and a male was seen near Olney. In 1971 three pairs successfully raised young at Grangelands, Dancersend and Lady Margery's Gorse, while another pair may have been successful at Ravenstone. A single male was present at Downley Bank, High Wycombe. The following year marked the end: birds were seen at Steps Hill, and at two sites in north Buckinghamshire, the last being seen on 22 Jun 1972.

The events in the county were part of a national near extinction of the species. The decline began in the middle of the 19th century and continued until 1989, when, for the first time, no pairs bred in the UK. Since then one or two pairs have occasionally bred. The cause of the decline is unclear although the most likely cause is the decrease in the population of the large insects which are the species' main prey, which in turn has been caused by the increased use of agricultural pesticides. The bird had always been a target for egg-collectors - indeed Clark Kennedy mentions the eggs being on sale in Eton, and this may have been a factor in the 19th and early 20th centuries. Much of one of its prime habitats - heathland - has been destroyed, but there is still plenty of apparently suitable areas of bushes in the Chilterns. Indeed the two last breeding sites, both nature reserves, still seem much as they were when shrikes bred there, but undoubtedly the habitat has degraded in some way.

There has only been one recent record, a first-winter male from 19 to 23 Sep, 2005 on a cut hedge near Astwood.

DMF

Great Grey Shrike
Lanius excubitor

Ivinghoe, 8 Oct 2008 — Ashley Stow

Rare winter visitor.

Clark Kennedy gives an undated record for Hampden.

The first dated record is:

1778: 1 shot on 8 Jan, Dinton Hall.

There were a further 13 records to 1969. Since 1970 about 52 birds have been recorded. They are shown on the graphs. From being an annual winter visitor, Great Grey Shrikes became very rare with only eight birds recorded between 1981 and 2005. Since then there has been a minor revival with six birds recorded between 2006 and 2008. It is possible the bird seen at Grendon Underwood in Jan 2006 was the same bird found at Botolph Claydon in Dec 2007 and Jan 2008 having been overlooked in the intervening winter. The map shows the distribution of records between 2007 and 2011.

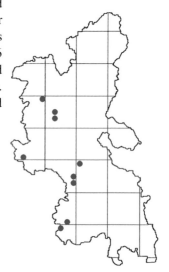

Woodchat Shrike
Lanius senator

Very rare vagrant. There have been three records.

1974: 1 on 5 Jun, Padburyhill Farm, Padbury.
1976: 1 on 16 May, Little Marlow.
2003: 1 male from 1 to 3 May, Langley Park.

Jay
Garrulus glandarius

Common resident.

In 1905 H & R considered Jays to be `very numerous residents', and `anxiously kept down by keepers'. By 1920 the species was `more or less common in all wooded districts' and had `increased in numbers considerably since 1914' (H & J), presumably because keepering had declined during the First World War. Since then CBC/BBS data shows a population fluctuating about a mean with an upsurge since 2000.

Prestwood, 10 May 2011   *Richard Billyard*

From the maps it can be seen that the distribution of Jays in Buckinghamshire reflects that of woodland in the county, with the majority of birds nesting in the Chilterns or to the south. Other favoured areas include the Brickhill Woods, the woods south of the Claydons, the Buckinghamshire part of Salcey Forest, Whaddon Chase and the areas west of Oakley. There has been a spread into the areas north of the Chilterns but the apparent increase in the north of the county is probably due to under-recording during the first survey. Jays are more secretive than the other corvids and more difficult to prove breeding. In Buckinghamshire, Jays breed in mature woodland of all types, including well wooded parks and suburban gardens.

In Chiltern beechwood CBC plots, breeding densities of about 10 territories per sq km have been found, with about 25 per sq km in the oaks of Church Wood in 1963 and 26 per sq km in the spruces of Wendover Woods in 1974. In the north, Shenley Wood in Milton Keynes held 21 per sq km in 1980. Jays often occur in gardens. The BBC Garden Birds Survey graph shows that the occurrence of Jays in the participating gardens fluctuates around 30%. A maximum of 12 have been seen at a time.

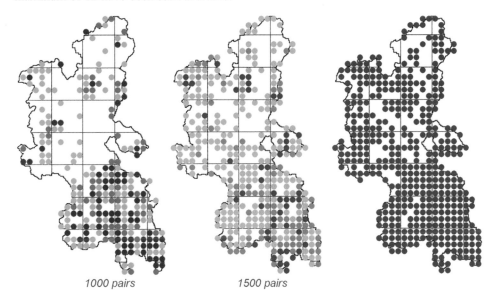

1000 pairs   1500 pairs

In autumn Jays can be much more visible and are more often seen away from woodland. Acorns are an important food source at this time. In some autumns Jays are more plentiful than usual. This happened in 1975 and in 1983 when there was a huge influx nationally, probably due to a shortage of acorns both in this country and on the continent. Some of this movement was seen in Buckinghamshire, with flocks of up to 45 seen moving west across the county in October.

RJT

Magpie
Pica pica

Common resident.

H & R and H & J regarded the Magpie as widely distributed in Buckinghamshire, though fairly scarce and local. This was partly because it was tightly controlled by keepering. H & J pointed to an apparent increase after the First World War, but clearly the species has undergone a vast expansion since then as it is now abundant everywhere in the county. The increase since the 1960s has been shown by the CBC/BBS data.

Beaconsfield, 21 Oct 2009   *David Ferguson*

The two breeding maps show an apparent colonisation of the far north of the county since the mid 1980s. This extension of range appears to be real rather than an artifact of under-recording in the first atlas as the Winter Atlas showed that this part of Buckinghamshire lay on the edge of an area extending through East Anglia in which there was a paucity of Magpies.

The species occurs in a variety of habitats, usually within range of thick cover of bushes or trees. It is found in woodland (mostly near the edge), in farmland (especially if the hedges are tall), and increasingly this century in parks and suburban gardens. The BBC Garden Birds Survey has shown that up to 1991 they occurred in 75% of participating gardens. Since then this figure has increased to an average of 87%. The maximum flock size is 27. A small sample of BTO nest record cards for S Buckinghamshire show that many nested in hawthorn and a few in blackthorn, with nests often 5-10 m from the ground. Typically, the young hatched in late April or early May.

CBC plots in the county show the highest breeding densities to be in small woods. Haleacre Wood, Little Kingshill has held up to 40 territories per sq km between 1977 and 1983; there were 20 per sq km in Shenley Wood, Milton Keynes and 25 per sq km in 1977 in Cowcroft Wood, Ley Hill. Most farmland plots had no more than 5 territories per sq km and some plots in large woods such as Burnham Beeches (1982-85) and Monkton Wood, Speen (1970-72) were devoid of Magpies.

After breeding, birds can be seen in parties of up to 20 or 30, often in hedgerows or scrub. During winter some roost communally. The size of the largest roosts has steadily increased since one of 50 birds in February 1984 near Ashley Green. On 5 Feb 1994 there were 120 at Little Marlow and 137 on 24 Dec 2000, which remains the highest number recorded. Smaller numbers have been seen at Hazlemere, Wendover and Milton Keynes.

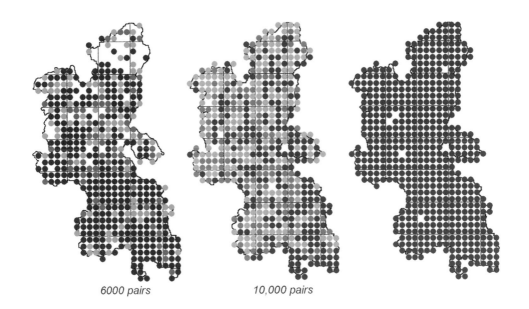

6000 pairs   *10,000 pairs*

RJT

Nutcracker
Nucifraga caryocatactes

Very rare vagrant. There have been three records.

1911: 1 killed on 7 Oct, Whitchurch.
1968: 1 on 22 Sep, Penn.
1968: 1 from Sep to 6 Oct, in the county near Berkhamsted.

The 1968 records were part of a large invasion into Britain of the Siberian slender-billed race.

Jackdaw
Corvus monedula

Common resident.

To H & R the species was 'by no means rare' in the county. H & J stated that the bird was 'common in many places, especially where there is much old timber'. Both refer to much persecution by keepers. The CBC/BBS index remained steady until the mid 1970s then showed a steady rise so that by 2010 it was double the 1975 figure.

Radnage, 19 Apr 2009   *Gerry Whitlow*

The first county breeding survey map shows a patchy distribution with many small gaps. The pattern is quite similar to that of the Rook with the birds shunning some of the higher parts of the Chilterns and some of the denser woodland areas such as Burnham Beeches. The two maps of the second survey show that they are now found throughout the county with the only significant gap in the Milton Keynes area.

309

As hole nesters Jackdaws prefer old trees. They occur frequently in small woods or in hedgerows and not so commonly in large woods. They also nest in buildings, sometimes in towns, and the nests are often in small colonies. Breeding Jackdaws usually feed in small flocks on open ground, often with Rooks.

Outside the breeding season, Jackdaws wander and disperse but seldom travel very far. The longest distances shown by ringing recoveries are to Devon and Worcestershire. From August until March they often roost communally with Rooks and are often found feeding with them in flocks on farmland. The first four-figure roost was recorded at Dorney on 21 Sep 1996 when 1300 birds were seen. In July and Aug 1998 over 2000 were found. At Little Marlow the roost reached 1000 for the first time on 24 Oct 1998. By October 2002 it had reached 2000+. Other notable roosts have been at Hyde Lane and Shardeloes.

Landfill sites are an attraction for this species. Over 500 have regularly been recorded at Hedgerley and Springfield Farm.

On 28 Aug 1995 an all silvery-grey bird was seen at Broughton.

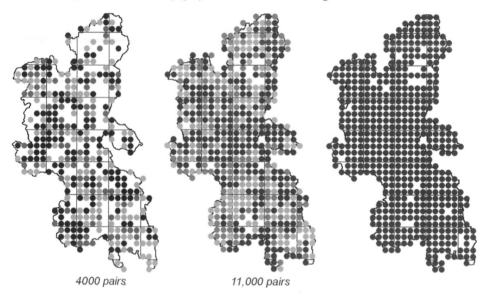

4000 pairs   11,000 pairs

RJT

Rook
Corvus frugilegus

Common resident.

Writing early this century both H & R and H & J were agreed that the Rook was very numerous, and that most parks had a rookery. There was little change until after the 1940s. There have been two post-war censuses, by Fisher in 1945/46 and by the BTO in 1975/76, and comparisons were reported by Sage and Vernon (1978). In the Thames Valley part of Buckinghamshire (using the

Winchmore Hill, 19 May 2011   David Ferguson

pre-1974 boundary) there was an increase of about 30% in nests counted compared with a national decrease in England and the Isle of Man of around 45%. In 1980 a census taken in a random selection of 10-km squares did not reveal any net change in the county.

In Buckinghamshire, Rooks start to incubate eggs in March. During the fieldwork for the first county breeding survey young could be heard calling in some nests by mid April, although a few nests were still being added to in the rookeries ®. J. Tomlin). In 1973-75 most rookeries were in farmland with a scattering of hedgerow trees and small copses. Large areas of woodland such as Burnham Beeches were shunned as were built-up areas. The nests were almost always in the crowns of large trees. Before Dutch elm disease destroyed the UK's elms, rookeries in the north of the county were almost all in English elms but in the Chilterns beech was the favoured tree (Tomlin & Youngman 1981). This is probably explained by the relative abundance of each tree species rather than any preference of Rooks for one or the other.

The two breeding maps show a somewhat patchy distribution with the later survey indicating a slight range extension. The profusion of grey dots on the second survey represents presence of Rooks but without known breeding. The map shows many clusters of rookeries and many areas with none. Rooks are particularly widespread and abundant in the Vale of Aylesbury, but less so in the higher parts of the Chilterns. However, the Rivers Chess, Misbourne and Wye can be traced on the map, since many of the Chiltern rookeries were in small copses on the sides of the valleys. Breeding was recorded in few tetrads in the north-east where coverage was sparse, and in the far south where there is much dense woodland and urban development.

The local figures from the 1975 census provide another view of the bird's distribution. The largest densities of nests were recorded in 10-km squares in the Vale. SP61 (Brill) had about 9 per sq km, SP71 (Waddesdon) and SP72 (Winslow) both had about 12 per sq km, and other high densities were 9.5 in SP83 (Milton Keynes) and 10 in SU99 (Amersham). Overall, the density in the county was 6.4 per sq km. The largest individual rookeries were at Coleshill (c180) and at Newton Longville (c190).

12,000 pairs   15,000 pairs

In the autumn and winter, Rooks continue to feed near their rookeries which they often visit during the day. In the evening they gather in larger flocks at a roost, usually accompanied by about half their number of Jackdaws. In the early autumn of 1971 there were three such roosts in the Amersham/Chesham area, in small copses at Shardeloes, Botley and The Lee. The first two were also the sites of rookeries of around 100 nests. In late October the Shardeloes and Botley roosts were abandoned, but birds continued to gather at them in late afternoon before flying off to the main roost at The Lee at which c5,000 Rooks and c3,000 Jackdaws spent each night until early March. During the winter of 1971/72 there were other roosts at Winchendon (c1,000 Rooks) and Wing (c2,000). Also there were three large roosts just outside the county at Sonning in Berkshire, and at Studham and Woburn in Bedfordshire. Many Rooks and Jackdaws were seen to fly to each of these from Buckinghamshire ®. J. Tomlin). A more recent record was 400 going to roost at Stowe on 30 Jan 2005.

Although Rooks are not noted garden birds but there were two in a garden in Oakley feeding on wild bird seed in May 2004.

RJT

Carrion Crow
Corvus corone

Common resident.

Dorney Lake, 24 Nov 2010   *David Ferguson*

In 1905 H & R considered that Carrion Crows were widespread throughout the county, scarce in well keepered country, but common in 'the grass country' of NE Buckinghamshire and north-west of Aylesbury. They considered that the bird was declining. While largely agreeing with this, H & J thought there had been an increase since the intervening war when keepering had diminished. Apparently crows are now appreciably more numerous than earlier in the century, and the national CBC/BBS has shown a continuation of this since the 1960s.

The maps show Carrion Crow to be one of the most widespread species in the county. Some of the gaps shown on the first survey map are no doubt due to under-recording, but the increase at the north-east end of the Chilterns where there is much woodland and several built-up areas, is certainly real.

During a survey in April 1975, in the area around Waddesdon, Quainton and the Claydons, quite a large proportion of hedgerow trees were seen to contain used nests. Local farmland CBC plots seemed to follow the national increase in the 1970s and some woodlands also showed an increase, although most plots only contained two or three territories. A Burnham Beeches plot contained no Carrion Crows in the late 1960s, but regularly one or two territories in the early 1980s. Two notable densities were 12 territories per sq km in Stowe Park in 1974 and a remarkable 47 per sq km near Claydon in 1986 in a small wood that also contained a large rookery.

The first edition stated that 'Outside the breeding season Carrion Crows are less gregarious than Rooks or Jackdaws'. This statement is no longer true. Carrion Crows are now a feature of landfill sites, often forming flocks of several hundred. It is likely that this change in behaviour has contributed to the population increase. Also, they often form night-time roosts of several hundreds. In the early 1970s there was regularly one at Bellingdon and one near

Dancers End. Both of these were occupied in the late autumn and winter and contained 200-300 birds. A roost at Stoke Common contained 485 birds on 30 Aug 1994.

6000 pairs   9000 pairs

RJT

Hooded Crow
Corvus cornix

Very rare vagrant. Formerly a regular winter visitor.

There has evidently been a change in the status of the Hooded Crow since 1868 when Clark Kennedy wrote 'may be observed on the banks of the Thames every winter'. Apparently it was common in winter near Drayton Beauchamp and found near Chesham in frosty weather. In 1920 H & J stated 'Winter visitor. Generally more or less scarce, but sometimes occurs in fair numbers. More common along the Thames Valley and on the plains near Cheddington, Mentmore, and Leighton Buzzard.'

Since 1946 there have been only seven records:

1951: 1 on 18 Mar, Pinewood.
1953: 1 on 8 and 22 Mar, Marlow.
1953: 1-3 wintered at Wendover, one remaining until 12 Apr.
1960: 1 on 29 Feb, Iver.
1964: 1 on 1 Jan, Stone.
1975: 1 on 12 Oct, Marsh Gibbon.
1975: 1 from 25 to 31 Oct, Freith.
1975: 1 on 2 Nov, Foxcote.

The UK boundary between Hooded and Carrion Crows has retreated northwards this century and this may account for the status change, although it is believed that most Hooded Crows wintering in England originate from Scandinavia (the Winter Atlas).

DMF

313

Raven
Corvus corax

Uncommon but increasing resident.

Prior to 1999 there were six records:

1828: 1 shot on 25 Mar, Dinton Hall.
1829: 1 shot on 16 Dec, Dinton Hall.
1887: 1 on 14 Aug, Farnham.
1932: 1 probable on 12 Nov, Boveney.
1947/1948: 1 seen at Ravenstone mobbed by Rooks.
1982: 1 on 25 Jan, Willen.

Pulpit Wood, 22 Aug 2011   *Richard Billyard*

The remarkable invasion of the county began with single birds being seen at Steps Hill and Stoke Goldington in the spring of 1999. The following year nine birds were seen at six sites. Sightings remained static until 2003 when the first signs of breeding were noted when a pair was observed displaying over Steps Hill. That year 19 birds were seen at eight sites which were scattered throughout the county. By 2005, pairs were seen at 13 sites and in 2006 breeding was finally confirmed.

The map show that birds are thinly distributed in the well wooded areas south of the Chiltern escarpment, the west and the north. They are missing from the Milton Keynes area and the agricultural land to the south where there no woods. Single birds are often seen flying purposefully to an unknown destination which accounts for the high percentage of 'present but not breeding' tetrads.

There is no obvious explanation for the population increase and range expansion, but it is almost certainly linked with the similar, though even more dramatic, change in the status of Common Buzzard. Reasons suggested are decreased persecution, an increasing rabbit population, and a reduction in the use of organochlorine pesticides.

Nests are usually high in isolated trees on at a wood edge but several pairs have made use of electricity pylons where there are no suitable trees.

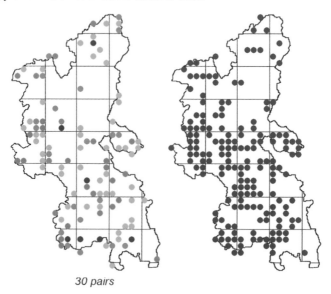

DMF   *30 pairs*

Starling
Sturnus vulgaris

Resident and winter visitor.

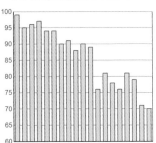

% of occupied gardens 1992 - 2011

Beaconsfield, 22 Mar 2012   *David Ferguson*

The Starling was once considered rare as a resident, following a large drop in numbers in the early nineteenth century. This may have been due to changes in agricultural practices, a period of abnormally severe winters, or a combination of the two. An increase was well under way by the middle of that century, as Clark Kennedy states it to be a 'very plentiful resident by 1860'. In 1920 H & J reported that there had been a huge increase in the preceding 50 years.

Since the 1980s there has been a national decline which is reflected in the two breeding maps. Woodland breeding populations have been particularly affected and this too is reflected in the Chilterns where gaps are apparent in the second atlas maps. Rural Starlings rely on a supply of soil invertebrates such as earthworms and leatherjackets which they obtain from permanent pasture, a habitat that has become degraded with the intensification of livestock rearing (Robinson *et al.* 2002. 2005b). Although this is a compelling reason for the decline of rural Starlings it does not explain the similar decline in urban Starlings, the cause of which is as yet unknown.

After a breeding season starting in mid April, young birds start to appear in flocks from early June, and from then on some quite large flocks can be seen roaming the fields. However, it is not until autumn and winter that the really large flocks appear, when residents are joined by many thousands from N and E Europe. The largest numbers are usually seen early and late in the day when the birds are going to or leaving their roosts.

Between 1972 and 1981 Starlings formed very large roosts in the county. The MTNHS report for 1972 mentioned two: one at Aston Clinton containing over one million birds had attracted publicity in local papers in March, while one at Wicken Wood near Deanshanger reportedly holding around half a million birds in November 1971 was considered to have doubled in size by mid January 1972. In early 1975 the Aston Clinton roost had built up to a total 'in excess of a million birds". Others have included one of over 50,000 at Drayton Parslow in March 1978 and another of similar size near Chesham at the same time. In 1981 there were possibly as many as a quarter of a million at Calvert.

Since then the only roosts of 10,000 or more birds to be recorded are: 20-25,000 at Calvert on 1 Mar 1985, 10,000 at Newton Longville on 9 Dec 1998, 15,000 in Aylesbury in Jan 2006, 10,000 at Calvert landfill in Dec 2006, and 10,000 at Foxcote on 3 Nov 2008.

Recoveries of birds ringed locally show that many of the winter visitors are from breeding populations in E Europe and that they do not necessarily return to the same wintering areas each year. One ringed at Bletchley in November 1971 was shot on the Black Sea coast of

Bulgaria in January 1979, and others have been found in the USSR (4), Latvia (3), Poland (5), Denmark (3), Finland (2), Sweden (1), Norway (1), Germany (12), the Netherlands (10) and Belgium (2). In addition, birds ringed in some of these countries have been found in Buckinghamshire. Most of the winter visitors have left for their breeding grounds by mid March. There is one record of longevity: a juvenile ringed at Little Marlow on 27 Jun 1988 was found dead at Lane End on 14 Apr 1997.

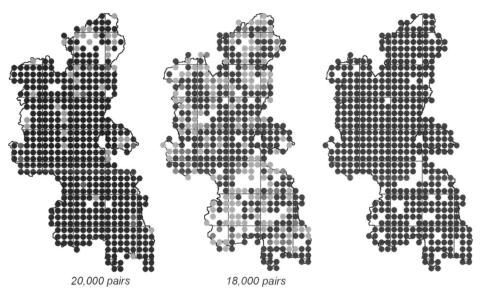

20,000 pairs   18,000 pairs

DBH

Rose-coloured Starling
Pastor roseus

Very rare vagrant. There have been two records.

There is an undated record in Gould of a bird shot at Iver Court.

1978: adult on 7 Nov, Bletchley.

Birds have been recorded in Britain in every month of the year, but November is one of the least likely for a genuinely wild individual to be found.

316

House Sparrow
Passer domesticus

Common resident.

% of occupied gardens 1992 - 2011

Beaconsfield, 6 Jun 2011   *David Ferguson*

All the older records name the House Sparrow as the commonest bird in the county and it is probably safe to assume that in Buckinghamshire, as elsewhere, the House Sparrow has been a resident in towns and villages and around farms and homesteads, indeed part of the everyday scene, for many generations past. In that sense it is very common, and, indeed, it was the second most widespread species in the first county breeding survey.

However, the national population of House Sparrows has been in decline since the 1970s. There is evidence that first-year survival rates and nest failure rates at the chick stage have contributed to this decline (Freeman & Crick, 2002). It is noticeable that very few farms now have House Sparrows, which is probably as a result of an increase in levels of tidiness and hygiene. Spilt grain is now a rarity on a modern farm. Other reasons for the decline are likely to be a reduction in food supply caused by crop-spraying, and the change to autumn sowing of cereals which has reduced the area of stubble available for winter feeding.

In urban and suburban areas the preferred habitat is often council houses with thick hedges. On modern housing estates, with their hedgeless gardens and bird-proof eaves, House Sparrows are non-existent. Toxic fumes from petrol has also been cited as a possible reason for the decline of urban House Sparrows although it is a puzzle as to why the species is so abundant in New York but in severe decline in London.

The bird is a prolific breeder and is adept at finding its way through tiles and loose bricks to find a dry spot in the roof or eaves of a building. In towns it also has a liking for lamp posts, particularly the older sort where presumably it derives some warmth from the lamp itself. This can be important as it uses the nest all the year round as a roost site.

With breeding over, Sparrows can be seen in flocks in hedgerows and shrubberies. They fly out in numbers to whatever food is available and can cause problems if this happens to be a cereal crop. The Handbook suggests that, during winter, cattle and horse feeds help nourish the House Sparrow. This no doubt still occurs but rural and urban bird tables are also a common substitute although the BBC Garden Bird Survey graph shows a steep decline in the percentage of gardens with House Sparrows which accords with the national decline.

F & Y mention a fully grown female ringed at Taplow in January 1957 being recovered there in May 1965. There are two long-distance recoveries. A bird ringed in the county in May 1977 was found at Ryton-on-Dunsmore, Warwickshire in April 1983, while an adult male ringed at Aston Abbots on 21 May 1987 was found at Ewell, Surrey on 12 Mar 1990.

50,000 pairs   *14,000 pairs*

DBH

Tree Sparrow
Passer montanus

Very local and decreasing resident.

The Tree Sparrow is a bird of fluctuating
fortunes whose whereabouts vary
considerably, both countrywide and locally.
A decline in one area may be balanced by an
increase elsewhere. Earlier authors suggest
that it was distinctly local in the middle and
late nineteenth century but had increased by
the 1930s, a situation which remained until
the mid 1970s. Since then there has been a
major decline, parallelled by the national

Gallows Bridge Farm, 28 Nov 2010   *Rod Scaife*

population (Summers-Smith 1989). The MTNHS report for 1979 mentions the bird as
becoming `uncommon in the area (or under-recorded)'. It is certainly unobtrusive, especially
in the breeding season, and when it flocks in the winter it may do so in the company of House
Sparrows, finches and buntings. If there are only a few Tree Sparrows in a large mixed flock
they can easily be overlooked.

As the maps show, there has been a huge decline with the distribution shrinking to just a few
enclaves in the west and north-west of the county. Nationally, this decline began before the
start of CBC recording in1965, stabilised in the 1970s then accelerated around 1980 until it
settled at about the present population level in 1990. The national population is now only 3%
of what it was in 1970. The species is on the red list of species of conservation concern.

To give an idea of previous numbers, Williamson (1972) reported that a small area of mature
deciduous woodland in the Chilterns held 62 pairs per sq km while both MTNHS and BBC

reports frequently mentioned sizeable flocks in autumn and winter which during the 1970s often exceeded 100. On 7 Dec 1980 300 were found in stubble at Bishopstone.

Tree Sparrows have a notably fluctuating population. Colonies can form, build up rapidly and then disappear for no apparent reason (New Atlas), but it is likely that the present decline is more permanent. Tree Sparrows are birds of hedgerows with large trees or open woodland where they form hole-nesting colonies. They utilise stubble fields in winter where they associate with flocks of buntings and finches. All these birds of farmland are in decline, most probably because of the change to winter sown cereals and to spraying. Of all the farmland birds Tree Sparrows have suffered the most serious decline.

A few local ringing recoveries suggest small scale movements. F & Y mention local birds found in Kent and Essex, and one ringed at Wheathamstead, Hertfordshire in July 1982 was found in Moulsoe Wood six months later.

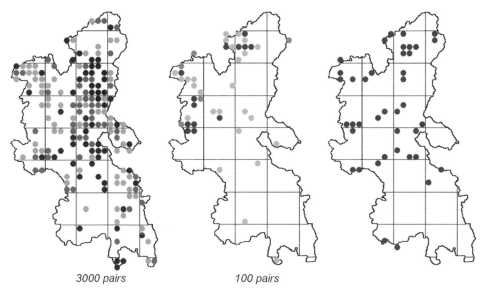

3000 pairs   100 pairs

DBH

Chaffinch
Fringilla coelebs

Very common resident, passage migrant and winter visitor.

H & R considered the Chaffinch to be one of the most common birds in Buckinghamshire, if not the most numerous species, and nesting virtually everywhere.

The county breeding surveys showed it still to be present as a breeding bird

Little Kimble, 7 Dec 2012   Richard Billyard

throughout the area. It is thought that there was a national decline in late 1950s, probably due to the effects of toxic chemicals used in agriculture, but national Common Birds Census figures suggest that this trend was reversed during the early 1960s. Since the early 1970s, the CBC shows the species to be slowly on the increase.

Chaffinches occupy a wide range of habitats, breeding wherever there are trees or bushes. Numbers tend to be highest in broad-leaved woodland but just about all habitats within the county will be utilised, including scrub, farmland hedgerows and gardens, even those in suburban areas. The Chaffinch is easily detected as it is strongly territorial and has a distinctive song and call-note, which means recording is quick even in less well covered areas, but the breeding season is rather short with usually only one brood being raised. The characteristic, neat nest is usually built in a hedge or tree from mid April onwards. During the breeding season, Chaffinches are insectivorous, feeding their young largely on caterpillars. At other times the diet is predominantly seeds. In winter they are common in gardens, the BBC Garden Survey recording them in 92% of gardens, with a maximum flock size of 200 birds. The considerable majority were taking artificial food.

Breeding birds within the county appear to be very sedentary, moving only short distances and tending to remain in the breeding area for most of their life. However, the population is swollen in late autumn and winter by immigrants from Scandinavia, N Germany and Finland. Most arrive in October and only leave again between March and mid April. This movement has been shown by ringing recoveries. For example, several birds ringed at High Wycombe in February or March have been recovered in Norway and Sweden in April, May and June, while others have been found in Germany and the Benelux countries at this time and in October. These continental birds, of the race *F. c. coelebs* are slightly larger and paler than the resident British birds. Between 20 September and 12 November 2009 fourteen counts were made at Steps Hill of flyover Chaffinches. They were in groups of 22 to 808 and totalled 2656 birds.

Winter flocks, which may number up to 300, birds can often be found in beechwoods in the Chilterns, where they feed on the fallen mast. The largest flock recorded is one of 1500 in West Wycombe Park on 23 Feb 2002. Other exception flocks were 750 at Ford in March 1981 and 6-700 at Bryants Bottom in March 2001.

Two aberrant Chaffinches have been recorded. An orange headed bird was seen at Prestwood from 1 to 5 March 1995 while an all blue-grey bird was present among a flock of 100 Chaffinches at Black Park on 13 February 2005.

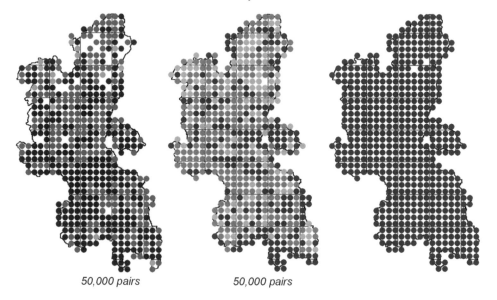

50,000 pairs   50,000 pairs

PAW

Brambling
Fringilla montifringilla

Winter visitor in low numbers.

It is evident that Bramblings have been regular winter visitors to Buckinghamshire in varying numbers since at least the days of Clark Kennedy, although the vast flocks that were occasionally reported in the 19th century are no longer encountered. Gould, in his *Birds of Great Britain*, wrote 'tens of thousands of Bramblings may now (25th March 1865) be seen at Stoke, Cliefden, and

Stowe, 19 Feb 2008   Phil Tizzard

Dropmore, in Buckinghamshire.' When in flight the flock at Stoke Park took 35 minutes to pass and Mr A G Atkins killed 45 with one shot. The Brambling was reported by H & R to be a regular winter visitor, although numbers were variable between years and higher when beech mast was plentiful. For example, flocks of several hundreds were seen in Chiltern beechwoods in the winter of 1905/06.

The first birds to arrive in Buckinghamshire are usually recorded during the second week of October, often from Steps Hill on the Chiltern Escarpment near Ivinghoe. Most reports in winter though come from the south-central part of the county between Amersham and Aylesbury and are associated with the Chiltern beechwoods. Beech mast forms the principal food of the species in the county, and birds will move around until they find an adequate source. If mast is in short supply or exhausted, they will utilise other habitats and food, such as cereal and weed seeds in open fields, and they will also visit gardens and take peanuts, particularly in late winter. Between 1992 and 2011 they were recorded in 16% of gardens taking part in the GBS, compared to 4% in the previous six years. Numbers in gardens are usually in single figures but some gardens have recorded very large flocks. In 2008 150 were present in a Daws Hill garden in February while the following month saw 56 in a Stowe garden and 50 in a garden in High Wycombe.

In Mar 2005 a roost of 200 birds was discovered in Penn Wood (Holt, 2008)although it is likely that Bramblings have utilised the area since the 1970s. Since recording began, numbers have found to vary considerably with a maximum of 900+ on 3 Apr 2007. Data from this roost has shown a probably localised number of birds throughout the winter boosted by migratory peaks in the second half of December and again in late March and early April. The birds roost in holly and rhododendrons in the centre of the wood and share the roost with Greenfinches and Chaffinches. It is possible this is the only known large Brambling roost in southern England.

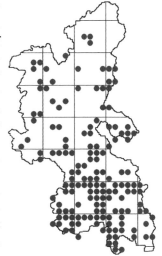

The number of birds wintering within the county is probably largely dependent on the size of the beech mast crop. Feeding flock sizes tend to be fairly small, 20 usually being a good number, but flocks of 200+ have been recorded at Tylers Green, Common Wood and Burnham Beeches. The largest number recorded away from Penn Wood was 600 at Sands,

High Wycombe in January 1981.

The wintering area of individuals varies from year to year, as shown by some local ringing recoveries. Birds wintering in Buckinghamshire in one year have been recovered as far apart as the Netherlands, Denmark, France and Italy in subsequent winters. Hard weather may force Bramblings to move out of the county, usually towards the south and west.

The birds wintering in Britain come mainly from breeding areas in Scandinavia, although ringing recoveries show that they may arrive via other NW European countries. A bird recovered at Cheddington in December 1983 had been ringed in Antwerp, Belgium 66 days previously.

The last birds are normally recorded in the last week of April, with the latest a female which stayed at Bradenham Woods until 4 May 1986. There is one summer record: a male was present at Flackwell Heath from 30 June to 22 Aug 1995.

PAW & DMF

Serin
Serinus serinus

Very rare vagrant. There has been one record.

1971: pair from 12 to 14 Mar, Bourne End. Only the male was seen on the second date.

Greenfinch
Carduelis chloris

Common resident and winter visitor.

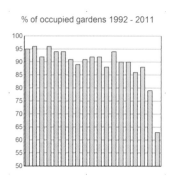

% of occupied gardens 1992 - 2011

Beaconsfield, 24 Sep 2009   David Ferguson

Specific historical information on the status and distribution of the Greenfinch within Buckinghamshire is somewhat sketchy. It seems to have been a very common resident and winter visitor since records began, occupying a range of habitats including gardens, farmland hedgerows and orchards.

The present distribution is little changed. Birds were found over the whole county during the two surveys. Breeding birds occur in small, loose colonies of a few pairs in a variety of habitat types where suitable shrub cover for nesting is available. National Common Birds Census data showed the population on farmland over the country as a whole to have been fairly stable since the mid 1960s, although the woodland data suggested a slight decrease over this period. BBS data shows an increase in England of 24% between 1995 and 2007.

Greenfinches are easily detected during the breeding season by the characteristic song, a nasal `dzwee" followed by a short trill. There is also a butterfly-like display flight, during which the male continues to sing. The nest is built in a bush, usually in April. There may be from two to four broods, which can extend the breeding season until as late as August.

There is no known regular movement of birds from their breeding areas in Buckinghamshire to any specific wintering grounds. However, birds do tend to wander and others come into the county as winter visitors. One bird ringed in France in January 1960 was recovered at Chesham in April 1961, another was ringed in Wexford (Ireland) in January 1982 and found at Mentmore that April, and birds ringed in the county in October have been found as far south-west as Cardiff and Exeter during the winter. A female ringed at Lowton, Greater Manchester in December 1982 journeyed to High Wycombe, where it was controlled 29 days later, before turning up at Lowton again in March 1983. There are also several records of birds travelling to and from East Anglia, suggesting perhaps a regular movement.

The Greenfinch enjoys a varied diet of seeds ranging from those of chickweed and dandelion to cultivated cereals, hornbeam and yew. Its main food in winter is the seed of agricultural weeds, although peanuts at garden feeding stations are also a significant food source. It was always in the top ten of most widespread birds in the BBC Garden Survey, being recorded in over 88% of all gardens, where it favoured artificial food. More visit gardens in late winter, especially during severe weather. Flocks of 100 or more occur in most winters in Buckinghamshire and may reach up to 400 in some years if there are good food supplies in one place. Exceptional flocks were 1500-2000 feeding on sunflowers at Dorney Common in Sep 1993 and 700 in a pre-roost at Shardeloes on 7 Dec 2002.

A leucistic bird was present in a garden in Burnham in the winters of 1992 and 1993.

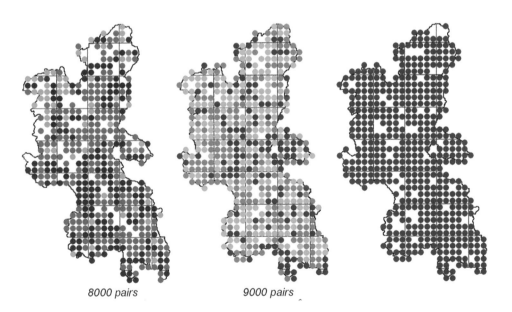

8000 pairs   9000 pairs

PAW

Goldfinch
Carduelis carduelis

Common resident and summer visitor.

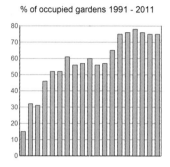

% of occupied gardens 1991 - 2011

Great Kimble, 26 Jun 2011   *Richard Billyard*

At the beginning of the present century H & R stated that the Goldfinch was nowhere common, although it was more regular in winter and on passage than as a breeding bird. It was seen occasionally and bred in limited numbers, but was decreasing in many places. H & R laid the blame for this squarely at the door of professional bird-trappers, as the species was a very popular cage-bird. The trappers were said to be particularly active in the hills above Wendover. By 1920, however, numbers of Goldfinches had increased considerably and the species could frequently be seen near Chesham, Beaconsfield, Cholesbury, Aylesbury, Wendover, Cheddington and Aston Abbots (H & J), and by 1947 it was considered by Price to be a common resident and passage bird.

The two county breeding surveys show the Goldfinch to be well distributed throughout the county with the many of the gaps in the earlier survey probably due to under-recording. There are indications that the local population has increased since then. The well watched area north of Tring had a rather sparse population in the 1980s but in the later survey birds were recorded in every tetrad in this region. The BBS shows an increase of 31% between 1995 and 2007. A range of habitats is occupied during the breeding season including farmland, gardens, parkland, scrub and woodland edge as well as areas of waste ground, provided there are tall bushes or trees for nesting. The birds will travel some distance from their nest to find food, which is mainly weed seeds, especially those of thistles and other Compositae. The national increase in garden sightings is reflected in the GBS graphs which show a change from 15% of occupied gardens in 1992 to 75% in 2006, a percentage that has since been maintained.

Feeding flocks are a familiar sight in August and September when birds visit wasteland, allotments, and rough pasture to feed on the seeds of dandelion, groundsel, ragwort, and particularly thistles. The birds' long, sharp beaks are well suited to extracting these seeds. Large flocks are present during the time although the 3-400 birds present on Ivinghoe Beacon on 8 Sep 2006 was exceptional.

It was stated in the first edition that 'It is likely that up to 80% of the summer population leaves the county by late October.' This may no longer be true. Winter flocks of 100+ are now more frequent while 500+ were present at Frieth in Jan 1999 and 300 at Old Wolverton in Feb 2003. It is possible that recent mild winters have persuaded many birds to forgo migration.

Ringing recoveries show that most of the birds travel to France or Spain. For example, two ringed at Lane End on 26 Sept 1964 were recovered in Spain in January and February 1965, while one ringed there in August 1967 was found in France in January 1968. A less distant recovery concerns a bird ringed at Marlow SF in August 1984 and recovered in Dorset in February 1985.

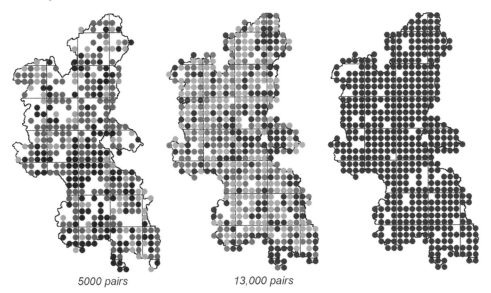

5000 pairs   13,000 pairs

PAW

Siskin
Carduelis spinus

Regular winter visitor which occasionally breeds.

% of occupied gardens 1992 - 2011

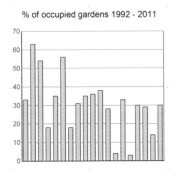

Speen, 28 Mar 2011   *Peter Symonds*

It would seem that the status of Siskin in the county has not changed significantly since the days of Clark Kennedy who considered it to be a winter visitor in variable numbers, occasionally appearing in large numbers, for instance in the winter of 1866/67.

The first county breeding survey shows the Siskin to be present in suitable habitat in four tetrads, two in the centre and two in the south of the county. There was no indication of breeding in the county until 1993 when a juvenile was seen near Wendover in June 1993. Further summer juveniles have been seen in Amersham in 1995 and Chalfont St Peter in 2000, 2003 and 2004. During the period of the second atlas juveniles were recorded in four tetrads which suggest an increase in the local breeding population. An extraordinary flock of 15-20 were seen at Prestwood on 6 June 2008 which may indicate a nearby small breeding colony.

The preferred habitat in the breeding season is coniferous woodland; the main food at that time of year is seeds of spruce and pine. There does not appear to be any sign of birds holding territory in Wendover Woods during the survey period, despite the fairly large expanse of apparently suitable habitat, although odd ones have been seen there subsequently.

The commercial planting of conifers has allowed the species to extend its breeding range from its original stronghold in the Scottish pine forests to Ireland and parts of England and Wales. The Siskin's nest is difficult to find, and although its song and calls are distinctive, the odd pair in extensive suitable habitat could easily be overlooked.

Siskins are more familiar in Buckinghamshire as winter visitors. The winter map shows records scattered over the county with a concentration in the more densely wooded south. The first usually arrive around mid September, though they may appear towards the end of August or not until late October. Ringing recoveries have shown these birds to be a mixture of British breeding birds and continental immigrants, with perhaps the majority being Scottish bred. One male was ringed in Hertfordshire in February 1982, controlled at Chalfont St Peter in March 1983 and again at Bonar Bridge, Highland two months later. Other British birds found wintering in Buckinghamshire had been ringed in N England and Dyfed, Wales during the summer. Continental immigrants seem mainly to arrive via Belgium and the Netherlands. Their countries of origin are indicated by ringing recoveries to be Norway, Sweden, Germany and Austria, and one bird was found bearing a Lithuanian ring.

This is an irruptive species, and the number of birds wintering within the county varies from year to year. In some winters they seem plentiful and widespread while in others they can be hard to find. Flocks normally number less than 100 but 200 have been recorded at Marlow and Hedgerley.

Birds may winter in widely separated places from one year to the next. Individuals caught in Britain in one winter have been found the following winter in the Netherlands, Belgium, France, Spain and Austria. One ringed in High Wycombe in Mar 1989 was recovered at Leningrad in Feb 1990. An unusual ringing recovery involved a two-year-old bird ringed at Aston Clinton on 14 Feb 1986 which was controlled at Dingwall, Scotland on 15 Mar 1995, which meant that the bird was eleven years old at the time. Local movements during the winter and spring of up to 20 km are common. A male ringed at Uxbridge, Middlesex on 1 Apr 1986 was controlled at Seer Green the following day, a distance of 11 km, and it was subsequently found dead at Fort William, Highland 43 days later.

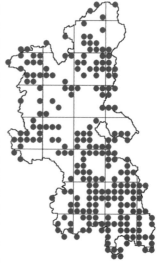

In winter, the main habitat is alder woods and copses, although Siskins can also be found in birches or larches. Their habit of visiting gardens was first noticed in the 1960s and is more a feature of late winter and early spring. They will readily take peanuts and seed. This has made them easy to catch and ring, thereby enabling more to be learnt about their movements. It can be seen from the graph that their occurrence in gardens varies considerably from winter to winter. During the period 1992 to 2011 the average was 31% of gardens recording Siskins which is a considerable increase on the 11% of the previous six years.

PAW

Linnet
Acanthis cannabia

Common but decreasing resident and summer visitor.

The Linnet was described by H & R as very common in the early part of this century, but it has shown a major national decline especially since the mid 1970s.

Breeding was confirmed during the first county breeding survey over much of the county, with the main gaps occurring in the north where coverage was poorest. Since then the distribution has contracted over

Great Kimble, 3 Jul 2011   *Richard Billyard*

much of its range within the county with only the Haddenham-Thame area and the Ivinghoe Hills showing the former continuous distribution.

A range of habitats is occupied during the breeding season including farmland, downland, heath, woodland edge, young plantations and areas of scrub. The Breeding Atlas estimated a mean of seven pairs per sq km (using CBC data) in 1972, and densities were found to be especially high in chalk grassland scrub and young conifer plantations. The basic requirements of the birds are bushes for nesting, and weed seeds which comprise the bulk of their food. They usually nest in small colonies of about half a dozen pairs, where their song and display flights make them easy to locate. Eggs are laid from mid April, to take advantage of the seasonal crop of fresh seeds, and breeding extends into early August which allows some pairs to raise as many as four broods.

The national Common Birds Census has recorded a major decrease in numbers both on farmland and in woodland habitats since the mid to late 1970s while BBS data has shown a decline of 34% in England between 1995 and 2007. This has been caused in the main by the increased use of herbicides, which has reduced the amount of weed seeds available for food. Birds have also been affected on their breeding grounds in France and Iberia where most of our birds winter. There is some reason to believe that the increase in the area of oilseed rape may be beneficial to the birds. The species is on the red list of Species of Conservation Concern.

Although some birds remain to winter in the county, the species is generally scarce between the end of September and the end of March. Ringing recoveries indicate that most go south, taking a similar route to the county's Goldfinches, although the Linnets probably leave a few weeks earlier. Their destinations have been shown to be the Low Countries, W France and Spain. Some southerly movement within Britain may also occur during hard weather.

Those birds that do remain form flocks which feed mainly on farmland, waste ground and game cover which has the weed seeds especially favoured by the birds, particularly brassicas, persicaria and fat hen. The largest gatherings tend to occur in autumn when they often number 200-300, but a flock of 600 was recorded on stubble fields at Dorney in August 1984, another of 800-1000 at Bradenham in Mar 1992 and one of 500-1000 in the wasteland of Hedgerley Tip in Oct 1999. Winter flocks generally do not exceed more than about 100 birds, but game cover at Drayton Parslow has regularly held up to 500 birds while nearby Mursley held 500 in a turnip field in Feb 2001 and 2004. Roosts within the county have numbered up to 400 birds, one such being recorded at Willen in January 1984. Birds tend to return from the Continent during April and early May.

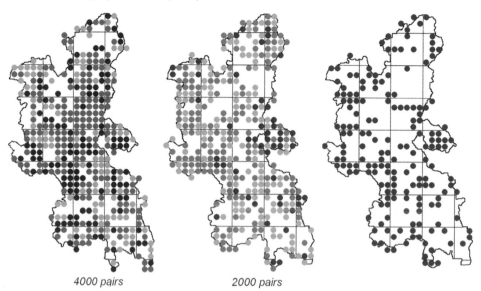

4000 pairs   2000 pairs

PAW

Twite
Carduelis flavirostris

Rare vagrant. All records are given.

1893: 21 Nov, caught by bird-catcher near Aston Clinton.
1893: 5 Dec, as above.
1898: 11 Nov, as above.
1902: 3 caught Feb, near Skirmett.
1949: 30 on 22 Aug, East Burnham.
1962: c25 on 1 Apr, Shardeloes.
1962: 40 on 8 Apr, Whaddon.
1964: 5 on 27 Sep, Weston Turville Res. One was caught and ringed.
1970: 1 on 5 Mar, Little Marlow.
1997: 1 on 22 Mar, Dorney Reach.
2000: 1 on 1 and 30 Jan, Hedgerley.
2003: 1 on 3 and 5 Oct, Steps Hill.
2006: fem/imm on 7 Nov, Steps Hill.

The flocks found in 1960s are remarkable considering the dearth of records since.

Common Redpoll
Carduelis flammea

Very rare vagrant. All records are given.

Early authors thought that this newly split species occurred in Buckinghamshire, but the first accepted record was:

1921: 20 from Dec to Mar 1922 at
    Weston Turville Reservoir.

Since then there have been just six records.

Speen, 8 Mar 2009   Rob Andrews

1982: 1 male in Mar, Newport Pagnell.
1996: 12 on 1 Mar, 4 on 7 Mar, Back
    Wood.
2001: 1 male on 2 Feb, Little Marlow.
2005: 1 on 13 Nov, Quainton was trapped and ringed.
2009: 1 male from a few days before 28 Feb to early April, Speen. It was present in a garden
    and photographed.
2010: 1 on 26 Dec in garden, Marlow Bottom.
2011: at least 10 from c10 to 12 Jan in garden, Beaconsfield. Arctic Redpoll was not
    eliminated in some cases.
2011: 1 on 17 Mar in garden, Marlow Bottom.
2011: 1 or 2 from 20 to 27 Mar in garden, Speen.

Separation of this species from Lesser Redpoll is extremely problematical. A number of claims have been made but only the above have satisfied the county rarities committee.

Lesser Redpoll
Carduelis cabaret

Uncommon resident and regular winter visitor.

When H & R published their account of birds in Buckinghamshire in 1905, there had been no authenticated record of Lesser Redpolls nesting within the county, although they were thought to breed occasionally and had been found nesting nearby in Hertfordshire. The species was known principally as a winter visitor. Price still recorded the Lesser Redpoll as a winter

Speen, 23 Mar 2011   Peter Symonds

visitor but also as breeding locally in small numbers. F & Y stated that it bred regularly in small numbers 'which appear to be increasing'.

The first county breeding survey showed that birds were patchily distributed throughout the county but with the majority in the east. The pattern is broadly similar to that discovered by the Breeding Atlas in 1968-72. Most breeding season reports seem to be associated with commons and wooded areas such as those around Burnham Beeches, the Chiltern escarpment and Wendover, although some records were from tetrads with little or no woodland at all, particularly in the north of the county. The second county atlas shows breeding birds to be confined to the Wendover and Brickhills area but much more widely distributed in winter.

The breeding population of the Redpoll is subject to an eruptive strategy, which, in Europe, depends upon the quantities of seed crops of birch and spruce. The local population also seems to be subject to considerable fluctuations which, as the maps show, is in decline.

The first atlas population estimate was calculated using a density of five pairs per 100 ha for mixed broad-leaved/coniferous woodland and 10 pairs per 100 ha for pure coniferous woodland, which gave a population, using the mapping data, of 400 pairs. By 2011 the population was probably no more than 10 pairs.

Traditionally, the birds favour birch woodland or scrub, tree-lined streams and chalk downland where scrub has invaded. They will also take to overgrown field hedgerows and have benefited in recent years from the growth in commercial forestry, favouring young conifer plantations with trees up to six metres high. Eggs are laid between late April and late May, with the breeding season extending to mid July, allowing two or three broods to be raised. The diet at this time consists of seeds and flowers of sallows, and seeds of a variety of herbaceous plants, as well as insects taken from opening tree buds.

In autumn and winter Lesser Redpolls are largely reliant on birch and alder seeds for their food, and their movements are largely governed by the abundance of these. Birds from N Britain move into S England around late September and October. Some may then cross into the Netherlands, Belgium, France or West Germany, stopping when they reach an abundant food source. If the birch seed crop in England is good, more birds tend to overwinter. There are three instances of birds ringed in Buckinghamshire in April or October being found in Belgium during the winter months. Wintering flocks within the county tend to be small, only occasionally numbering over 100.

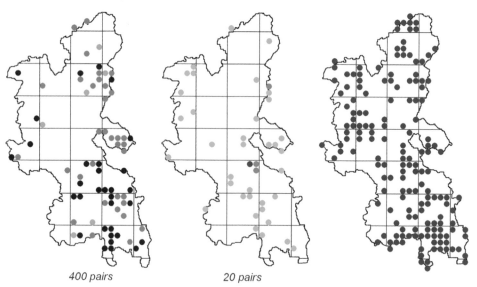

400 pairs   20 pairs

PAW

330

Two-barred Crossbill
Loxia leucoptera

Very rare vagrant. There is one record.

2003: 1 male from 27 Jan to 14 Feb, Hedgerley (McManus & McManus, 2004).

Common Crossbill
Loxia curvirostra

Irregular winter visitor and occasional breeding bird.

Wendover Woods, 11 Apr 2012   Ann Bolton

H & R considered the Crossbill to be a frequent winter visitor, rare or absent in some years but numerous in others. They also made reference to what may have been the first breeding record in the county, at Dinton Hall in 1791. The first definite record of breeding came from a Mr R. Bulstrode who was shown a nest with four eggs near Gerrards Cross on 1 Apr 1910. The young were still in the nest on 23 April.

The Crossbill is an irruptive species, and most breeding reports relate to birds which irrupted in the previous summer and stayed on. The breeding season is early, usually from February to April, but is dependent on an adequate food supply and can be at almost any time of the year. The habitat occupied is dictated by the Crossbill's food of conifer seeds. Coniferous plantations of pine, larch, spruce and fir are all utilised. The nest is placed in thick foliage high up in a tree, and hence it is difficult to prove breeding.

Movements of birds usually occur when the new crop of seeds is forming. In the case of European birds, which feed largely on spruce, this happens in late June and July. Birds will move from areas where the new crop is poor and settle where it is good. In some years large numbers of birds move out of their normal range, travelling anything up to 4,000 km. The reason for such irruptions is not fully understood, but they probably arise from the combination of a high population of birds and a poor food crop.

In recent years there have been a number of large countrywide invasions. Birds appeared in the county in mid June 1985, and again in the following October. There were flocks of up to 34 at Wendover Woods and 60 at Woburn golf course at this time. A number of these birds stayed on until at least 1989. Then 1990 saw another large invasion. The first birds were seen on 27 May 1990 and by July birds were found at 40 sites within the county, though only five of these were in the north. The largest flocks were 74 at Wendover Woods on 10 Jul 1990, 40+ near Kingsash on 20 Nov 1990, and 40 at Seer Green Railway Station on 2 Dec 1990. In 1997 an even larger invasion took place. It began with 14 birds in Wendover Woods on 23 June which peaked at 100 in July but decreased to 20 by the end of the year. Black Park held 225 on 29 June. Numbers then declined to 10 by the end of the year. Elsewhere birds were recorded at 37 sites. Birds remained in the county until July, a time when they normally arrive!

A pair was seen with nest material at Black Park, Iver on 15 Mar 1984, and a pair bred at

Wendover Woods in 1985. In 1986 pairs were seen in the Brickhill Woods and Wendover Woods, and a female and two juveniles at the Bernwood. In 1988 three pairs bred in Wendover Woods but the birds had gone by February 1989. The huge invasion of 1990 did not lead to any proved breeding in 1991 year although it almost certainly took place. The 1997 invasion led to breeding in Wendover Woods and probably Brickhill Woods. Breeding has occurred sporadically in the county since.

There has been one ringing recovery: a female ringed in Wiltshire on 15 Mar 2003 was recovered at Halton Wood on 7 May 2003.

PAW

Bullfinch
Pyrrhula pyrrhula

Common resident.

Clark Kennedy considered that the Bullfinch 'was less numerous than it had been a few years before' and thought the culprits were London bird-catchers and indiscriminate nest robbers. Bullfinches, with their colourful plumage and attractive song were popular cage birds at the time. They were also under threat from fruit growers who regarded the species, which eats the flowers of fruit trees, as a pest. However, F & Y believed there were signs of an increase, in spite of these

Little Kimble, 10 Dec 2011   *Richard Billyard*

attentions, which would seem to have been supported by the national Common Birds Census data although since 1976 the CBC suggests that it has decreased considerably, especially on farmland.

The first breeding survey showed the species to be breeding over much of the county, although there were gaps in the Vale of Aylesbury and what is now Milton Keynes, although the latter were probably due to under recording. By the time of the second survey the species had disappeared from much of the Chilterns and the far south of the county. The gap in the Milton Keynes area is now probably real as the urbanisation of the area is inimical to Bullfinches. BBS data shows a decline of 11% in England between 1995 and 2007. The decline is part of a national trend whose causes are not understood. The Bullfinch is on the amber list of Species of Conservation Concern.

The species occupies a range of habitats, provided there are sufficient bushy thickets for nesting. Woodland edge, scrub, and overgrown churchyards and gardens are typical.

Bullfinches do not form winter flocks, although several may gather at a good feeding site, such as a fruiting ash tree. As in the breeding season, they are more likely to be encountered in pairs or sometimes small groups of two or three pairs. 28 at Drayton Parslow on 23 Dec 1992 was noteworthy. They occupy much the same habitats during winter as in summer, but this is dependent upon food availability.

A small autumn passage has been noted at the Ivinghoe Hills with a maximum of 35 over Steps Hill on 19 Oct 2002. On 18 Oct 2004 several individuals of the continental race *P.p.borealis* were noted among a count of 30. Others were thought to be present at Broughton (Aylesbury) and Little Marlow. They were part of a major invasion into the UK.

There have been two long-distance ringing recoveries: a male ringed at West Wycombe in May 1961 was recovered at Chichester in January 1962, a distance of about 125 km, and one found wintering on 31 Dec 1969 at Sherington, Newport Pagnell had been ringed four months earlier at Gibraltar Point, Lincolnshire.

A part albino bird was present at Calvert from Dec 2007 to Mar 2008.

4000 pairs   4000 pairs

PAW & DMF

Hawfinch
Coccothraustes coccothraustes

Scarce and declining resident now possibly extinct. Scarce winter visitor.

In the latter part of the nineteenth century Hawfinches were known to breed at Burnham Beeches and near Chesham, Aylesbury, Langley, Stowe Park and Marlow; it had also been noted at Halton, Wendover, Beaconsfield, Cholesbury, Cheddington and Aston Abbots.

Emerson Valley, Milton Keynes   *Ashley Beolens*

The first county breeding survey produced reports of confirmed breeding in only two tetrads, and of probable or possible breeding in another 14. These came from similar areas to those mentioned above, such as the Ashridge estate near Tring, the Chesham/Amersham area, Beaconsfield, Great Missenden, High Wycombe and Marlow. However, there was a noticeable absence of records from Burnham Beeches, despite reasonable coverage in that area. During the second survey there was only one record during the breeding season, a pair flushed from a road near Fulmer. Although the species is likely to be under-recorded as the birds are unobtrusive and easily overlooked it is evident that a catastrophic reduction in the breeding population took place in the 25 years since the first survey.

The causes are not known, but increased recreational use of their woodland habitat may be a factor. It may be significant that several of their former strongholds, for example Ashridge Forest and Burnham Beeches, have considerably increased numbers of visitors, although woods at Flackwell Heath, which were a stronghold, are private and little visited.

Hawfinches are usually located during the breeding season by their call note, a Robin-like `tic", and may be seen among the topmost branches of a tree or, more likely, as they fly away. They are most easily located in early April, when they seem to call more frequently, and pairs can sometimes be observed chasing through the treetops.

Their favoured habitat within the county, as elsewhere, is mature deciduous woodland, especially where beech and hornbeam are prominent, such as at Chesham Bois and parts of the Ashridge estate. They will sometimes breed in orchards, parks or large gardens, and a pair was recorded nesting in a garden at Great Marlow in 1891.

The winter map shows Hawfinches were recorded in 12 tetrads during the four year survey period. The records in the north of the county are probably of visitors from Europe but the cluster of records in the south may indicate an undiscovered breeding colony. Their habitat use in winter is much the same as in the breeding season, although wintering sites are not regularly used, presumably due to a variable food supply. In winter small flocks used to build up and the birds become marginally easier to find. Maximum flock sizes varied from six to about 20 with most reports coming from the Chesham area.

Very little is known about the movements of Hawfinches. It would seem likely that the birds in Buckinghamshire are mainly sedentary, although a bird ringed in November 1968 at High Wycombe, was retrapped at Tunbridge Wells, Kent in May 1974, a distance of about 100 km.

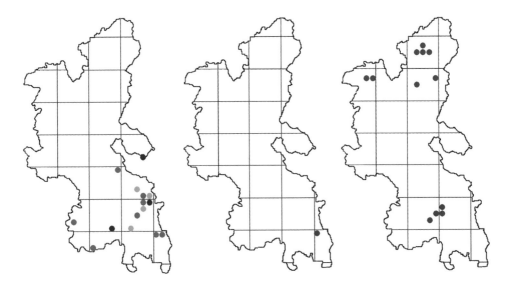

PAW

Lapland Bunting
Calcarius lapponicus

Very rare vagrant and winter visitor. All records are given.

Lodge Hill, 20 Oct 2010   *Mike Wallen*

1982: 1 male from 21 to 22 Apr, Willen.
1984: 2 on 11 Oct, with Skylarks on Dorney Common.
1987: of 3 present at Slough SF (Berks) different individuals strayed to Dorney Common on 21 Jan and 10 Feb.
1990: 1 on 24 Nov, Drayton Parslow rising to 5 on 31 Dec. Between 1 and 3 birds were seen to 2 Feb when a single bird was seen.
1991: 1-3 birds from 9 to 17 Feb, Boveney.
2008: 1 from 13 to 14 Oct and again on 21 Oct, Ivinghoe Beacon.
2008: 1 from 20 to 29 Oct, Dorney Lake.
2010: 3 on 12 Oct, Steps Hill.
2010: 1 from 17 to 21 Oct, Lodge Hill.
2010: 1 on 24 Oct, Dorney Lake.
2010: 1 on 24 Oct, Ivinghoe Beacon.

Although typically found on the coast in winter, Lapland Buntings occasionally winter inland. The events of the autumn of 2010 were, however, unprecedented. The six birds recorded were part of a widespread passage through England and, given the unobtrusive nature of the species, must represent a small percentage of the total number of birds present. Indeed, the Lodge Hill bird, which fed in a stubble field within a few metres of the observers, was, at times, incredibly difficult to see while little was seen of the birds at Drayton Parslow on the ground, and identification was based almost entirely on their, thankfully distinctive, flight-calls.

Snow Bunting
Plectrophenax nivalis

Rare vagrant. All records are given.

Ivinghoe Beacon, 12 Dec 2005   *Mike Wallen*

1776: 1 on 8 Jan, Dinton Hall.
1895: large flocks near Tring Res.
1901: 1 male shot on 4 Nov, Drayton Lodge.
1903: 1 Ivinghoe Beacon.
1956: 1 male on 23 Feb, Ballinger.
1960: 1 on 8 Nov, Foxcote Res.
1973: 1 male from 8 Nov to early May 1974, Fulmer.
1976: 2 on 31 Jan, Willen.
1976: 1 female on 23 and 25 Nov, Oakley.
1981: 1 on 24 Mar and 1 Apr, Willen.
1981: 1 on 15 Nov, Willen.
1983: 1 female on 16 Oct, Linford.
1984: 1 first-winter female on 27 Jan, Pitstone Hill.
1987: 1 on 1 Feb, Hulcott.
1992: 1 first-winter male from 15 Nov to 13 Mar 1993, Caldecotte.
1997: 1 first-winter male on 7 Feb, Willen.
1999: 1 first-winter male on 20 Nov, Calvert.
2005: 1 adult female on 30 Apr, Little Marlow.
2005: 1 first-winter male from 11 to 12 Dec, Ivinghoe Beacon.
2008: 5 on 1 Nov flew over Ivinghoe Hills.
2011: 1 adult female on 6 Nov, Ivinghoe Beacon.
2011: 1 male on 28 Nov, Broughton Grounds.
2011: 1 first-winter male from 12 Dec to 17 Feb 2012, Startopsend Res. It frequented the shingle edge of the reservoir by the county boundary.

The long-staying bird at Fulmer frequented a garden and, at the end of its stay, attained breeding plumage.

Yellowhammer
Emberiza citrinella

Common resident.

The status of Yellowhammers was described by H & J as 'common', while Price wrote 'very common'. The first atlas map shows a bird widely distributed throughout the county with most gaps coinciding with urban areas. Since the early 1980s there has evidently been a decrease in range. The development of Milton Keynes is shown on the second atlas maps as a hole in the species range and demonstrates its aversion to urban areas. The loss of Yellowhammers in the far south-east of

Gallows Bridge Farm, 24 Jun 2011   *Rod Scaife*

the county is much more difficult to explain except as part of the national decline of this species.

Yellowhammers are virtually the type-species for agricultural land with hedges. In this habitat they nest at the base of hedges and feed in field margins. Destruction of hedges and increased use of pesticides have had a detrimental effect on Yellowhammer populations by reducing the number of sites suitable for nesting and by decreasing the invertebrate food supply that the young require. Like the other bunting species, Yellowhammers are seed-eaters during the winter. The change from spring-sown cereal, which involves leaving winter stubble fields, to autumn-sown cereal has reduced the supply of seeds and thus has had a further detrimental effect on Yellowhammer populations.

Yellowhammers are also found in scrub and, less frequently, in young conifer plantations and woodland clearings. Scrub areas in the Chilterns can hold high densities of breeding Yellowhammers. A study on Steps Hill (Williamson 1975) showed that there were an average of 42.5 pairs per 100 hectares in hawthorn scrub. This compares with a national population density of 10.8 pairs per 100 hectares for farmland. Using these two figures and first atlas mapping data a county population of 16,000 pairs was calculated. Using second atlas and BBS data the population has reduced to 9000 pairs. Yellowhammers are on the Species of Conservation Concern red list.

During winter Yellowhammers form flocks. One of 500 feeding on stubble at Bishopstone on 7 Dec 1980 is the largest recorded. There were flocks of 400 at Latimer on 19 Jan 1985 and at Drayton Parslow in Dec 1989 and Jan 1990. Since then the only flocks over 200 were 225 at Drayton Parslow in Jan 2002 and at the same site in Jan 2004. There have been no three-figure flocks since 2005, which reflects the decline in the breeding population.

All ringing recoveries have been within the county. None has involved a movement of more than 10 km. This is consistent with national ringing recoveries which indicate that 70% of adult Yellowhammers winter within 5 km of their breeding territories.

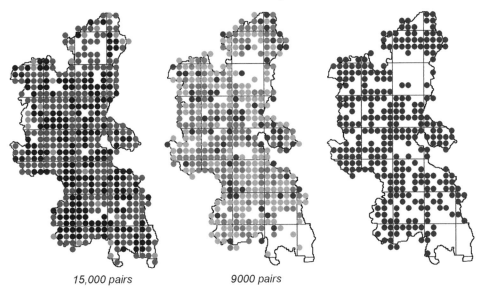

15,000 pairs   9000 pairs

DMF

Cirl Bunting
Emberiza cirlus

Formerly a local resident, no records since 1985.

H & J described the Cirl Bunting as breeding regularly in the Chilterns, and list localities from Ivinghoe to Princes Risborough, the birds being commonest between Wendover and Risborough. Elsewhere it occurred at Ashley Green, Drayton Beauchamp, and occasionally near Marlow. The decline that has occurred since is hinted at by their disappearance from the Tring area since 1917.

In 1947 Price described the population as only a few pairs, a situation which remained until the early 1980s. The main centre of population was still the Chiltern escarpment, and there were also records for Bourne End, Burnham, Turville, Downley, and the Ivinghoe area.

The 1982 BTO survey resulted in birds being found at four sites, with breeding proved at only one. The following year the range had decreased to a single locality at West Wycombe, where the last bird was seen on 13 May 1985. The County Breeding Survey found birds to be probably breeding in only two tetrads: SU89H and SP80G. The birds bred in open country with scattered trees, usually on or near the Chilterns escarpment. In winter some dispersal took place, with birds being found in neighbouring areas such as the canal at Wendover.

Cirl Buntings were first discovered in south Devon in 1800 by Col. G Montagu. From there they expanded rapidly until, by the mid-19th century, they were locally common in southern England with a peak population of about 10,000 pairs (Evans, 1997). A slow decline began after 1945 which resulted in only 167 pairs in six counties in 1982 (Sitters, 1982) and 83 pairs in 1989 when the species had returned to its original core population in south Devon.

The reasons for these changes in population are almost certainly caused by changes in climate. During the 1980s the isolated location of West Wycombe was probably the most northerly breeding site in the world. Undoubtedly these birds, whose population centre is the Mediterranean, were at the extreme edge of their climatic tolerance, so that any small unfavourable changes, combined with the effects of modern farming practices, could easily bring extinction. The northern limit of the European range approximately coincides with the 3 - 5°C January isotherm, which suggests that winter temperatures are a significant factor (the Winter Atlas).

The present population is now about 700 pairs although it is still confined to south-west England. This dramatic increase has been brought about by research into their requirements which has resulted in sympathetic farmers leaving winter stubble instead of planting with winter cereals and reducing spraying with herbicides. Birds appear to disperse no more than a few kilometres so the range seems unlikely to increase naturally.

DMF

Little Bunting
Emberiza pusilla

Very rare vagrant. There has been one record.

1987: male from 17 Mar to 26 Apr, Woodlands Park, near Iver Heath. It was in song towards the end of its stay.

Only 15% of the British records are for the spring, so this is a rather unusual record. It is possible that the bird wintered in the area.

Reed Bunting
Emberiza schoeniclus

Little Marlow, 1 Apr 2007   *Julia Eyles*

Local and decreasing resident and migrant.

Reed Buntings are generally associated with the edges of lakes and rivers. H & J described the status of Reed Buntings as 'not rare in suitable places on rivers and reservoirs', while Price described it as 'a common resident'. During the 1960s a population increase occurred, probably because of a succession of mild winters, and the excess population moved into drier habitats. Examples of sites include the dry slopes of Ivinghoe Beacon and young conifer plantations in the Chilterns. A decline occurred in the 1970s, probably because of more severe winters and the increased use of herbicides, so that the species reverted to more traditional habitats although birds are still found in rape fields.

Since the 1980s, when the first atlas survey was carried out, the species has undergone a decline. The first atlas map shows a wide distribution north of the Chilterns with gaps which may be due to under-recording. South of the Chilterns escarpment birds were found in the Misbourne, Chess, Colne and Thames Valleys. Since then the population has decreased with birds disappearing from the Colne Valley and much of the Vale of Aylesbury. The establishment of Milton Keynes has also destroyed many breeding sites. Reed Bunting is on the Species of Conservation Concern amber list.

The cause of this decline is not clear but is likely to be linked with the population declines of the other bunting species. This involves the increased use of pesticides, which reduces the number of insects during the breeding season, and the change from spring-sown cereals to winter sown which decreases the availability of seeds during the winter.

During the period of the first atlas the CBC gave an average density of 50-70 pairs per square km in typical wetland habitats, but Glue and Bodenham (1974) recorded 208 pairs per square km at Aylesbury Sewage Farm. The average Common Birds Census population density and the mapping data gave a population for the county of 3,000 pairs. Since then the distribution has decreased by 25% while the population density has also decreased. There may be no more than 1500 pairs in the county.

In winter the birds tend to form small flocks which are often found in hedges in agricultural areas. In severe winters they also move into gardens. This is the time when the species is most at risk as a long period of snow cover can have a detrimental effect on this ground-feeding bird. The largest flock recorded is one of 144 birds in Central Milton Keynes on 21 Sep 1982. The species may roost communally. The one at Dadford held 100 birds on 27 Sep 1986, while that at Weston Turville Reservoir consisted of at least 170 birds on 22 Jan 1989. Since then there have been only four records of three-figure flocks. There were 2-300 at Wing Park Farm on 26 Feb 1994, 300+ in a turnip fields and game cover at Mursley in Jan 2004, 150 at the same location in Nov 2005 and 100 at Little Marlow in Dec 2005. A small and declining passage occurs at the end of March and early April.

Seven ringing records support the view that winter flocks of Reed Buntings comprise birds from a wide area. Two birds ringed in the county during the winter were recovered during the summer in Cambridgeshire and Hampshire while birds ringed in Norfolk, Leicestershire, Nottinghamshire and Cleveland were recovered in the county. A bird ringed in Sweden on 12

Sep 2000 was recovered at Wing Park Farm on 20 Jan 2000. Finally, there was a bird that went the other way: a juvenile ringed at Little Marlow on 17 Dec 2005 was recovered at Zammel, Antwerpen, Belgium on 3 Nov 2006.

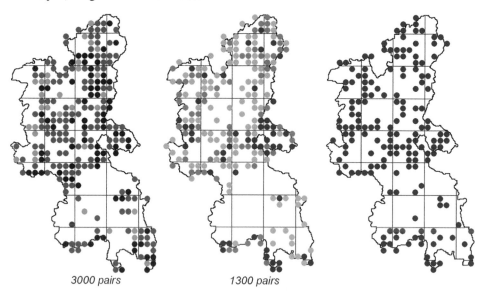

3000 pairs   1300 pairs

DMF

Corn Bunting
Emberiza calandra

Uncommon and decreasing resident.

Since Clark Kennedy wrote in 1868 'A common resident and very generally dispersed' numbers of Corn Buntings have deteriorated dramatically. The next comment came from H & J who stated 'not actually rare in arable districts, but nowhere numerous'. By 1947 this had been amended by Price to 'A common resident, found in arable districts, local in distribution'. A national decline began in the mid 1970s.

Rowsham, 24 Jul 2012   Mike Wallen

Locally, by the mid 1980s Corn Buntings had disappeared from many parts of the county although they were still widespread in the Vale of Aylesbury and the Ivinghoe area. By the time of the second atlas they were almost confined to these two areas and at a lower population density. They are on the Birds of Conservation Concern red list.

Corn Buntings are birds of arable land, their jangling song typically being sung from hedgerow perches and wires. They are one of a group of farmland species which have shown similar declines. During the late summer breeding season the nestlings are fed on invertebrates. The increased use of pesticides has resulted in lower numbers of insects and an increased level of starvation of nestlings (Brickle, 2000). Also, because the lower density of

340

invertebrates requires the parents to spend more time away from the nest foraging, there is an increased likelihood of predation.

During the winter Corn Buntings feed on seeds. It is noticeable that they tend to thrive where farmers continue to spring sow, leaving stubble throughout the winter. There is some correlation between Corn Bunting populations and barley (O'Connor and Shrubb, 1986). In areas where barley is comparatively rare, such as the Chilterns, they are uncommon or absent.

The average population density given by the National Common Birds Census and the mapping data gave a population for the county of 700 pairs in 1986. It is possible there are now less than 70 pairs.

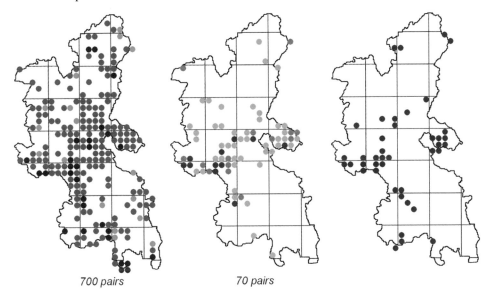

700 pairs   70 pairs

In winter Corn Buntings form flocks. The largest recorded flocks are a roosting flock of c300 birds at Weston Turville on 3 Jan 1972 and 300 at Quarrendon on 26 Feb 1995. Since then the largest recorded flock has been 72 at Haddenham on 11 Mar 2001 although most years have recorded a flock of about 50, usually in the Haddenham - Princes Risborough area or the Ivinghoe Hills. In the past, regular roosts have occurred at Weston Turville Reservoir, Dadford, Drayton Parslow, and Mursley.

DMF

INTRODUCED AND ESCAPED SPECIES

A number of deliberate attempts have been made at introducing species not native to Buckinghamshire. Some have involved birds native to other parts of Britain, while others have been of exotic species. All of them quickly failed and are usually poorly documented.

In addition a number of species have escaped from captivity. Escaped wildfowl may survive for many years and may wander around the county quite extensively, but smaller birds usually quickly succumb to the hostile conditions. The species involved can be fairly bizarre, and some can present challenging identification problems.

The following list is somewhat selective. It does not includes records of obviously escaped cagebirds but it does include accounts of the various attempts at introducing gamebirds and the more regular feral wildfowl species, some of which have bred. Accounts of feral species were not published until 1982, and there is no doubt that many observers do not bother to report observations. The following list is therefore likely to be very incomplete.

Rufous Tinamou
Rhynchotus rufescens

This native of South America was first introduced into Britain in the 1880s. In July 1901 one was shot near Olney, some 30 km from Woburn where the Duke of Bedford had turned down a number that did fairly well for 'a good many years' before finally capitulating to the cold, wet climate and the foxes which killed the sitting hens.

Black Swan
Cygnus atratus

Adult birds have been recorded in most years since 1982. One or two juveniles were recorded at Marlow between Sep and Dec 1989 and an adult and juvenile on the Thames at Marlow on 27 Jan 1991.

Bar-headed Goose
Anser indicus

Birds have been recorded in every year since 1982. Goslings were seen at Little Marlow in 2002, 2003.

Snow Goose
Anser caerulescens

Small numbers of clearly feral birds are regularly seen on some of the larger waters of the county. Two young were seen at Stony Stratford in 1986, but the breeding locality is not known. A minority of birds are of the uncommon blue phase.

Ross's Goose
Anser rossi

There have been four records of single birds since 1983 including the rare blue phase. Two blue phase birds were seen at Little Marlow in 2007.

Ruddy Shelduck
Tadorna ferruginea

A bird was shot at Wotton Lakes in Dec 1908. There were four records of single birds between 1983 and 1991 at Willen and Medmenham. In addition three males were seen with three Shelducks at Willen on 8 Sep 1987. Since 1992 groups of up to five birds have been recorded in all but four years. A female with three goslings was present at Calvert from 23 to 30 August 2009.

Cape Shelduck
Tadorna cana

There were three records of single birds between 1988 and 1990 at Linford, Weston Turville Res, and Marlow.

Wood Duck
Aix sponsa

Birds have been recorded in 10 years since 1973. Pairs have occasionally been seen but there has been no evidence of breeding.

Hooded Merganser
Mergus cucullatus

A female or immature seen at Willen on 28-29 December 1983 and accepted by the BBRC has recently been reviewed by the same body. It is no longer considered more likely to be wild than other recent occurrences in Britain.

White-headed Duck
Oxyura leucocephala

A male was present at Shardeloes from 11 April to 9 May 2003. Interestingly, it was dominant over the resident Ruddy Ducks.

Shardeloes, 12 Apr 2003   *Rob Andrews*

Black Grouse
Tetrao tetrix

Single males were shot at Hyde Heath in 1852 and near Penn House, near Amersham in 1863. Birds were introduced into Surrey in 1815 from where they apparently spread. The origin of the Buckinghamshire birds came is not known.

Capercaillie
Tetrao urogallus

In the autumn of 1855 a pair was shot at Burnham Beeches. These birds were certainly escapes or releases.

Greater Prairie-chicken
Tympanuchus cupido

This native of the plains of North America was introduced into the county in June 1903, when 'a good many' pairs were put down. Of these a hen was shot at Wing in October of the same year.

Northern Bobwhite
Colinus virginianus

Birds going under this name or California Quail were introduced at Marlow in 1867 and bred there for a short time.

Chukar
Alectoris chukar

Chukars, which are natives of SE Europe and the southern Palaearctic, were first introduced into Britain in 1894 in Peeblesshire. Between the wars they were kept fully-winged at Woburn and Whipsnade but they died out. Releases of game farm birds began in 1971 but they were not recorded in the county until 1990. The lateness of the first records may be due to a lack of awareness by observers. After 1990 records became more frequent, although numbers were small compared to the Red-legged Partridge population.

Some alarm has been expressed by the introduction of Chukars as they hybridise with Red-legged Partridges to produce 'Ogridges'. Eventually, it is thought this may eliminate the population of pure Red-legged Partridges which, although also an introduction, are now generally regarded as a native species, and one which has a rather restricted world distribution.

This potential degradation of the Red-legged Partridge population has resulted in the release of Chukars being prohibited from 1993. However, Red-legged Partridges prefer to breed with each other and pure Chukars seldom breed successfully in our climate, being adapted to much hotter conditions. Hybrids have genetic problems and low breeding success. *Alectoris* partridges will only survive in the long term if there is sufficient pure Red-leg blood in the population (Game Conservancy Trust, pers comm). The last birds were seen in 1994 at Linford, Little Marlow and Bourne End.

Snowy Owl
Nyctea scandiaca

One was seen from 31 Jul-c4 Aug, 1912 at Yewdon Manor, Hambleden. The time of year suggests that the bird was an escape.

Monk Parakeet
Myiopsitta monachus

About 100 birds of this South American species are present in south-east England where they are the subject of a cull by DEFRA who regard them as a potential pest. Two birds were seen in Aylesbury on 29 July 2011.

Chough
Pyrrhocorax pyrrhocorax

There have been two problematical records. First was a female was found dead on 29 Dec 1991 by the road between Beaconsfield and Gerrards Cross. It had been ringed as a nestling on Islay on 31 May 1986 and had bred at Islay in 1990 but did not reappear in 1991. When it was found, the three colour rings it had been wearing were missing. It is very unlikely that this bird was a genuine vagrant. It is more likely that it reached southern England as a captive and subsequently escaped or was released. Consequently the record has not been admitted to the county list.

The second record was a bird flying over Incombe Hole, Steps Hill on 22 Jun 2003. Although the identification was not in question, the unlikelihood of this non-migratory species appearing so far from its nearest breeding area in mid-summer strongly suggests a captive origin.

Trumpeter Finch
Bucanetes githagineus

One seen between 2 and 4 Jul 1990 at Haverfield, Great Missenden was believed to be an escaped cage bird.

SPECIES NO LONGER RETAINED
ON THE COUNTY LIST

Assessing the validity of old records of rare birds is beset with problems. Sight records do not always have written descriptions, and for those that do, the details recorded typically fall far short of today's requirements of the county and national records committees and leave room for doubt that sufficient care was taken over the identification. Even the best of 19th-century ornithologists can hardly have had the experience and field skills, and certainly not the powerful optical equipment, that is commonplace nowadays.

According to the epigram, what's hit is history: but even specimen records often leave doubt that the finding circumstances were exactly as recorded or that, if the whereabouts of the specimen are still known, it is the same one referred to in the original literature. Apart from the famous 'Hastings rarities', there are many cases where specimen records of British birds are known or believed to be invalid - because the corpse was imported from abroad, or because the specimen was not continuously in responsible hands. Even where identification and provenance are clearly established, knowledge of escape likelihood of many species in earlier decades is insufficient for a proper assessment to be made of the bird's likely origin.

A review of old Buckinghamshire rarity records has been begun by the Records Committee of the Buckinghamshire Bird Club, and is continuing. Despite the very poor documentation of many of the records, we believe it would not be right to reject all those not meeting present-day standards. Rather, we wish to re-examine the records in the context of our present knowledge of the status of the species in Buckinghamshire and in Britain as a whole. Some claims are clearly not worthy of any serious attention. No credence can be placed, for different reasons, in claims of Great Auk (W. Macgillivray, 1852, *A History of British Birds*, page 361) or Rufous Tinamou (A Allen, *The Field*, 1st March 1902) (see page 293). These records have been ignored, clearly deliberately, by earlier authors.

The following species have been included in previous lists and reports of Buckinghamshire birds but, after review, the Records Committee now finds all records unacceptable and has deleted the species from the county list.

Little Crake
Porzana parva

1954: 1 calling on 3 Jun, Marlow.

No details are recorded of this record. Confusion may perhaps have arisen with Water Rail, since the repertoire of that species is not fully described in The Handbook or in the then new Peterson field guide.

Scops Owl
Otus scops

1833: 1 shot near Brill.

There is no published description of this bird, and no indication that the specimen was ever seen by a competent ornithologist. Further, the bird was said to have been taken on the county border and may in fact relate to Oxfordshire. The date is 1833 in the original reference, not 1838 as quoted in H & R.

Black Woodpecker
Dryocopus martius

Clark Kennedy claims he watched one in Ditton Park for half a minute at close range, busily engaged on a tall elm till it flew off with an undulating flight, in March 1867. No details are given. Like all other British claims of this species this record is widely believed to be erroneous.

Savi's Warbler
Locustella luscinioides

1897: 1 in May, Olney.

No details are recorded to support this difficult identification. The species was not recorded breeding in Britain between the middle of the 19th century and 1960 (BOU 1971).

Moustached Warbler
Acrocephalus melanopogon

1965: 1 trapped on 31 Jul, Weston Turville Res

A review of the status of the Moustached Warbler in Great Britain in 2000 concluded that the above occurrence was the sole record (Bradshaw, 2000), but a further review determined that even this record could not be substantiated (Melling, 2006). The reasons are compelling.

The bird had pale legs and lacked a dark crown and black streaking on the mantle. It was very pale without any chestnut, had pale ear coverts, no moustache and no rufous on the flanks. Furthermore the tongue was described as canary yellow rather than the bright orange of Moustached Warbler. However, it did have a wing formula which fitted Moustached and not Sedge. Unlikely though it may seem, there is a possibility that the bird was a Paddyfield Warbler. The biometrics fitted Paddyfield and worn birds in June and July apparently can be difficult to separate (Shirihai et al, 1996).

EXTRA SPECIES RECORDED WITHIN THE PRE-1974 AND PRE-1995 COUNTY BOUNDARIES

There have been several significant changes to the political county boundary: in 1974 the area from Slough to Wraysbury was ceded to Berkshire while New Wavendon Heath was transferred to Bedfordshire. In 1995 the area south of the M4 which includes Old Slade and Colnbrook was transferred to Berkshire. The main species accounts have been compiled from records that have occurred within the present political county boundary so that records from the ceded areas have been lost even though they were in Buckinghamshire at the time of the record. The following lists those records for the rarer species pre-1974 (for Slough and Wraysbury) and pre-1995 (for Old Slade and Colnbrook), that is those records that warrant an individual mention.

The first list details records of species that are additional to the main Buckinghamshire list.

Short-toed Lark
Calandrella brachydactyla

1985: 1 from 29 to 30 April, Wraysbury Reservoir.
1987: 1 from 2 to at least 16 Jan, Slough SF.

Shore Lark
Eremophila alpestris

1971: 1 from 22 Dec to 1 April 1972, Wraysbury.
1972: 1 on 3 Dec, Wraysbury.

Arctic Redpoll
Carduelis hornemanni

1991: 1 from 21 to 28 Mar, another from 23 to 24 Mar, New Wavendon Heath.

The identification of the Marsh Sandpiper listed in the first edition was, at the time, considered to be probably correct but the description lacked the full suite of features required for confirmation (Swash, 1996).

These additions complete the avifauna for the Watsonian vice-county number 24 (Buckinghamshire).

The second list details records of the rarer species.

Scaup
Aythya marila

1970: 1 male on 21 Feb, Old Slade.

Red-throated Diver
Gavia stellata

1972: 1 on 2 Nov, Wraysbury
1972: 1 on 3 Dec, Wraysbury

Black-throated Diver
Gavia arctica

1966: 1 on 5 Nov, Old Slade.
1971: 1 on 27 Feb, Wraysbury

Great Northern Diver
Gavia immer

1971: 1 from 9 to 10 Jan, Wraysbury

Manx Shearwater
Puffinus puffinus

1970: 1 flying over on 1 Jul, Old Slade.
1974: 1 on 3 Sep. Wraysbury.

Leach's Petrel
Oceanodroma leucorhoa

1972: 1 on 9 Nov, Wraysbury

Petrel sp.
Oceanodroma sp.

1974: 1 on 14 Jan, Wraysbury.

Gannet
Morus bassanus

1981: 1 from 16 to 26 Apr, Old Slade. The bird was finally found dead.

Spoonbill
Platalea leucorodia

1940: 8 May, Slough SF.

Marsh Harrier
Circus aeruginosus

1954: 1 on 31 May, Slough SF.

Hen Harrier
Circus cyaneus

1949: 1 on 23 Apr 1949, Slough SF.

Harrier sp.
Circus sp.

1950: ringtail on 22 Oct, Slough SF.

Rough-legged Buzzard
Buteo lagopus

1972: 17 Oct, Wraysbury.

Spotted Crake
Porzana porzana

1980: 1 on 19 Aug, Old Slade.

Black-winged Stilt
Himantopus himantopus

1945: 2 on 22 Jun, Slough SF.

Little Ringed Plover
Charadrius dubius

1948: 1 on 11 Apr, Slough SF.

Temminck's Stint
Calidris temminckii

1955: 1 on 31 May, Slough SF.
1957: 1 on 3 Oct, Slough SF.

Pectoral Sandpiper
Calidris melanotus

1944: 1 Aug, Slough SF.

Great Snipe
Gallinago media

1956: 1 on 29 Sep, Slough SF.

Lesser Yellowlegs
Tringa flavipes

1953: 21 Nov, Langley SF.

Red-necked Phalarope
Phalaropus lobatus

1940: 3 from 10 to 15 Oct, Slough SF.

Grey Phalarope
Phalaropus fulicarius

1957: 3 Oct, Slough SF.
1958: 22 Nov, Slough SF.

Pomarine Skua
Stercorarius pomarinus

1972: 26 Nov - 7 Dec, Wraysbury.

Sabine's Gull
Larus sabini

1987: juvenile on 17 Oct, flying NE over Colnbrook.
1987: adult on 21 Oct, 3 adults from 22 to 24 Oct, 1 from 26 to 28 Oct, Colnbrook.

Iceland Gull
Larus glaucoides

1940: 6 Apr, Slough SF.

Glaucous Gull
Larus hyperboreus

1966: 24 Sep, Old Slade.

Puffin
Fratercula arctica

1973: 11 Feb, Wraysbury.

Cetti's Warbler
Cettia cetti

1989: 1 on 12 Aug, Old Slade.

Aquatic Warbler
Acrocephalus paludicola

1944: 6, 9, 10 Aug, Slough SF.

Twite
Carduelis flavirostris

1966: 1 on 21 Mar, Old Slade.

BREEDING LOSSES AND GAINS SINCE 1900

The 20th and 21st centuries have seen significant changes in the fortunes of many of the county's birds which has resulted in a number of breeding birds becoming lost to the county. These losses have been more than matched by the number of gains, but it should be noted that many of these are of introduced species. The losses and gains between 1900 and 2011 are summarised below.

Losses	Year last bred	Gains	Year first bred
Corncrake	c1947	Woodcock	1926
Northern Wheatear	1954	Curlew	1946
Stone-curlew	1964	Mandarin	1955
Red-backed Shrike	1971	Little Ringed Plover	1955
Whinchat	1983	Collared Dove	1961
Cirl Bunting	1984	Black Redstart	1965
Wryneck	1985	Common Tern	1968
Wood Warbler	1992	Firecrest	1971
Redstart	1997	Greylag Goose	1972
Stonechat	2003	Ring-necked Parakeet	1974
		Shelduck	1975
		Ringed Plover	1975
		Gadwall	1985
		Red Kite	1992
		Egyptian Goose	1996
		Oystercatcher	2000
		Herring Gull	2000
		Black-headed Gull	2001
		Lesser Black-backed Gull	2002
		Goosander	2007
		Peregrine	2011

In addition, three species arrived and departed during this time. They are:

Lady Amherst's Pheasant	c1905 - c2005
Ruddy Duck	1980 - 2008
Dartford Warbler	2003 - 2007

352

THE POPULATION ESTIMATES

An attempt has been made to estimate the populations of most of the regular breeding birds of Buckinghamshire. It should be said at once that these estimates are not accurate, but should be regarded as conjectures based upon the best available information. Each estimates is given as a single figure. Ranges are not shown as this implies that the limits of the range are accurate, which would not be the case.

Bird populations vary from year to year (see Marchant et al 1990). For most species the annual variation is masked by the inaccuracies of the estimates, but the populations of some birds have changed significantly since the mapping period (1980-1986). In these cases two population estimates are given, one for 1986 and another for 1991. The estimates are given in pairs, even when this is known to be inappropriate (eg Woodcock), and are shown under the maps.

For each species, an estimate was made of the breeding population using the tetrad maps. Three sets of data are required

1. The area of each broad habitat type in every tetrad in the county

   This was estimated using already available habitat data and by calculating areas using OS maps. It was not possible to differentiate between the different types of agricultural land, but woodland was divided into three broad types: broad-leaved, mixed broad-leaved/coniferous, and coniferous.

2. Population densities for each broad habitat type

   These were estimated using CBC data. Where figures were not available then informed guesses were made.

   The BTO are very circumspect about using the absolute population densities calculated from CBC data because of the small sample sizes. Furthermore, they do not distinguish between the various types of woodland. It is likely that beechwood has lower densities of birds than oakwood and that as a consequence Buckinghamshire has densities of woodland birds which are below the national average. The population densities of conifer-nesting birds are usually not known.

3. The BBC maps

   Most species have been under-recorded, which results in lower population estimates. No differentiation has been made between the three levels of breeding.

The population of each species was calculated using a computer program which worked in the following way:

Each species map was scanned tetrad by tetrad. If the species occurred in the tetrad then it was assumed to be present in every habitat in the tetrad which has a population density figure for that species, and at those densities. If the species did not occur in that tetrad then its population was taken as zero. The calculated tetrad populations for each species were then totalled to given the county population.

CHANGES IN DISTRIBUTION

The maps of breeding distribution show many changes in the fortunes of the county's birds. The tables shown below are an attempt to quantify these changes. The numbers are the numbers of tetrads occupied by possible, probable or confirmed breeding birds. Tetrads recording birds that are known not to be breeding are excluded. These are usually migrants or colonial nesters that range widely, such as Grey Heron. These tetrads are shown as grey dots on the maps.

The county's breeding species have been divided into six broad categories in order to highlight the effect of habitat and migration on the changes. Species that were known to have bred in the county during the first survey but were not mapped are excluded.

Under-recording during the first survey exaggerates the positive changes and diminishes the negative. This can be seen by studying the figures of the most widely distributed species which can be found in the last table. The apparent increases in the distributions of Woodpigeon, Blackbird and others can only be an artifact of under-recording.

Summer visitors	1981-86	2007-11	Change	% change
Turtle Dove	299	32	-267	-89
Spotted Flycatcher	295	109	-186	-63
Willow Warbler	446	296	-150	-34
Cuckoo	368	250	-118	-32
Swift	335	233	-102	-30
Yellow Wagtail	209	131	-78	-37
Tree Pipit	81	5	-76	-94
House Martin	347	296	-51	-15
Wood Warbler	36	0	-36	-100
Sedge Warbler	131	111	-20	-16
Nightingale	23	15	-8	-35
Common Redstart	8	0	-8	-100
Grasshopper Warbler	56	51	-5	-9
Sand Martin	27	28	1	4
Little Ringed Plover	16	25	9	56
Lesser Whitethroat	249	266	17	7
Swallow	440	463	23	5
Reed Warbler	73	105	32	44
Garden Warbler	192	256	64	33
Blackcap	398	515	117	29
Common Whitethroat	349	494	145	42
Chiffchaff	317	512	195	62

Introductions	1981-86	2007-11	Change	% change
Little Owl	209	195	-14	-7
Lady Amherst's Pheasant	4	0	-4	-100
Red-legged Partridge	223	254	31	-14
Egyptian Goose	0	51	51	-
Mandarin Duck	4	65	61	1525
Ring-necked Parakeet	0	72	72	-
Greylag Goose	0	103	103	-
Pheasant	387	510	123	32
Canada Goose	80	225	145	181
Red Kite	0	294	294	-

Farmland	1981-86	2007-11	Change	% change
Corn Bunting	210	70	-140	-67
Tree Sparrow	176	44	-132	-75
Grey Partridge	215	118	-97	-45
Yellowhammer	468	431	-37	-8
Linnet	383	348	-35	-9
Lapwing	278	250	-28	-10
Curlew	40	22	-18	-45
Skylark	451	485	34	8
Meadow Pipit	50	99	49	98
Rook	314	428	114	36
Barn Owl	13	170	157	1208
Green Woodpecker	278	504	226	81
Kestrel	202	449	247	122

Woodland	1981-86	2007-11	Change	% change
Willow Tit	142	7	-135	-95
Tawny Owl	244	176	-68	-28
Lesser Spotted Woodpecker	88	24	-64	-73
Treecreeper	239	193	-46	-19
Woodcock	53	14	-39	-74
Hawfinch	15	1	-14	-93
Marsh Tit	148	139	-9	-6
Firecrest	9	37	28	311
Nuthatch	182	225	43	24
Coal Tit	222	280	58	26
Goldcrest	255	322	67	26
Sparrowhawk	197	303	106	54
Jay	251	362	111	44
Long-tailed Tit	293	455	162	55
Great Spotted Woodpecker	262	481	219	84

Wetland	1981-86	2007-11	Change	% change
Ringed Plover	11	7	-4	-36
Redshank	26	22	-4	-15
Little Grebe	91	92	1	1
Little Egret	0	5	5	-
Cormorant	0	10	10	-
Oystercatcher	0	13	13	-
Shelduck	0	16	16	-
Tufted Duck	103	125	22	21
Cetti's Warbler	0	25	25	-
Coot	166	193	27	16
Grey Heron	8	35	27	337
Great Crested Grebe	55	89	34	62
Kingfisher	74	109	35	47
Moorhen	335	376	41	12
Mute Swan	99	180	81	82
Grey Wagtail	53	136	83	157
Mallard	299	406	107	36
Pied Wagtail	303	416	113	37

Others	1981-86	2007-11	Change	% change
Mistle Thrush	367	330	-37	-10
Starling	498	482	-16	-3
Reed Bunting	243	233	-10	-4
House Sparrow	485	481	-4	-1
Herring Gull	0	1	1	-
Peregrine	0	2	2	-
Lesser Black-backed Gull	0	2	2	-
Bullfinch	365	390	25	7
Collared Dove	422	457	35	8
Blackbird	515	553	38	7
Song Thrush	480	532	52	11
Woodpigeon	499	553	54	11
Chaffinch	497	552	55	11
Carrion Crow	492	552	60	12
Dunnock	477	537	60	13
Stock Dove	384	444	60	16
Wren	481	547	66	14
Robin	485	552	67	14
Blue Tit	483	550	67	14
Great Tit	479	549	70	15
Greenfinch	438	518	80	18
Magpie	460	540	80	17
Raven	0	111	111	-
Goldfinch	382	524	142	37
Jackdaw	353	526	173	49
Buzzard	0	509	509	-

ARRIVAL AND DEPARTURE DATES OF MIGRANTS 1971-2011

Jim Rose

The tables that follow contain information on the arrival and departure of migrant species based upon data collected for the years 1971 to 201.

The species concerned have been split into three groups :-

1) Summer visitors
2) Spring and autumn migrants
3) Winter visitors

Not all migrant species seen in the county are included in the tables. Where possible the commoner migrant species are included. The rarer species are not usually included as there are often insufficient data to make arrival and departure dates meaningful. Where a graph showing the occurrence of the species has been provided then that species is not usually included in these tables. In addition it has not been possible to include some species that are normally regarded as common summer visitors (eg Blackcap) because of the regular winter sightings of this species.

The data used as the basis for the tables has been obtained from the annual reports published by the Middle Thames Natural History Society (MTNHS - up until 1979) and the Buckinghamshire Bird Club (from 1980). The MTNHS reports covered an area of east Berkshire and the whole of Buckinghamshire. On occasion only dates for Berkshire birds are given. As it was the intention to only use Buckinghamshire records in the compilation of these tables, wherever Buckinghamshire dates have not been given, the numbers of dates used as the basis for determining the earliest arrival date, latest departure date or the SD, may vary. A similar problem occurs when the editor of the annual report may omit, for some reason, vital data for a species that is normally covered in depth. Referring back to the original records was considered but found to be impractical.

Summer visitors	Earliest Arrival Date	Average Earliest Arrival Date	Average Latest Departure Date	Latest Departure Date
Garganey	9 Mar	9 Apr	29 Sep	22 Dec
Hobby	2 Apr	20 Apr	10 Oct	12 Nov
Little Ringed Plover	2 Mar	21 Mar	10 Sep	15 Oct
Ringed Plover	28 Jan	15 Feb	26 Sep	17 Nov
Quail	20 Apr	27 May	26 Jul	6 Sep
Common Tern	27 Mar	10 Apr	26 Sep	27 Oct
Turtle Dove	20 Mar	23 Apr	16 Sep	17 Oct
Cuckoo	30 Mar	11 Apr	25 Aug	6 Oct
Swift	12 Apr	21 Apr	20 Sep	2 Nov
Sand Martin	24 Feb	17 Mar	1 Oct	24 Oct
Swallow	13 Mar	27 Mar	3 Nov	5 Dec
House Martin	19 Mar	4 Apr	28 Oct	5 Dec
Tree Pipit	15 Mar	9 Apr	18 Sep	19 Oct
Yellow Wagtail	23 Mar	1 Apr	12 Oct	29 Nov
Nightingale	4 Apr	21 Apr		20 Aug
Common Redstart	17 Mar	14 Apr	23 Sep	06 Nov
Grasshopper Warbler	10 Apr	17 Apr	21 Aug	25 Sep
Sedge Warbler	31 Mar	9 Apr	23 Sep	22 Oct
Reed Warbler	25 Mar	18 Apr	01 Oct	13 Nov
Lesser Whitethroat	8 Apr	20 Apr	29 Sep	8 Nov
Common Whitethroat	2 Apr	16 Apr	25 Sep	13 Oct
Garden Warbler	13 Mar	19 Apr	21 Sep	21 Oct
Wood Warbler	14 Apr	1 May	27 Aug	10 Sep
Willow Warbler	13 Mar	28 Mar	29 Sep	16 Oct
Spotted Flycatcher	19 Apr	4 May	28 Sep	28 Oct

Migrants *Spring*	Earliest Arrival Date	Average Earliest Arrival Date	Average Latest Departure Date	Latest Departure Date
Greenshank	13 Mar	21 Apr	24 May	
Common Sandpiper	5 Mar	1 Apr	31 May	
Whinchat	16 Mar	22 Apr	15 May	
Northern Wheatear	6 Mar	18 Mar	23 May	
Ring Ouzel	15 Mar	5 Apr	28 Apr	22 May

Autumn	Earliest Arrival Date	Average Earliest Arrival Date	Average Latest Departure Date	Latest Departure Date
Greenshank		10 Jul	8 Oct	28 Dec
Common Sandpiper		26 Jun	24 Oct	31 Dec
Whinchat		3 Aug	9 Oct	11 Nov
Northern Wheatear		1 Aug	18 Oct	10 Nov
Ring Ouzel	8 Sep	4 Jul	27 Oct	3 Dec

Winter visitors	Earliest Arrival Date	Average Earliest Arrival Date	Average Latest Departure Date	Latest Departure Date
Bewick's Swan	19 Oct	23 Oct	15 Feb	6 May
Whooper Swan	1 Oct	30 Oct	1 Mar	20 Apr
Wigeon		9 Aug	11 May	
Pintail	10 Aug	19 Sep	23 Mar	24 Jun
Scaup	6 Sep	26 Oct	8 Mar	12 May
Goosander	8 Oct	2 Nov	15 Apr	17 May
Goldeneye		13 Oct	26 Apr	15 May
Smew	2 Nov	6 Dec	4 Mar	6 Apr
Golden Plover	25 Jun	24 Aug	23 Apr	25 May
Green Sandpiper	3 Jun	23 Jun	5 May	20 May
Short-eared Owl	15 Sep	24 Oct	15 Apr	28 May
Fieldfare	17 Aug	30 Sep	30 Apr	28 May
Redwing	21 Jul	24 Sep	21 Apr	23 May
Brambling	18 Aug	9 Oct	24 Apr	8 May

EARLIEST ARRIVAL DATES

The displayed graphs show the three year moving averages of the earliest arrival dates of our most numerous summer visitors. With the exception of Hobby, whose start year is 1973, the records start from 1971. Almost all the graphs show that our summer visitors are arriving earlier. The most obvious explanation for this is climate change, but it is likely that fewer birders were sending in their records during the early 70s.

There are four species which are not arriving earlier: Turtle Dove, Cuckoo, Tree Pipit and Spotted Flycatcher. All are in decline. Although their increasing rarity means that they are more difficult to find so that the earliest arrivals are less likely to be found, there may be a less trivial explanation. It has been shown that many birds are breeding earlier so as to synchronise the hatching of young with the main supply of food. There are many factors involved in the declining populations of these species but an inability to adapt to a changing climate may also be one of the problems.

The horizontal lines on the graphs are at four day intervals.

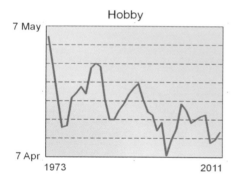

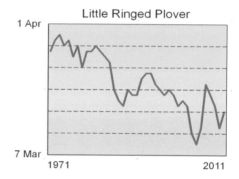

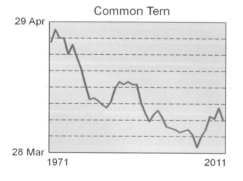

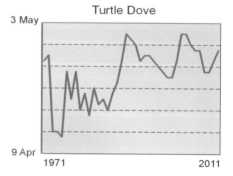

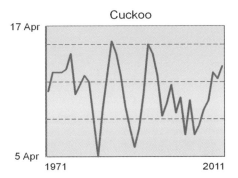

Cuckoo

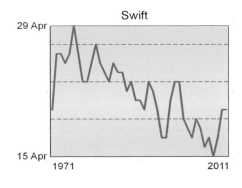

Swift

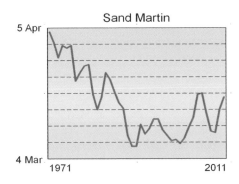

Sand Martin

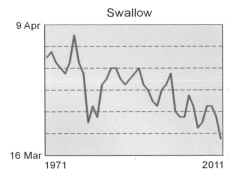

Swallow

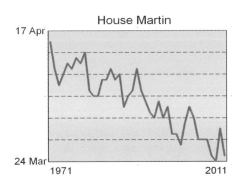

House Martin

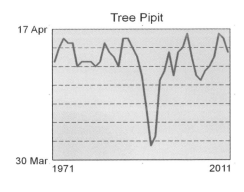

Tree Pipit

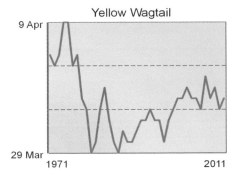

Yellow Wagtail

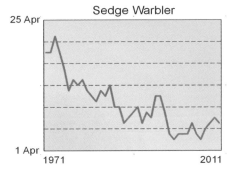

Sedge Warbler

361

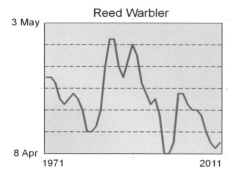

Reed Warbler

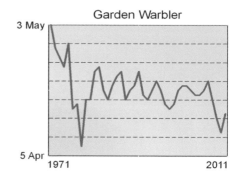

Garden Warbler

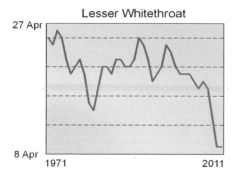

Lesser Whitethroat

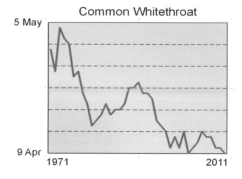

Common Whitethroat

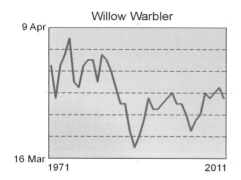

Willow Warbler

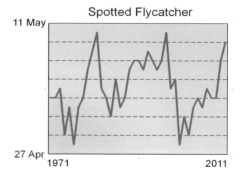

Spotted Flycatcher

THE GARDEN BIRD SURVEY

John Gearing

In November 1986 Arthur Brown created a Garden Bird Survey for Club members, which has continued in some form ever since, with administration by Graeme Taylor from 1992 until 2010/11, followed by John Gearing in 2011/ 2012.

The Club's GBS is divided into three nine week periods running from early October through until the end of March and participants keep notes of birds feeding on natural foods in their gardens and on the foods they provided for them throughout winter. A log is also kept of the birds' use of water over this period. From the data gathered a report is compiled for each period and the data compared to previous years using a five year episode to give a historical picture of the changes occurring in Buckinghamshire gardens.

The number of participant gardens covered was at a maximum of 90 in 1992. The total number of British species recorded, so far, is 101 including some species lost now to the county, Wood Warbler and Willow Tit to name but two. In addition three escapee species have also been seen in member's gardens. Among rarities visiting: in October 2006 one surveyed garden paid host to a visiting Yellow-browed Warbler while during severe weather in December 2010 a Bar-tailed Godwit spent a short time trying to feed in a garden in Gerrards Cross. Recent additions to the GBS list include in 2010/11 Waxwing feeding in four gardens while five gardens now have regular visits from Ring-necked Parakeets.

The table below shows the 40 most frequent occurring species visiting gardens during the last five years 2007/12 with, for comparison, those reported in the original five years of the GBS from 1986/92. The final four columns of the chart show the latest species activity in the gardens reporting, with in most cases maximum activity happening in the survey's 3rd period, February to April, when food support and water needs are greatest.

As can be seen some significant changes have occurred over the time of the GBS with four species dropping out of the top 40 - Treecreeper, Rook, Reed Bunting and Willow Tit. Woodpigeon, Goldfinch, and Fieldfare have become substantially more common as visitors while Blackcap, Mistle Thrush, Nuthatch, Starling and House Sparrow have declined significantly as garden birds. Who would have predicted 20 years ago that Red Kite would have become a regular garden bird !

	2007/12 % of total gardens	1986/1992 % of total gardens	2011/2012 Garden Activity			
			Artificial food	Natural food	Using Water	Max flock size
Blackbird	100.0%	98.7%	84%	84%	72%	14
Robin	100.0%	98.5%	90%	73%	73%	5
Blue Tit	99.8%	98.7%	91%	67%	46%	17
Wood Pigeon	99.4%	53.0%	82%	56%	50%	29
Great Tit	96.8%	90.2%	87%	60%	27%	8
Dunnock	96.4%	89.2%	86%	79%	27%	4
Chaffinch	95.0%	91.7%	83%	62%	40%	38
Magpie	88.8%	75.2%	71%	33%	18%	17
Collared Dove	84.2%	75.8%	83%	38%	30%	22
Greenfinch	79.6%	88.3%	90%	37%	39%	28
Goldfinch	78.0%	18.3%	84%	43%	35%	22
Wren	77.6%	75.0%	14%	64%	6%	2
Long Tailed Tit	76.4%	35.6%	84%	49%	12%	15
Coal Tit	73.6%	62.4%	76%	23%	21%	4
Starling	73.0%	96.0%	88%	35%	47%	60
Song Thrush	71.6%	78.5%	41%	70%	27%	4
House Sparrow	63.8%	90.5%	87%	50%	42%	35
Gt Sp Woodpecker	52.2%	30.3%	80%	35%	5%	3
Redwing	50.8%	18.0%	22%	65%	11%	35
Carrion Crow	48.6%	31.1%	52%	35%	15%	5
Jackdaw	39.4%	13.7%	68%	15%	12%	30
Fieldfare	37.0%	12.9%	21%	55%		80
Pied Wagtail	36.6%	25.1%	60%	27%	20%	2
Blackcap	35.4%	7.6%	45%	32%	18%	2
Green Woodpecker	34.6%	15.4%	8%	80%	10%	3
Jay	34.4%	29.6%	45%	53%	27%	4
Sparrowhawk	30.8%	10.8%		32%		2
Bullfinch	27.2%	23.6%	53%	33%	13%	4
Pheasant	27.0%	13.7%	62%	60%	15%	8
Siskin	24.6%	11.0%	73%	50%	25%	6
Goldcrest	24.2%	17.5%	10%	67%	30%	3
Nuthatch	23.4%	21.8%	82%	47%	13%	4
Red Kite	22.8%		64%	7%		30
Brambling	17.6%	4.3%	60%		20%	1
Marsh Tit	13.6%	8.0%	89%	20%	22%	3
Mistle Thrush	12.8%	25.0%		60%	17%	5
Mallard	10.6%		80%	70%		32
Grey Heron	10.2%			50%		2
Chiffchaff	10.0%			20%		1
Black-headed Gull	10.0%	7.5%	67%	29%		23

THE BUCKINGHAMSHIRE LIST

The 294 species recorded in the present county up to 31 December 2011 are:

Mute Swan	Local resident.
Bewick's Swan	Scarce winter visitor.
Whooper Swan	Scarce winter visitor.
Bean Goose	Rare vagrant.
Pink-footed Goose	Scarce migrant.
White-fronted Goose	Scarce migrant and rare winter visitor.
Greylag Goose	Introduced local resident.
Canada Goose	Introduced resident
Barnacle Goose	Introduced resident.
Brent Goose	Scarce migrant.
Egyptian Goose	Introduced local resident.
Shelduck	Scarce resident and regular migrant.
Mandarin Duck	Introduced local resident.
Wigeon	Regular winter visitor
Gadwall	Local resident and local winter visitor.
Eurasian Teal	Regular winter visitor. Has bred.
Green-winged Teal	Very rare vagrant, 5 Records.
Mallard	Common resident and winter visitor.
Pintail	Uncommon migrant and winter visitor.
Garganey	Scarce migrant and winter visitor.
Shoveler	Scarce resident and local migrant and winter visitor.
Red-crested Pochard	Uncommon migrant, most of which are probably feral.
Common Pochard	Scarce resident but common winter visitor and migrant.
Ring-necked Duck	Very rare vagrant. 7 records.
Ferruginous Duck	Rare vagrant. 10 records. All may be escapes.
Tufted Duck	Common resident, migrant and winter visitor.
Scaup	Scarce migrant and winter visitor.
Eider	Very rare vagrant. 3 records.
Long-tailed Duck	Rare vagrant and winter visitor.
Common Scoter	Scarce migrant.
Velvet Scoter	Very rare vagrant. 4 records.
Bufflehead	Very rare vagrant. 1 record.
Goldeneye	Local winter visitor.
Smew	Scarce winter visitor.
Red-breasted Merganser	Rare vagrant and winter visitor.
Goosander	Local winter visitor. Has bred twice.
Ruddy Duck	Former very local resident and scarce migrant.
Red-legged Partridge	Fairly common introduced resident.
Grey Partridge	Uncommon and decreasing resident.
Quail	Rare summer visitor; occasionally breeds.
Common Pheasant	Introduced common resident.
Golden Pheasant	Introduced or escaped in very small numbers.
Lady Amherst's Pheasant	Former introduced resident in very small numbers.
Red-throated Diver	Rare vagrant. 18 records.
Black-throated Diver	Rare vagrant. 12 records.

Great Northern Diver	Rare vagrant. 17 records.
Little Grebe	Fairly common resident and winter visitor.
Great Crested Grebe	Local resident and winter visitor.
Red-necked Grebe	Scarce migrant and winter visitor.
Slavonian Grebe	Scarce migrant and winter visitor.
Black-necked Grebe	Scarce migrant,
Fulmar	Very rare vagrant. 9 records.
Great Shearwater	Very rare vagrant. 1 record.
Manx Shearwater	Rare vagrant. 19 records.
Storm Petrel	Very rare vagrant. 7 records. Last record in 1929.
Leach's Petrel	Rare vagrant. 17 records.
Gannet	Rare vagrant. 16 records.
Cormorant	Very local resident and regular visitor.
Shag	Scarce migrant and winter visitor.
Bittern	Regular winter visitor in very small numbers.
Little Bittern	Very rare vagrant. 5 records.
Night-heron	Very rare vagrant. 5 records.
Cattle Egret	Very rare vagrant. 2 records.
Little Egret	Very local resident and regular visitor.
Great White Egret	Very rare vagrant. 5 records.
Grey Heron	Local resident and winter visitor.
Purple Heron	Very rare vagrant. 4 records.
Black Stork	Very rare vagrant. 1 record.
White Stork	Rare vagrant. 12 records.
Glossy Ibis	Very rare vagrant. 2 records.
Spoonbill	Very rare vagrant. 9 records.
Honey-buzzard	Scarce migrant. May breed.
Red Kite	Introduced locally common resident.
Black Kite	Very rare vagrant. 2 records.
White-tailed Eagle	Very rare vagrant. 4 records.
Marsh Harrier	Scarce migrant.
Hen Harrier	Scarce migrant.
Montagu's Harrier	Very rare vagrant. 5 records.
Goshawk	Very rare resident.
Sparrowhawk	Fairly common resident.
Common Buzzard	Common resident.
Rough-legged Buzzard	Very rare vagrant. 8 records.
Osprey	Scarce migrant.
Kestrel	Common resident and partial migrant.
Red-footed Falcon	Very rare vagrant. 3 records.
Merlin	Uncommon winter visitor and migrant.
Hobby	Uncommon breeding summer visitor.
Peregrine	Very rare resident and scarce winter visitor.
Water Rail	Rare resident and local winter visitor.
Spotted Crake	Very rare vagrant. 6 records.
Corncrake	Very rare migrant. Formerly a breeding summer visitor.
Moorhen	Common resident and winter visitor.
Coot	Common resident and winter visitor.
Common Crane	Rare vagrant. 12 records.

Oystercatcher	Very local breeding summer visitor and scarce migrant.
Black-winged Stilt	Very rare vagrant. 1 record.
Avocet	Rare vagrant.
Stone-curlew	Very rare migrant. Former local summer visitor.
Little Ringed Plover	Scarce breeding summer visitor and migrant.
Ringed Plover	Scarce breeding summer visitor and migrant.
Kentish Plover	Very rare vagrant. 1 record.
Dotterel	Very rare vagrant. 7 records.
American Golden Plover	Very rare vagrant. 1 record.
Golden Plover	Locally common winter visitor.
Grey Plover	Scarce migrant and very rare winter visitor.
Lapwing	Common but decreasing resident and winter visitor.
Knot	Scarce migrant.
Sanderling	Scarce migrant.
Little Stint	Scarce migrant.
Temminck's Stint	Rare migrant.
Least Sandpiper	Very rare vagrant. 1 record.
Pectoral Sandpiper	Very rare vagrant. 4 records.
Curlew Sandpiper	Scarce migrant.
Purple Sandpiper	Very rare vagrant. 3 records.
Dunlin	Regular migrant and rare winter visitor.
Ruff	Scarce migrant and rare winter visitor.
Jack Snipe	Uncommon winter visitor.
Snipe	Common migrant and winter visitor; irregular breeder.
Great Snipe	Very rare vagrant. 1 record.
Woodcock	Very local resident and local winter visitor.
Black-tailed Godwit	Scarce migrant.
Bar-tailed Godwit	Scarce migrant.
Whimbrel	Scarce migrant.
Curlew	Local summer visitor and uncommon migrant.
Common Sandpiper	Common migrant and very rare winter visitor. Has bred.
Spotted Sandpiper	Very rare vagrant. 1 record.
Green Sandpiper	Fairly common migrant and uncommon winter visitor.
Spotted Redshank	Scarce migrant.
Greenshank	Uncommon migrant and very rare winter visitor.
Lesser Yellowlegs	Very rare vagrant. 1 record.
Wood Sandpiper	Scarce migrant.
Redshank	Local summer visitor, uncommon migrant and winter visitor.
Turnstone	Scarce migrant.
Wilson's Phalarope	Very rare vagrant. 2 records.
Red-necked Phalarope	Very rare vagrant. 6 records.
Grey Phalarope	Rare vagrant. 10 records.
Pomarine Skua	Very rare vagrant. 5 records.
Arctic Skua	Very rare vagrant. 2 records.
Long-tailed Skua	Very rare vagrant. 1 records
Great Skua	Very rare vagrant. 4 records.
Kittiwake	Scarce migrant.
Black-headed Gull	Very rare resident; common migrant and winter visitor.

Little Gull	Scarce migrant.
Franklin's Gull	Very rare vagrant. 1 record.
Sabine's Gull	Very rare vagrant. 8 records.
Mediterranean Gull	Scarce migrant and winter visitor.
Common Gull	Common migrant and winter visitor.
Ring-billed Gull	Rare vagrant. 11 records.
Lesser Black-backed Gull	Very rare resident; common migrant and winter visitor.
Herring Gull	Very rare resident; common migrant and winter visitor.
Yellow-legged Gull	Regular migrant.
Caspian Gull	Scarce migrant and winter visitor.
Iceland Gull	Scarce winter visitor.
Glaucous Gull	Scarce winter visitor.
Great Black-backed Gull	Uncommon winter visitor.
Little Tern	Scarce migrant.
Caspian Tern	Very rare vagrant. 3 records.
Whiskered Tern	Very rare vagrant. 2 records.
Black Tern	Local migrant.
White-winged Black Tern	Very rare vagrant. 1 record.
Sandwich Tern	Scarce migrant.
Common Tern	Local summer visitor and migrant.
Roseate Tern	Very rare vagrant. 6 records.
Arctic Tern	Local migrant.
Guillemot	Very rare vagrant. 1 record.
Razorbill	Very rare vagrant. 1 record.
Little Auk	Rare vagrant. 17 records.
Puffin	Rare vagrant. 11 records.
Pallas's Sandgrouse	Very rare vagrant. 3 records, none since 1908.
Rock Dove / Feral Pigeon	Common resident.
Stock Dove	Common resident.
Woodpigeon	Very common resident.
Collared Dove	Common resident.
Turtle Dove	Rare and decreasing summer visitor.
Ring-necked Parakeet	Very local but increasing introduced resident.
Cuckoo	Uncommon summer visitor.
Barn Owl	Uncommon but increasing resident
Little Owl	Uncommon introduced resident.
Tawny Owl	Fairly common resident.
Long-eared Owl	Rare resident and scarce winter visitor.
Short-eared Owl	Scarce winter visitor and migrant.
Nightjar	Irregular summer visitor and rare migrant.
Swift	Common summer visitor.
Alpine Swift	Very rare vagrant. 3 records.
Kingfisher	Local resident.
Bee-eater	Very rare vagrant. 9 records.
Roller	Very rare vagrant. 1 record.
Hoopoe	Rare vagrant. Has bred once.
Wryneck	Scarce migrant which used to breed.
Green Woodpecker	Common resident.
Great Spotted Woodpecker	Common resident.

Lesser Spotted Woodpecker	Scarce and declining resident.
Woodlark	Occasional summer visitor and rare migrant.
Skylark	Common resident, migrant, and winter visitor.
Sand Martin	Very local summer visitor and common migrant.
Swallow	Common summer visitor and migrant.
Red-rumped Swallow	Very rare vagrant. 1 record.
House Martin	Common summer visitor and migrant.
Richard's Pipit	Very rare vagrant. 3 records.
Tree Pipit	Rare summer visitor.
Meadow Pipit	Scarce resident; fairly common migrant and winter visitor.
Rock pipit	Scarce migrant.
Water Pipit	Scarce migrant.
Yellow Wagtail	Uncommon and decreasing summer visitor and migrant.
Grey Wagtail	Local resident and winter visitor.
Pied Wagtail	Common resident and migrant.
Waxwing	Erratic winter visitor.
Dipper	Very rare vagrant.
Wren	Very common resident.
Dunnock	Very common resident.
Robin	Very common resident.
Nightingale	Rare and declining summer visitor.
Bluethroat	Very rare vagrant. 2 records.
Black Redstart	Irregular breeding summer visitor and scarce migrant.
Redstart	Uncommon migrant. Former breeding summer visitor.
Whinchat	Uncommon migrant. Former breeding summer visitor.
Stonechat	Scarce migrant and winter visitor. Has bred.
Northern Wheatear	Local migrant. Former breeding summer visitor.
Black-eared Wheatear	Very rare vagrant. 1 record.
Ring Ouzel	Very local migrant.
Blackbird	Very common resident, migrant and winter visitor.
Fieldfare	Common winter visitor.
Song Thrush	Common resident, migrant and winter visitor.
Redwing	Common winter visitor.
Mistle Thrush	Common resident.
Cetti's Warbler	Very local resident and rare migrant.
Grasshopper Warbler	Scarce summer visitor.
River Warbler	Very rare vagrant. 1 record.
Aquatic Warbler	Very rare vagrant. 2 records.
Sedge Warbler	Local summer visitor.
Marsh Warbler	Very rare vagrant. 4 records including one of breeding.
Reed Warbler	Local summer visitor and migrant.
Great Reed Warbler	Very rare vagrant. 2 records.
Icterine Warbler	Very rare vagrant. 2 records.
Blackcap	Common summer visitor and migrant; uncommon winter visitor.
Garden Warbler	Fairly common summer visitor.
Lesser Whitethroat	Fairly common summer visitor.
Common Whitethroat	Common summer visitor.

Dartford Warbler	Very rare occasional resident, migrant and winter visitor.
Yellow-browed Warbler	Very rare vagrant. 5 records.
Wood Warbler	Rare migrant; former summer visitor.
Chiffchaff	Common summer visitor and migrant; scarce winter visitor.
Willow Warbler	Common summer visitor and migrant.
Goldcrest	Common resident and winter visitor.
Firecrest	Very local summer visitor; scarce migrant & winter visitor.
Spotted Flycatcher	Uncommon and decreasing summer visitor and migrant.
Red-breasted Flycatcher	Very rare vagrant. 2 records.
Pied Flycatcher	Scarce migrant. 2 breeding records.
Bearded Tit	Rare winter visitor.
Long-tailed Tit	Common resident.
Blue Tit	Very common resident.
Great Tit	Very common resident.
Coal Tit	Common resident.
Willow Tit	Very rare resident.
Marsh Tit	Uncommon resident.
Nuthatch	Fairly common resident.
Treecreeper	Fairly common resident.
Golden Oriole	Rare vagrant. 14 records including 1 breeding.
Red-backed Shrike	Very rare vagrant. Former breeding summer visitor.
Great Grey Shrike	Rare winter visitor.
Woodchat Shrike	Very rare vagrant. 3 records.
Jay	Common resident.
Magpie	Common resident.
Nutcracker	Very rare vagrant. 3 records.
Jackdaw	Common resident.
Rook	Common resident.
Carrion Crow	Common resident.
Hooded Crow	Very rare vagrant. None since 1975.
Raven	Uncommon but increasing resident.
Starling	Very common resident and winter visitor.
Rose-coloured Starling	Very rare vagrant. 1 record.
House Sparrow	Common resident.
Tree Sparrow	Very local resident.
Chaffinch	Very common resident.
Brambling	Uncommon winter visitor.
Serin	Very rare vagrant. 1 record.
Greenfinch	Common resident and winter visitor.
Goldfinch	Common resident and summer visitor.
Siskin	Uncommon winter visitor that occasionally summers.
Linnet	Common but decreasing resident.
Twite	Rare vagrant. 12 records.
Common Redpoll	Very rare vagrant. 5 records.
Lesser Redpoll	Scarce and declining resident; uncommon winter visitor.
Two-barred Crossbill	Very rare vagrant. 1 record.
Common Crossbill	Irregular visitor and breeder.

Bullfinch	Common resident.
Hawfinch	Very rare migrant and winter visitor. Former local resident.
Lapland Bunting	Very rare vagrant. 7 records.
Snow Bunting	Rare migrant and very rare winter visitor. 20 records.
Yellowhammer	Common but declining resident.
Cirl Bunting	Former scarce resident. Last record 1985.
Little Bunting	Very rare vagrant. 1 record.
Reed Bunting	Local and declining resident.
Corn Bunting	Scarce and declining resident.

GAZETTEER

The sites listed below are either mentioned in the text of this book or are of local interest. Against each site is given the 4-figure OS National Grid reference, the nearest town, its bearing, and its distance from the town in kms.

Site	Grid ref	Town	Bearing	Km
Ashridge	SP 98 13	Tring	ENE	5
Aston Sandford	SP 75 07	Thame	ENE	4
Aylesbury STW	SP 79 14	Aylesbury	West	
Bacombe Hill	SP 86 07	Wendover	SW	1
Balham's Wood	SU 75 89	Stokenchurch	SSW	7
Beacon Hill (Ellesborough)	SP 83 06	Wendover	SW	3
Berghers Hill	SU 91 87	Beaconsfield	SSW	2
Bernwood Forest	SP 61 10	Thame	WNW	10
Bernwood Meadows	SP 60 11	Thame	WNW	11
Berryfields	SP 78 16	Aylesbury	WNW	2
Bishopstone	SP 80 10	Aylesbury	SSW	2
Black Park Country Park	TQ 01 06	Slough	NE	3
Bledlow Ridge	SU 79 97	High Wycombe	NNW	2
Bletchley Brick Pits	SP 86 31	Bletchley		
Bletchley STW	SP 88 34	Bletchley		
Blue Lagoon	SP 86 32	Bletchley		
Bockmer End	SU 81 86	Marlow	W	3
Booker	SU 83 91	High Wycombe	SW	1
Botolph Claydon	SP 73 24	Aylesbury	NW	12
Boveney	SU 93 77	Slough	WSW	3
Bradenham Woods	SU 83 98	High Wycombe	NW	3
Burnham Beeches	SU 95 85	Slough	NNW	3
Caldecotte Lake	SP 89 35	Milton Keynes	E	
Calvert Sailing Lake	SP 68 25	Buckingham	SSW	8
Calvert Jubilee Reserve	SP 68 25	Buckingham	S	8
Campbell Park	SP 85 38	Milton Keynes	Central	
Castlethorpe Mill	SP 78 44	Wolverton	NW	4
Chalfont Park & Lake	TQ 01 89	Beaconsfield	ENE	5
Chartridge	SP 93 03	Chesham	NW	3
Chearsley	SP 71 10	Thame	N	4
Chequers	SP 84 05	Wendover	SW	3
Chesham Bois Woods	SP 96 00	Chesham	S	1
Chesham Cress Beds	SP 96 00	Chesham	SSE	0.5
Chesham Moor	SP 96 00	Chesham	SSE	1
Chesham STW	SU 97 99	Chesham	SSE	2
Chesham Waterside	SP 96 00	Chesham	SSE	0.5
Chess Valley	SU 99 98	Amersham	E	2
Cholesbury	SP 93 07	Chesham	NNW	4
Church Wood	SU 97 87	Beaconsfield	SE	4
Claydon Lakes	SP 71 25	Buckingham	SSE	8
Cliveden	SU 91 85	Beaconsfield	SSW	5
Coleshill	SU 94 95	Beaconsfield	N	3

College Lake	SP 93 13	Tring	NNE	1
Common Wood	SU 91 94	High Wycombe	ENE	3
Coombe Hill	SP 84 06	Wendover	SW	2
Cosgrove	SP 79 42	Wolverton	WNW	2
Dadford	SP 66 38	Buckingham	NW	5
Dancersend	SP 90 09	Wendover	ENE	3
Dagnall	SP 99 16	Tring	ENE	7
Denham Country Park	TQ 04 86	Gerrards Cross	E	5
Dinton Hall	SP 77 11	Aylesbury	WSW	5
Dipple Wood	SU 93 87	Beaconsfield	S	2
Doddershall Wood	SP 69 20	Thame	N	14
Dorney Common	SU 93 79	Slough	WSW	3
Dorney Lake	SU 92 78	Slough	WSW	4
Dorney Reach	SU 91 79	Slough	WNW	3
Dorton	SP 68 12	Thame	NNW	12
Downley Common	SU 85 95	High Wycombe	NW	3
Drayton Beauchamp	SP 89 12	Tring	WNW	1
Drayton Parslow	SP 84 28	Bletchley	SSW	5
Dropmore	SU 92 86	Beaconsfield	S	4
East Claydon	SP 74 25	Aylesbury	NW	12
Edgecott	SP 68 22	Buckingham	SSW	11
Egypt Woods	SU 95 86	Beaconsfield	SSE	3
Emberton Country Park	SP 88 50	Great Linford	NNE	8
Eythrope	SP 77 14	Aylesbury	W	3
Fawley	SU 75 86	Marlow	WSW	7
Finemere Wood	SP 71 21	Aylesbury	NW	11
Foxcote Reservoir	SP 71 36	Buckingham	NNE	2
Fulmer Marsh & Lake	SU 99 86	Gerrards Cross	S	2
Gallows Bridge Farm	SP 66 20	Aylesbury	WNW	16
Grangelands & Pulpit Hill	SP 82 04	Wendover	SW	5
Great Brickhill	SP 90 30	Bletchley	ESE	4
Great Hampden	SP 84 01	High Wycombe	N	7
Hambleden	SP 78 86	Marlow	W	5
Hampden Bottom	SP 86 02	High Wycombe	N	8
Hartigan's GP **	SP 88 38	Milton Keynes E		
Haversham	SP 83 43	Wolverton	NNE	2
Hedgerley	SU 96 87	Beaconsfield	SE	4
Hockeridge & Pancake Woods	SP 97 06	Chesham	NNE	3
Hodgemoor Woods	SU 96 94	Beaconsfield	NE	3
Homefield Wood	SU 81 86	Marlow	NE	3
Howe Park Wood	SP 83 34	Milton Keynes W		
Hughenden Park and Manor	SU 86 95	High Wycombe	N	1
Hyde Lane Lake	SP 72 35	Buckingham	ENE	2
Iver GP	TQ 03 80	Slough	E	3
Iver STW	TQ 04 80	Slough	E	4
Ivinghoe Hills	SP 96 15	Tring	NE	4
Jubilee River (Marsh Lane)	SU 91 80	Slough	W	3
Jubilee River (Lake End)	SU 92 79	Slough	WSW	2
Kings Wood (Tylers Green)	SU 89 94	High Wycombe	ENE	1

Langley Park Country Park	TQ 00 84	Slough	NNE	2
Latimer Park & Lake	SU 99 98	Amersham	E	2
Lenborough	SP 70 31	Buckingham	S	1
Linford Wood (MK)	SP 84 40	Milton Keynes N		
Linford/Newport Pagnell Lakes	SP 84 43	Great Linford	NNW	1
Little Britain Country Park	TQ 05 81	Slough	E	5
Little Linford Wood	SP 83 45	Great Linford	NNW	3
Little Marlow GPs	SU 88 87	Marlow	ENE	2
Little Marlow STW	SU 87 87	Marlow	ENE	2
Littleworth Common	SU 93 86	Beaconsfield	S	4
Lodge Hill	SP 79 00	Stokenchurch	NW	5
Loughton Valley Park	SP 83 37	Milton Keynes W		
Marlow Low Grounds	SU 84 84	Marlow	SSW	1
Marsworth Reservoir	SP 92 13	Tring	N	2
Medmenham	SU 80 84	Marlow	SW	4
Moorend Common	SU 80 90	Marlow	NW	5
Moulsoe	SP 91 42	Willen	ENE	3
Mursley	SP 81 28	Bletchley	SW	6
Naphill Common	SU 84 97	High Wycombe	NNW	3
Newport Pagnell	SP 86 43	Great Linford	NE	2
Newton Longville	SP 83 41	Bletchley	SSE	2
Old Rectory Meadows	TQ 03 87	Slough	NE	8
Old Slade	TQ 03 77	Slough	ESE	3
Olney	SP 88 50	Great Linford	NNE	9
Padbury	SP 72 31	Buckingham	SE	3
Park Wood	SU 82 98	High Wycombe	NW	4
Penn Wood	SU 91 96	High Wycombe	ENE	4
Philipshill Wood	TQ 00 94	Amersham	ENE	4
Pickeridge Quarry**	SU 98 85	Slough	N	5
Pitstone Hill	SP 95 14	Tring	NE	3
Quainton Hills	SP 75 21	Aylesbury	NW	8
Ravenstone	SP 84 50	Great Linford	N	7
Ringshall	SP 98 14	Tring	ENE	7
Rushbeds Wood	SP 66 15	Thame	NNW	10
Salcey Forest	SP 81 50	Wolverton	N	9
Shabbington Wood	SP 61 10	Thame	NNW	10
Shardeloes	SU 94 98	Amersham	W	2
Sheephouse Wood	SP 70 23	Buckingham	S	10
Startops End Reservoir	SP 92 13	Tring	N	1
Steps Hill	SP 95 15	Tring	NE	4
Stockgrove Country Park	SP 91 29	Bletchley	SE	5
Stoke Common	SU 98 85	Gerrards Cross	WSW	3
Stoke Hammond	SP 88 29	Bletchley	S	2
Stony Stratford NR	SP 78 41	Milton Keynes N		
Stowe	SP 67 37	Buckingham	NNW	4
Taplow Court	SU 90 82	Slough	WNW	3
Taplow GP	SU 91 81	Slough	W	3
Temple Island Meadows	SU 76 84	Marlow	WSW	7
The Lee	SP 91 04	Chesham	WNW	6

Three Locks	SP 89 28	Bletchley	SSE	4
Tilbrook	SP 89 35	Milton Keynes E		
Tilehouse GPs	TQ 03 89	Slough	NNE	10
Tongwell	SP 87 41	Milton Keynes E		
Tyringham Park	SP 85 46	Great Linford	N	4
Wapseys Wood WDS	SU 97 88	Beaconsfield	ESE	3
Watermead	SP 82 15	Aylesbury	N0.5	
Wavenden Wood	SP 91 35	Bletchley	ENE	4
Wendover Canal	SP 88 10	Wendover-Tring		
Wendover Woods	SP 89 08	Wendover	ENE	1
West Wycombe Park	SU 83 94	High Wycombe	WNW	1
Westbury Wild	SP 62 37	Buckingham	WNW	7
Westcott	SP 71 17	Aylesbury	WNW	8
Weston Turville Reservoir	SP 86 09	Wendover	NNW	1
Whitecross Green Wood	SP 60 14	Thame	NW	13
Willen Lake	SP 88 40	Milton Keynes E		
Wilstone Reservoir	SP 90 13	Tring	NW	2
Wotton Lakes	SP 67 16	Thame	NNW	10
Wycombe Rye	SU 87 92	High Wycombe		
Yiewsley GP	TQ 04 80	Slough	E	3

Abbreviations:

GP - Gravel Pit
NR - Nature Reserve
STW - Sewage Treatment Works
WDS - Waste Disposal Site
** - site no longer exists

ATLAS FIELDWORKERS

The main contributors to the atlas are listed below.

Mick A'Court	Anna Field	Rob Norris
Lars Ahlgren	Paul Field	Peter Ogden
G P Anderson	Neil Fletcher	Duncan Orr-Ewing
Rob Andrews	Jennifer Ford	Kenneth Panchen
Derek Antropik	Neill Foster	Bill Parker
Stephen Appleby	Gavin Foster	Dave Parmenter
Kate Ashbrook	Robert Fowles	Richard Pearson
Peter Austin	Nicholas Foxton	Chris Pendleton
Derek Barker	P Franklin	Julia Riddell
John Barnes	Peter Garner	Jonathan Ridge
W H Beglow	John Gearing	J J Robertson
Richard Billyard	Howard Ginn	Steve Rodwell
Richard Birch	David Glue	Jim Rose
John Birkitt	David Godfrey	John Rotheroe
Wendy Black	Richard Goodlad	Martin Routledge
John Bleby	Mark Griffin	Sue Rowe
Christine Booth	Ed Griffiths	Jeremy Rowley
Brian Boyland	Robert Gritton	David Rugg
Martin Britnell	R D Gross	Louise Russell
Stephanie Brown	John Hale	Patricia Scobie
Michael Bryant	Rosie Hamilton	Margaret Shackell
Bob Bullock	Andy Harding	A Slater
Chris Bullock	Tony Hardware	Wally Smith
Ian Burrus	Sheila Harry	Peter Stevens
Mike Campbell	R Hicks	Ashley Stow
George Candelin	Carolyn Hill	Colin Strudwick
Gordon Caw	Rob Hill	Gerry Studd
Martin Chadwick	Trevor Hill	Martin Sullivan
Peter Cherry	Kevin Holt	John Sweeney
Andrew Chipchase	Graham Hughes	Andrew Taylor
David Clark	Michael Hunt	Tessa Taylor
Brian Clews	Stephen Jones	Malcolm Tinnelly
Mike Collard	Rosemary Kemp	Phil Tizzard
David Cook	George Kernahan	Richard Tomlin
Chris Coppock	Graham Knight	Andy Tomczynski
Brian Crathorne	Judith Knight	Mike Tubb
Richard Crawford	Lynne Lambert	Bill Tunnicliffe
Andrew Cristinacce	C M Lansley	Esther Turnbull
Jonathan Daisley	David Lee	Mark Vallance
Rob Dazley	T Lewis	John Warren
Angela de Muynck	Keith Linger	Roger Warren
R A Dewey	Kevin Lovett	Tim Watts
Sandi Dobson	Neil Lukes	Peter Weisner
Nigel Dodd	Sandy Macfarlane	Michael Wells
J Dowling	Nick Marriner	Andrew Westwood
Ken Earnshaw	D G Marsh	J M Winyard
Jez Elkin	Roger Morton	Nicholas Wood
Colin Everett	Angus Murray	Rebecca Woodell
Samuel Farnsworth	Peter Newbound	
David Ferguson	Simon Nichols	

REFERENCES

Many records and information about individual species are taken from the series of reports covering the county, published by the Oxford Ornithological Society until 1953, the Middle Thames Natural History Society (1954 to 1979 inclusive) and the Buckinghamshire Bird Club from 1980 to the present. Specific references to the accounts in the systematic species accounts are rarely referred to individually and do not appear in the following list of references. However specific papers and notes published separately as part of the reports are noted here.

ALEXANDER, W. B. and D. LACK. 1944. Changes in status among British breeding birds. Brit. Birds 38:42-45,62-69,82-88.

ANDREWS, R & J. WALLINGTON. 1998. The River Warbler at Linford. Buckinghamshire Bird Report 1997.

ASTLEY, H. D. 1900. My Birds in Freedom and Captivity. Dent, London.

BAILLIE, S. R. 1990. Integrated population monitoring of breeding birds in Britain and Ireland. Ibis 132:151-166.

BAINBRIDGE, I. P. and C. D. T. MINTON. 1978. The migration and mortality of the Curlew in Britain and Ireland. Bird Study 25: 39-50.

BALMER, D.E., S.Y.ADAMS and H.Q.P.CRICK. Report on Barn Owl release scheme: monitoring Project Phase II. Research Project 250. BTO. Thetford.

BATTEN, L .A. 2007. Firecrests breeding in Buckinghamshire. Brit. Birds 64:11, 473-475.

BERTHOLD, P. and S. B. TERRILL. 1988. Migratory behaviour and population growth of Blackcaps wintering in Britain and Ireland: some hypotheses. Ringing & Migration 9:153-159.

BONHAM P. F. and J. T. R. SHARROCK. 1974. Sedge Warblers singing in fields of rape. Brit. Birds 67:9, 389-390.

BOU. 1971. The status of birds in Britain and Ireland. Blackwell Scientific Publications, Oxford.

BOU. 1992. Checklist of birds of Britain and Ireland. British Ornithologists' Union, Tring.

BRADSHAW, C. 2000. From the Rarities Committees files. The occurrence of Moustached Warbler in Britain. Brit. Birds 93: 29-38.

BROWN, A. F. and N. H. F. STONE. 1991. Mute Swan census in Buckinghamshire 1990. Buckinghamshire Bird Report 1990:8-13.

BROWN, L. 1976. British Birds of Prey. Collins, London.

BRUCKER, J. W., A. G. GOSLER and A. R. HERYET (eds). 1992. Birds of Oxfordshire. Pisces, Newbury.

BURTON, P. J. K. 1986. Ringing recoveries of Chilterns Sparrowhawk. Buckinghamshire Bird Report 1984:3-5.

BURTON, P. J. K. 1993. Nest-boxes as a monitoring tool for Kestrel (*Falco tinnunculus*) breeding performance. Biology and Conservation of Small Falcons (M.K.Nicholls & R.Clarke, eds). Hawk and Owl Trust, London.

CADBURY, C. J. 1980. The status and habitats of the Corncrake in Britain 1978-79. Bird Study 27:203-218.

CADWALLADER, D. A. and J. V. MORLEY. 1973. Sheep grazing preferences on a saltings pasture and their significance for Wigeon (*Anas penelope*) conservation. Journal of the British Grassland Society 28:235-242.

CAMPBELL, B. 1960. The Mute Swan census in England and Wales 1955-56. Bird Study 7:208-223.

CAVÉ, A. J. 1968. The breeding of the Kestrel, *Falco tinnunculus* L., in the reclaimed area Oosterlijk Flevoland. Neth. J. Zool. 18:313-407.

CHANDLER, R. J. 1981. Influxes into Britain and Ireland of Red-necked Grebes and other water-birds during winter 1979/79. Brit. Birds 74:2, 55-81.

CLEMENTS, R. 2002. The Common Buzzard in Britain: a new population estimate. Brit. Birds 95:8, 377-383.

COLLARD, M. 2011. An 'Eastern' Lesser Whitethroat in Buckinghamshire. Buckinghamshire Bird Report 2010.

COOK, A. 1984. Winter wildfowl at Weston Turville Reservoir. Buckinghamshire Bird Report 1982:2-6.

CRAMP, S. and K. E. L. SIMMONS (eds). 1977-1992. The Birds of the Western Palaearctic. Vols 1-6. University Press, Oxford.

CRUTTENDEN, P. 1990. The Aquatic Warbler at Botolph Claydon. Buckinghamshire Bird Report 1990.

DAVIS, P. 1966. The movement of Pied Wagtails as shown by ringing. Bird Study 13:147-162.

DOBINSON, H. M. and A. J. RICHARDS. 1964. The effects of the severe winter of 1962-63 on birds in Britain. Brit. Birds 57:10, 373-434.

DYMOND J. N., P.A. FRASER, and S. J. M. GANTLETT. 1989. Rare Birds in Britain and Ireland. Poyser, Calton.

ERAUD, C., J-M BOUTIN, M. RIVIERE, J. BRUN, C. BARBRAUD & H. LORMEE. 2009. Survival of Turtle Doves in relation to western Africa environmental conditions. Ibis 151: 186-190.

EVANS, A. 1997. Cirl Buntings in Britain. Brit Birds 90:7, 238-250.

EVANS, L. 2009. The White-Winged Black Terns at Wilstone - a first for Buckinghamshire. Buckinghamshire Bird Report 2008.

FERGUSON, D. 2009. The Roller in Great Missenden - a first for Buckinghamshire. Buckinghamshire Bird Report 2008.

FERGUSON-LEES, I. J., I. WILLIS and J. T. R. SHARROCK. 1983. The Shell Guide to Birds of Britain and Ireland. Michael Joseph, London.

FITTER, R. S. R. 1959. The Ark in our Midst. Collins, London.

FRASER, A. C. 1954. The Birds of the Middle Thames. Middle Thames Natural History Society, Slough.

FRASER, A. C. and R. E. YOUNGMAN. 1976. The Birds of Buckinghamshire and East Berkshire. Middle Thames Natural History Society, Slough.

FULLER, R. J. 1981. Aspects of counting Lapwings and Curlews breeding on lowland grasslands. Wader Study Group Bulletin 33: 14-16.

FULLER, R. J. 1990. Wintering Golden Plovers in central Buckinghamshire: annual variation in numbers and distribution. Buckinghamshire Bird Report 1988:4-8.

FULLER, R. J., J. K. BAKER, R. A. MORGAN, R. SCROGGS and M. WRIGHT. 1985. Breeding populations of the Hobby on farmland in the southern midlands of England. Ibis 127: 510-516.

FULLER, R. J. and D. E. GLUE. 1978. Seasonal activity of birds at a sewage-works. Brit. Birds 71:235-244.

FULLER, R. J. and D. E. GLUE. 1980. Sewage works as bird habitats in Britain. Biol. Conserv. 17:165-181.

FULLER, R. J. and R. E. YOUNGMAN. 1979. The utilisation of farmland by Golden Plovers wintering in southern England. Bird Study 26:37-46.

GEARING, J. 2009. The Black Stork at Lower Winchendon - a first for Buckinghamshire. Buckinghamshire Bird Report 2008.

GIBBONS, D. W., J. B. REID and R. A. CHAPMAN. 1993. The New Atlas of Breeding Birds in Britain and Ireland: 1988-1991. Poyser, Calton.

GILES, N. and R. WRIGHT. 1986. Reproductive success of Canada and Greylag Geese on gravel pits. Game Conservancy Annual Review 18:142-145.

GILLINGS, S., AUSTIN, G. E., FULLER, R. J. & SUTHERLAND, W. J. (2006) Distribution shifts in wintering Golden Plover *Pluvialis apricaria* and Lapwing *Vanellus vanellus*. Bird Study 53:274-284.

GLADWIN, T. and B. SAGE. 1986. The Birds of Hertfordshire. Castlemead, Ware.

GLUE, D. E. (ed.) 1982. The Garden Bird Book. MacMillan, London.

GLUE, D. E. and D. BODENHAM. 1974. Bird-life at a modern sewage farm. Bird Study 19:81-90.

GLUE, D. E. and D. BODENHAM. 1985. Changes in the breeding bird community of Aylesbury sewage works during 1970-1983. Buckinghamshire Bird Report 1983:2-9.

GLUE, D. E. and R. A. MORGAN. 1972. Cuckoo hosts in British habitats. Bird Study 19:187-192.

GLUE, D. E. and D. SCOTT. 1980. Breeding biology of the Little Owl. Brit. Birds 73:167-180.

GRANT, P. J. 1986. Gulls. A Guide to Identification. 2nd edn. Poyser, Calton.

HARDING, A. 1982. Waders at Willen Lake. Buckinghamshire Bird Report 1981:2-6.

HARRISON, G. 1934. A Bird Diary. Dent, London.

HARRISON, G. R., A. R. DEAN, A. J. RICHARDS and D. SMALLSHIRE. 1982. The Birds of the West Midlands. West Midlands Bird Club.

HARTERT, E. and W. ROTHSCHILD. 1905. Birds. Pp. 128-152 in A History of Buckingham (ed. W. Page). Constable & Co., London.

HARTERT, E. and F. C. R. JOURDAIN. 1920. The birds of Buckinghamshire and the Tring reservoirs. Novitat. Zool. 27:171-259.

HAYWARD, H. H. S. 1947. The birds of the Tring Reservoirs. Records of Buckinghamshire 15:51-62.

HEARD, C. 2002. Kumlien's Gull at Withybridge, March 2001. Buchinghamshire Bird Report, 2001.

HEATH, J., E. POLLARD, and J. THOMAS. 1984. Atlas of Butterflies in Britain and Ireland. Viking, Harmondsworth.

HIBBERT-WARE, A. 1937-8. Report of the Little Owl food inquiry, 1936-7. Brit. Birds 31:162-187, 205-229, 249-264.

HILL, D. A. 1984. Laying date, clutch size and egg size of the Mallard *Anas platyrynchos* and Tufted Duck *Aythya fuligula*. Ibis 126:484-495.

HILL, R. 1995. Great White Egret - a first for Buckinghamshire. Buckinghamshire Bird Report 1994.

HÖHN, E. O. 1943. Some observations on the Common Pochard. Brit. Birds 37:6, 102-107.

HUDSON, R. 1972. Collared Doves in Britain and Ireland during 1965-1970. Brit. Birds 65:4, 139-155.

HUDSON, R. 1973. Early and late dates for summer migrants. British Trust for Ornithology, Tring.

HUGHES, S. W. M., P. BACON, and J. J. M. FLEGG. 1979. The 1975 census of the Great Crested Grebe in Britain. Bird Study 26:213-226.

HUTCHINSON, C. D. and B. NEATH. 1978. Little Gulls in Britain and Ireland. Brit. Birds 71:563-582.

IMBODEN, C. 1974. Zug, Fremdansiedlung und Brutperiode des Kiebitz *Vanellus vanellus* in Europa. Orn. Beob. 71:5-134.

JENKINS, J. G. 1967. Chequers. A History of the Prime Minister's Buckinghamshire Home. Pergamon Press, Oxford.

JUILLARD, M. 1984. La chouette chevêche. Nos oiseaux. Société Romande pour l'étude et la protection des oiseaux.

KENNEDY, A. W. M. CLARK. 1868. The Birds of Berkshire and Buckinghamshire, a Contribution to the Natural History of the two Counties. Eton and London.

KENWARD, R. E. 1979. Winter predation by Goshawks in lowland Britain. Brit. Birds 72:2, 64-73.

KIRBY, J. 1988. Westerly movement of Buckinghamshire Ringed Plovers. Buckinghamshire Bird Report 1987:3-4.

KNIGHT, J. and N. H. F. STONE. 1988. Census of the Mute Swan in Buckinghamshire 1983. The Buckinghamshire Bird Report 1986:3-4.

LACK, P. 1986. The Atlas of Wintering Birds in Britain and Ireland. Poyser, Calton.

LEACH, I. H. 1981. Wintering Blackcaps in Britain and Ireland. Bird Study 28:5-15.

LEVER, C. 1987. Naturalised Birds of the World. Longman Scientific & Technical, Harlow.

LLYN-ALLEN, E. 1956. A Partridge Year. A.W.P. Robertson.

LLOYD, C., M. L. TASKER and K. PARTRIDGE. 1991. The status of seabirds in Britain and Ireland. T & A D Poyser, London.

MARCHANT, J. H., R. HUDSON, S. P. CARTER and P. WHITTINGTON. 1990. Population Trends in British Breeding Birds. British Trust for Ornithology, Tring.

MARCHANT, J. H. and P. A. HYDE. 1980. Aspects of the distribution of riparian birds on waterways in Britain and Ireland. Bird Study 27:183-202.

McMANUS, M & P. McMANUS. 2004. The Two-barred Crossbill at Hedgerley - a new bird for Buckinghamshire. Buckinghamshire Bird Report 2003.

MEAD, C. J. and K. W. SMITH. 1982. Hertfordshire Breeding Bird Atlas. HBBA, Tring.

MELLING, T. 2006. Time to get rid of the moustache: a review of British records of Moustached Warbler. Brit. Birds 99:9, 465-478.

MILSOM, T. P. 1984. Diurnal behaviour of Lapwings in relation to moon phase during winter. Bird Study 31:117-120.

MORGAN, R. A. 1980. The 1978 Mute Swan Survey in Buckinghamshire. Buckinghamshire Bird Report 1980:5-7.

MORGAN, R. A. and D. E. GLUE. 1977. Breeding, mortality and movements of Kingfishers. Bird Study 24:15-24.

MORRIS, F. O. 1970. A History of British Birds. Vol.5. Groombridge & Sons, London.

MURTON, R. K. 1966. Natural selection and the breeding seasons of the Stock Dove and Wood Pigeon. Bird Study 13:311-327.

NEWSON, S. E., A. JOHNSTON, A. R. RENWICK, S. R. BAILLIE, R. J. FULLER. 2011. Modelling large-scale relationships between changes in woodland deer and bird populations. Journal of Applied Ecology.

NEWTON, I. 1972. Finches. Collins, London.

NEWTON, I. 1986. The Sparrowhawk. Poyser, Calton.

NICHOLS, S. 2004. The Red-rumped Swallow at Furzton Lake - a first for Buckinghamshire. Buckinghamshire Bird Report 2002.

NIGHTINGALE, B. 2005. The Status of Lady Amherst's Pheasants in Britain, Bird Study, Jan 2005, 98, 20-25.

O'CONNOR, R. J. and C. J. MEAD. 1984. The Stock Dove in Britain 1930-80. Brit. Birds 77:5, 181-201.

O'CONNOR, R. J. and M. SHRUBB. 1986. Farming and Birds. University Press, Cambridge.

OGILVIE, M. A. 1967. Population changes and mortality of the Mute Swan in Britain. Wildfowl Trust Annual Report 18:64-73.
OGILVIE, M. A. 1977. The number of Canada Geese in Britain, 1976. Wildfowl 28:27-34.

OSBORNE, P. 1982. Some effects of Dutch elm disease on nesting farmland birds. Bird Study 29:2-16.

OWEN, M., G. L. ATKINSON-WILLES and D. G. SALMON. 1986. Wildfowl in Great Britain, 2nd ed. University Press, Cambridge.

OWEN, M. and D. G. SALMON. 1988. Feral Greylag Geese *Anser anser* in Britain and Ireland, 1960-86. Bird Study 35:37-45.

PARMENTER, D and M. COLLARD 2011. The Waxwing invasion - winter 2010/11. Buckinghamshire Bird Report 2010.

PARSLOW, J. 1973. Breeding Birds of Britain and Ireland. Poyser, Berkhamsted.

PLOSZAJSKI, T. 2000. Great Shearwater at Willen Lake, Milton Keynes. Buckinghamshire Bird Report 1999.

PRICE, K. 1947. The Birds of Buckinghamshire. Records of Buckinghamshire 15:20-31.

RADFORD, M. C. 1966. The Birds of Berkshire and Oxfordshire. Longman, Green & Co., London.

REDFERN, C. P. F. 1982. Lapwing nest sites and chick mortality in relation to habitat. Bird Study 29:201-208.

RICHARDSON, P. W. 1982. Northamptonshire Bird Report 1982.

RIDDIFORD, N. 1983. Recent declines of Grasshopper Warblers at British observatories. Bird Study 30:143-148.

RIDDIFORD, N. and P. FINDLAY. 1981. Seasonal movements of summer migrants. BTO Guide no.18. British Trust for Ornithology, Tring.

ROSE, J & M. WALLEN. 1993. Black-eared Wheatear - a first for Buckinghamshire. Buckinghamshire Bird Report 1992.

ROSE, J. 2008. The Alpine Swift in South Bucks. Buckinghamshire Bird Report 2006.

SHIRIHAI H, D. A. CHRISTIE, & A. HARRIS. 1996. The Macmillan Birder's Guide to European and Middle Eastern Birds.

SAGE, B. L. 1959. A History of the Birds of Hertfordshire. Barrie & Rockliff, London.

SAGE, B. L. and J. D. R. VERNON. 1978. The 1975 national survey of Rookeries. Bird Study 25:64-86.

SHRUBB, M. 1980. Farming influences on the food and hunting of Kestrels. Bird Study 27:109-115.

SIBLEY, C.G. and B. L. MONROE, Jr. 1990. Distribution and Taxonomy of Birds of the World. Yale University Press, New Haven.

SHARROCK, J. T. R. 1976. The Atlas of Breeding Birds in Britain and Ireland. Poyser, Berkhamsted.

SHAWYER, C. R. 1987. The Barn Owl in the British Isles: its Past, Present and Future. The Hawk Trust, London.

SITTERS, H. P. 1982. The decline of the Cirl Bunting in Britain, 1968-80. Brit. Birds 75, 7: 105-108.

SITTERS, H. P. 1986. Woodlarks in Britain, 1968-83. Brit Birds 79,3: 105-116,

SMITH, C. J. 1980. Ecology of the English Chalk. Academic Press, London.

SMITH, K. W. 1983. The status and distribution of waders breeding on wet lowland grasslands in England and Wales. Bird Study 30:177-192.

SMITH, K. W. and N. H. F. STONE. 1984. Survey of breeding waders of wet meadows. Buckinghamshire Bird Report 1982:8-10.

SMYTHE, W. H. 1864. Aedes Hartwelliana. Nicholls & Son, London.

SNOW, D. W. 1968. Movements and mortality of British Kestrels. Bird Study 15:65-83.

SNOW, B. and D. W. SNOW. 1988. Birds and Berries. Poyser, Calton.

SOVON. 1987. Atlas van de Nederlandse Vogels. SOVON, Arnhem.

SWASH A., P. STANDLEY, N. J. BUCKNELL, I. D. COLLINS. 1996. The Birds of Berkshire. Berkshire Atlas Group.

STEVENS A, M. McQUAID & C. BULLOCK. 2004. Black Kite at Little Marlow. Buckinghamshire Bird Report 2003.

STUTTARD, P. and K. WILLIAMSON. 1971. Habitat requirements of the Nightingale. Bird Study 18:9-14.

SUMMERS-SMITH, J. D. 1989. A history of the Tree Sparrow *Passer montanus* in the British Isles. Bird Study 36:23-31.

TAYLOR, K. 1985. Crossbill Invasion. BTO News 140:1.

TAYLOR, K. and J.H. MARCHANT. 1983. Population changes for waterways birds, 1981-82. Bird Study 30:121-126.

TAYLOR, K., R. HUDSON and G. HORNE. 1988. Buzzard breeding distribution and abundance in Britain and Northern Ireland in 1983. Bird Study 35:109-118.

TAYLOR, K. 2000. Franklin's Gull at Willen Lake. Buckinghamshire Bird Report 1999.

TOMPKINS, D. M., R. A. H. DRAYCOTT and P. J. HUDSON. 2002. Field evidence for apparent competition mediated via the shared parasites of two gamebird species. Ecology Letters 3: 10 -14.

TOMLIN, R. J. and R. E. YOUNGMAN. 1982. Rookeries in Buckinghamshire. Buckinghamshire Bird Report 1981:8-11.

TRODD, P. and D. KRAMER. 1991. The Birds of Bedfordshire. Castlemead, Ware.

TUNNICLIFFE, R. 2008. Wilson's Phalarope at Hillesden. Buckinghamshire Bird Report 2006.

TUNNICLIFFE, W. R. 1993. Caspian Tern at Willen. Buckinghamshire Bird Report 1992.

VILLAGE, A. 1990. The Kestrel. Poyser, Calton.

WALLEN, M. 1997. The Razorbill at Caldecotte. Buckinghamshire Bird Report 1996.

WALLEN, M. 2003. The Black Kite at Ivinghoe Beacon. Buckinghamshire Bird Report 2003.

WARD, C. 1992. The American Golden Plover at Broughton, Milton Keynes. Buckinghamshire Bird Report 1991:12-14.

WATSON, M., N. J. AEBISCHER, G. R. POTTS and J. A. EWALD. 2007. The relative effects of raptor predation and shooting on overwinter mortality of grey partridges in the United Kingdom. Journal of Applied Ecology 44. 972 - 982.

WHITE, T. H. 1953. The Goshawk. Jonathan Cape, London.

WILLIAMSON, K. 1972. The conservation of bird life in the new coniferous forests. Forestry 45:87-100.

WILLIAMSON, K. 1975. The breeding bird community of chalk grassland scrub in the Chiltern Hills. Bird Study 22:59-70.

WITHERBY, H. F., F. C. R. JOURDAIN, N. F. TICEHURST and B. W. TUCKER. 1938-1941. The Handbook of British Birds. Vols 1-5. Witherby, London.

WRIGHT, R. M. and N. GILES. 1988. Breeding success of Canada and Greylag Geese (*Branta canadensis* and *Anser anser*) on gravel pits. Bird Study 35:31-36.

YOUNGMAN, R. E. 1977. Great Crested Grebes breeding on rivers. Brit. Birds 70:12, 544-545.

INDEX OF BIRD NAMES

This index does not include references to the birds mentioned in the tables towards the end of the book as almost all species are listed there.